D0463801

# THE AUDUBON NATURE ENCYCLOPEDIA

# THE AUDUBON NATURE ENCYCLOPEDIA

SPONSORED BY THE NATIONAL AUDUBON SOCIETY

## VOLUME 9

PR-SE

CURTIS BOOKS
*A division of*
The Curtis Publishing Company
Philadelphia – New York

CREATED AND PRODUCED BY
COPYLAB PUBLISHING COUNSEL, INC., NEW YORK



First Printing
 Library of Congress Card Catalog Number 64-8877.

Published simultaneously in Canada by
Curtis Distributing Company, Ltd., Toronto.

Printed in the United States of America

PICTORIAL ACKNOWLEDGEMENTS, Volume 9

Luoma Photos*, VIII —Lena Scott Harris, 1593, 1650, 1696, 1722, 1724, 1727, 1750 —Allan D. Cruickshank*, 1594, 1596, 1598, 1615, 1618, 1620, 1631, 1632, 1654, 1662 bottom, 1699, 1704-05, 1706, 1707, 1718, 1720, 1770-71, 1736 bottom, 1737 bottom, 1749 top —Hugh M. Halliday*, 1601, 1736 1741—George Porter*, 1605, 1730-31 —Richard Phillips, 1607 —Joe Van Wormer*, 1608 —John K. Terres, 1609, 1634, 1695, 1773, 1774 —Lewis Wayne Walker*, 1611 —Ray Glover*, 1612 —American Museum of Natural History, 1613 —Allan Brooks, 1619, 1622, 1645, 1646, 1745, 1758 —Soil Conservation Service, 1621, 1710 —Frank F. Gander*, 1625, 1626 —W. D. Berry, 1628, 1648, 1649, 1769 —Lynwood Chace*, 1629, 1789, 1791 —The New York State Conservationist, 1630 —John H. Gerard*, 1635 top, 1703, 1663 bottom, 1790 —Charles J. Ott*, 1635 bottom —L. W. Kephart, 1639 (courtesy of the United States Department of Agriculture) —Robert C. Hermes*, 1651, 1757, 1761 —Stephen Collins*, 1655 —Edmund J. Sawyer, 1656, 1753 —Michael H. Bevans, 1659, 1754 —Save-the-Redwoods League, 1660 —Charles M. Bogert, 1664, 1669, 1673, 1678, 1680, 1683, 1685, 1689, 1690, 1662 top, 1663 top —United States Fish and Wildlife Service, 1665, 1675, 1768 —William M. Rush*, 1697 —Roger Tory Peterson, 1701 —Arthur B. Williams, 1709 (courtesy of the Cleveland Museum of Natural History) —D. A. Treat, 1711 —Robert Jackowitz, 1713 —Jack E. Boucher, 1716 (courtesy of the National Park Service) —National Audubon Society Photograph 1721 —Joseph F. Pechamec, 1723 (courtesy of the United States Department of Agriculture) —Art Bilsten, 1725, 1726 —United States Forest Service, 1734 —F. L. Jaques, 1738-39 —G. Ronald Austing*, 1743 —Karl Maslowski* and Woodrow Goodpaster*, 1747 —Ben East, 1749 —J. A. Starkey, 1751 —Dade Thornton*, 1759 —United States Department of Agriculture, 1760 —Edgerton*, 1762 —Joseph Shoman, 1775 —Virginia Fisheries Laboratory, 1776 top, 1777 —Byron Ashbaugh, 1776 bottom —Karl W. Kenyon*, 1764 —W. T. Davidson*, 1785 —John R. Clawson*, 1790 left —Henry Mayer*, 1790 right

*Photographs from Photo-Film Department of National Audubon Society

*Prickly pear has many branching flat pads*

## PRICKLY PEAR

**Western Prickly Pear**
**Other Common Names**—Thicket tuna, prickly-pear cactus
**Scientific Name**—*Opuntia occidentalis*
**Family**—Cactaceae (cactus family)
**Range**—Ventura County, California to northern Baja California, occasionally reaching the coast from Los Angeles County southward
**Habitat**—Subcoastal hillsides and washes; Upper Sonoran Zone
**Time of Blooming**—April through July

This picture shows only one lobe of the prickly pear, with its flowers. This plant is shrublike and has "branches" made up of these flat lobes—each lobe is set on the top rim of another lobe. There are no leaves. Sometimes these branches are round instead of flat. The flowers are yellow, orange, rose color, or greenish. They sit in "cups" that later form the fruit or prickly pear. Many people, as well as birds and mammals, eat this fruit. The sharp spines are sometimes poisonous to human flesh. Prickly pear is common along the coast and in sandy valleys (*See also Cactus*).

*Prickly pear*

## PROBLEM BIRDS

**Problems of Bird Control**

For centuries it has been recognized that birds are helpful to farmers because they help control insects and rodents. Following World War II, however, the rapid intensification of agricultural production created conflicts of interest between birds and the agriculturist. This conflict has led to use of a new term, *problem birds*, a term that became applicable especially to blackbirds, starlings, city pigeons, and house (English) sparrows. At about the same time gulls and other birds living near airports also created a hazard for aircraft taking off and landing. These problems arose not because birds had suddenly changed their ways but because man had failed to include the habits of birds in his computations as he designed new ways of growing crops or of increasing air traffic at airports.

For example, claims that blackbirds have increased in numbers have little or no foundation in fact. There is no question that the numbers of starlings has increased, but red-winged blackbirds and grackles, which are true blackbirds, may or may not be more numerous than they were years ago. There are, of course, more depredations in corn and rice fields, and upon other crops by concentrations of blackbirds in the fall, but this is as likely to be the result of certain agricultural practices that lure these birds as it is to any real increase in their numbers.

*The European starling was introduced into the United States in 1890. Since that time it has expanded its range and its numbers*

The total number of birds and agricultural practices present two very different problems and should be considered separately. Increasing numbers of conservationists and ecologists question whether modern farmers are devoting adequate attention to the problem of maintaining quality while increasing production. They quote a famous American wildlife manager, Aldo Leopold, who said, "Though the art of land doctoring is being practiced with vigor, the science of land health is yet to be born."

In California citrus orchards entomologists have found that predatory and parasitic insects do, as a rule, keep pest insects below economically destructive levels, but these predators and parasites are themselves often damaged more by spray operations than are the pests the spray was intended to control.

Soil health may be similarly affected by such heavy-handed techniques. Ecologist Charles Elton claims that a lifetime of study has convinced him that the only stable environments are those that contain as diversified a population of plants and animals as nature has developed in that area; without such biotic diversity there appears to be no stability (*See Balance of Nature; and under Wildlife: The Wildlife Community*).

Biological evidence points up the fact that native bird populations, like the soil's flora and fauna of which many people are hardly aware, have important biological roles to play in keeping the environment productive and attractive. One often hears the all-to-common question of the uninformed, "What good are they?" being asked about problem birds. The answer is neither economic nor esthetic, as many have argued in the past. Instead, the answer is to be found in the biological and ecological values of these species—values of unquestioned significance to almost everyone. The National Audubon Society therefore opposes the tendency to classify any native birds as pests and something to be rid of. Some species do pose local and temporary problems but the sensible approach is to control the damage they may do without eliminating the birds or drastically reducing their numbers.

One of the most discussed blackbird problems concerns the rice-growing region of Texas, Louisiana, Arkansas, and California. Rice-growers have been very outspoken about the need of blackbird control and some have already taken things into their own hands and have resorted to aerial application of TEPP, a very dangerous poison that is not approved for such use by the United States Fish and Wildlife Service.

When one looks into the background of this problem one finds that a large proportion of all milled rice stocks are owned by the federal government. In other words, the conflict of interest to be faced is one created by the price support policy of one government department, the United States Department of Agriculture, while another department, the Department of the Interior, is asked to eliminate the headaches generated by a policy over which it has no control. This is much more than a bird depredation problem. It is a problem of overall resource-use policy, and an intelligent solution will require modifying policy all around.

People must learn how to protect and perpetuate the diversity of nature that makes for long-run stability and prosperity. This is the particular responsibility of researchers and educators at all levels. It will require a reasonable spirit of give and take.

For example, the United States Fish and Wildlife Service has discovered that the birds in big roosts of blackbirds are often not the ones that do the rice damage. It would, therefore, be blind to advocate or condone roost reduction, both because it would kill birds that perform an important role in the natural scheme of things, and because it probably would bring no material relief to the complainants. It is known, also, that by reducing competition, the decimation of winter populations may actually increase the total production of young during the summer, unless these winter reductions are so drastic as to jeopardize the entire population. This nobody wants. —R.C.C.

**Control of Problem Birds**

In the summer of 1959, a group of southern Indiana farmers hired an aerial crop-duster to treat three acres of river-bottom land with parathion, a highly toxic organic phosphate insecticide. The area, covered by a dense growth of giant ragweed, constituted a small portion of a 25-acre roost site for 300,000 to 500,000 blackbirds that were causing extensive damage to nearby cornfields. Approximately 65,000 red-winged blackbirds and starlings reportedly were killed as a result of the pesticidal treatment. The only other casualty reported was a lone Cooper's hawk.

The above incident was but one of a growing number of aerial operations carried out with the hope of alleviating bird damage to agricultural crops. The practice is not restricted to the United States. In 1958 olive growers in Tunisia applied the same chemical to five acres of brushland and destroyed approximately three million starlings. South Africans have also conducted a campaign that involved similar treatment to 540 acres of scattered woodland roosts to eliminate 56 million red-billed queleas, or finches.

This trend toward airplane applications of highly lethal insecticides on concentrations of blackbirds and starlings is a matter of serious concern to the United States Bureau of Sport Fisheries and Wildlife. The bureau is the federal agency responsible for the protection and management of the nation's migratory wild bird populations. The Bureau places great emphasis on the benefits of birds, but it also recognizes that the habits of certain species are at times detrimental to human interests. It also recognizes the right of citizens to apply reasonable and legally permissible measures for the protection of private property.

The bureau is disturbed over the fact that parathion-treated acres constitute a potential hazard to humans, domestic animals, and wildlife for periods of 10 days or more after the spraying, depending on climatic conditions. It does not regard this chemical as suitable for general use in bird control.

While crop damage by large concentrations of birds is not new, it appears to be growing. This may be in part due to changed agricultural practices. In some regions of the United States, it has been aggravated by the westward movement and growth of starling populations.

While bird damage to cereal grains such as corn and rice is the most frequent cause of complaint, requests to the Bureau of Sport Fisheries and Wildlife for assistance in bird control cover a wide variety of problems. These range from starling raids on backyard feeding stations to their fouling the engine intakes of high speed aircraft. Although the seriousness of these problems is

*Because of their habit of feeding on grain, blackbirds have become problem birds*

very real, there are encouraging findings from research that are proving helpful for dealing with some of them. Work completed and underway in this field includes:

1. Scare devices—rope firecrackers, exploding shells, carbide exploder, artificial hawk, twirlers, and recorded distress calls to repel birds.

2. Chemical repellents—commercially available bird "goo" for application on building ledges, and seed protectant formulations.

3. Exploratory studies in the development of electronic and ultrasonic devices to repel birds from specific areas.

4. Mechanical protectants—woven paper and plastic netting.

5. Investigation of sterility-producing chemicals.

6. Studies of habitat manipulation and changes in agricultural practices.

7. Development of bird-resistant varieties of corn and new methods of cultivation.

8. Investigation of the light trap.

9. Search for specific lethal agents.

By virtue of its statutory authority the Bureau attempts to assist farmers in minimizing bird depredations. When rendering such assistance, the Bureau will recommend methods for dispersing concentrations of nuisance birds. In situations where these procedures are inadequate and where serious economic losses occur or public health and safety are endangered, the Bureau will recommend limited killing of bird populations, providing selective methods are known and are acceptable to responsible state and local agencies.

The selection of lethal materials and devices for bird control are based on research studies that include an evaluation of their hazards to other forms of life. The use of such methods is not recommended in areas where important wildlife values are endangered. Continuous efforts are made to limit the application of lethal measures and to further the development of other methods of preventing crop or property damage with least harm to fishes and other wildlife.

W.W.D.

**PRONGHORN**
**Other Common Names**—Pronghorn antelope, antelope
**Scientific Name**—*Antilocapra americana*
**Family**—Antilocapridae (pronghorn)
**Order**—Artiodactyla
**Size**—Male: body length, 47 to 56 inches; height at shoulder, 35 to 41 inches; weight, 100 to 140 pounds. Females somewhat smaller
**Range**—Southern Alberta, Saskatchewan, and Manitoba south in western United States to central eastern Mexico. Absent from coastal California, Oregon, western Washington, northern Idaho, extreme western Montana, and the tip of Baja California

**Habits of the Pronghorn**

The pronghorn, or pronghorn antelope, *Antilocapra americana,* is native only to North America. Nowhere else in the world is the pronghorn or any of its near relatives found, and its ancestors were all North Americans too. The pronghorn differs from all other horn-bearing mammals. It grows a true set of horns that lie over a boney core like those of the Bovidae, which family includes the cattle, sheep, goats, and the true antelopes, yet unlike the Bovidae, which keep the original horns throughout life, the pronghorn sheds these horns annually, as the Cervidae, or deer, shed their antlers (*See under Deer; and under Mammal*).

The pronghorn is classified in a family by itself, Antilocapridae. Unlike the solid horned or antlered deer, which have no horn core and drop their complete antlers, the pronghorn is never without a visible horn. The growth of the pronghorn's horn is unique. Before the outer horn sheath falls off the new horn has already begun to grow beneath it. This growth begins at the tip of the bone core and proceeds down the core to the base; thus the core becomes covered with the new growth before the covering sheath falls off. After the sheath, or the old horn, is shed the material at the core tip enlarges and takes on the shape of the new horn including the prong. By late winter or early spring the horns have reached their full growth and have hardened. Most females also carry horns but they are generally small and are sometimes lacking.

The pronghorn prefers the open plains or the rolling foothills where its great speed is not hampered or its vision restricted, for it is dependent upon its swiftness of foot and its keen eyesight for protection. Pronghorns have the distinction of being the fleetest four-legged animal in North America and rightfully so, for it has been clocked by competent observers at 60 miles an hour.

The pronghorn lives from southern Alberta and southern Saskatchewan south to central Mexico and Baja California. In the American Southwest and in Mexico, the pronghorn lives in desert regions. There water is scarce and it is believed that the animals obtain water from feeding on many of the water-storing cacti (*See under Desert*). Pronghorns also feed on grasses, weeds, and browse, sagebrush being one of its favorite food plants.

The coat of the pronghorn is coarse and pithy, a good protection against heat and cold. On the rump there are elongated white hairs that the animal can erect at will, forming a conspicuous white disk. This is used by pronghorns as a signal to others of danger and can be observed at a long distance.

In the spring the female pronghorns (does) leave for the kidding ground which is often a secluded valley with enough low ground cover to afford protection for the kids. There the young are born, generally one or two. The mother does not spend much time with her young the first few days after birth, only occasionally coming to nurse it, but she is never far away and is watching warily for intruders. For the first day or two the young pronghorn is rather wobbly on its legs and depends upon its ability to hide for its protection. Within a week's

*The pronghorn, or antelope, a mammal of the plains, was reduced by hunting to a few scattered bands. Under protection, it is now rapidly increasing its numbers*

time, however, it is strong afoot and it requires the swiftness of a good dog to catch one.

Pronghorns seem to enjoy their ability to run. Frequently they will race alongside a speeding motor car and then dash across the road ahead of it. They are not jumpers, much preferring to go through or under a fence to going over it.

At one time the pronghorn almost rivaled the bison in numbers but indiscriminate hunting reduced it to a few scattered bands. Fortunately conservationists came to its rescue. Sanctuaries were developed and hunting curtailed and it has made a very satisfactory recovery.

Besides the typical species, which inhabits most of the western plains, there are subspecies or races: the Oregon pronghorns, *Antilocapra americana oregoni*, of Oregon, Washington, and northern California; the Mexican pronghorn, *Antilocapra americana mexicana*, of Texas, southern New Mexico, southern Arizona, and most of northern Mexico; the Sonoran pronghorn, *Antilocapra americana sonoriensis*, of northwestern Mexico; and the peninsula pronghorn, *Antilocapra americana peninsularis*, of Baja California.

It would be a sad day if our great plains were no longer graced by this beautiful animal. It is a fine tribute to the foresighted men and women who fought to conserve the pronghorn that one can still see a herd of these splendid animals running across the plains, however it still needs protection. Most Americans hope that it will continue to roam the plains, where it rightly belongs, for all future generations to see. —T.D.C.

*Recommended Reading*

**American Mammals**—William J. Hamilton. McGraw-Hill Company, New York.

**Mammals of North America**—Victor H. Cahalane. The Macmillan Company, New York.

## PROTECTION OF BIRDS

### Birds of Prey

When the first issue of *Bird-Lore,* now called *Audubon Magazine,* appeared in 1899, only five states offered any legal protection to eagles, hawks, and owls.

In its fiftieth year of publication, six states—Alabama, Arkansas, Georgia, Idaho, New Mexico, and Virginia—still failed to protect any of the birds of prey. Maine, Maryland, Michigan, Nevada, New Hampshire, and Oklahoma gave no protection to hawks and owls, and some of these states even included shrikes on the unprotected list. Montana laws failed to protect eagles and all hawks; Rhode Island did not protect hawks (except the osprey), owls, and shrikes; Connecticut protected no hawks except the osprey.

In 1899 at least 30 states offered no protection to any of the birds of prey. In 1949 at least 30 states protected all hawks and owls, except the bird hawks—Coopers, sharp-shinned, and goshawk

Slowly Americans have recognized the value of hawks, owls, and other birds of prey in the control of insects and rodents that exact a yearly tribute of millions of dollars worth of farm crops, but recognition by legal protection for them, and by law enforcement, is far from being complete or sufficiently effective. In 1850 Kentucky passed a law to protect "the small-eared owl" (probably the screech owl), but it was not until shortly after the turn of the century that the legal protection of birds of prey began to gain favor.

There were far more laws protecting predatory birds in 1949 than there were in 1899, but some of them were contradicted by state game codes, written by officials legally bound to support them. For example, on page four of South Carolina's *Digest of Game Laws* for 1949, both the bald and golden eagles were listed among the birds that could be destroyed, yet on page 40 of the same publication, "killing one of these birds is punishable by a fine of not less than $25 nor more than $100, or imprisonment for not more than 30 days."

Some states, with some justification, have based their legal protection of predatory birds on scientific research into their food habits. Commercial interests have influenced others in their legislation, particularly some of the western and southern states where golden eagles are shot the year around. Ignorance and lethargy have played their part, too. In Idaho and Georgia, nighthawks were not protected because these insectivorous birds bore the misnomer "hawk." Superstitions handed down from the Middle Ages concerning owls being "birds of ill omen" and the pets of witches have influenced some codes of law.

In 1899 three states protected only the bald eagle, nine protected the vultures, one protected only songbirds, one protected the shrike (vultures and shrikes have been included with the truly raptorial birds), and one the osprey. Utah protected all hawks and owls.

Although protective laws for birds of prey in 1949 contrasted favorably with those of half a century previously, they were often inconsistent. Three states—Montana, South Carolina, and Wyoming—listed the bald eagle as unprotected, although it was protected by federal law. Nearly all states protect the vultures, but Delaware authorized a bounty on them. Most states regarded the shrikes as songbirds, but eight considered them "destructive predators" (*See Predator*). Vermont and several other states included the kingfisher in the same category (*See Fish-eating Birds*).

Nearly every state has shown some progress during the half century preceding 1950 in the protection of raptors, but there was still much to be done. The head of the conservation department of a state that adopted what some people consider a model code, wrote an article that was published in 1948 in that state's conservation magazine. In it he stated that some hawks and owls made serious inroads upon gamebird populations and by implication included practically all species of predatory birds (*See Predation*). It is astonishing how consistently some state game commissions and the wardens in their employ overlook the very laws they are paid to enforce.

In Ohio all birds of prey are protected unless they are "found doing damage to property." However, this can be stated in such a way that a farmer or any other individual need not wait until the bird has been seen doing damage, but may shoot a hawk or owl to prevent damage. This is not at all what legislators intended when such a law was passed.

In Ohio, "hawk hunting" has been, as in many other states, common practice. Many people, particularly "city hunters," made a hobby of it. On Sunday afternoons they drove over country roads equipped with scope-mounted rifles, looking for any hawk that offered a target. All predatory birds—from the little sparrow hawk to the gentle, inoffensive broad-winged hawk—were an acceptable trophy.

Every time these men killed a hawk they broke four different laws distinctly set forth in the Ohio game code. They were shooting on Sunday; killing a protected species; shooting from the road; and—since they always retrieved their booty to exhibit to their friends, walking across the farmer's land to pick it up—they were breaking the trespass law. Often nothing was done about it.

A city hunter in northern Ohio killed what he thought was a very large hawk. When he retrieved it, he discovered that it was a bald eagle, protected by both federal and state law. Alarmed at what he had done, he sought out the game warden and informed him of his plight.

The game warden reassured the hunter that he had done no crime and advised him to give the dead eagle to a science teacher for exhibit. That was usually the attitude taken by game protection agents in this state and in many others. The Pennsylvania hawk laws, which supposedly protected all except the three accipitrine species (*see Accipiter*) were a tragic example of destruction under the guise of protection. The Pennsylvania Game Commission continued to pay a $5 bounty on goshawks and great horned owls. The antiquated bounty system has been staunchly upheld by the heads of the commission, despite the findings and alleged advice for its discontinuation by the commission's own technicians. The goshawk bounty is actually an incentive to kill all hawks (*See Bounty System*).

A conservation official from a midwestern state was asked why his department so consistently avoided the issue of the birds of prey, since they were as much in need of conservation as were pheasants and rabbits. He replied that his department was so busy trying to keep enough pheasants in the field to make the hunters happy that they could not take time for anything else.

Despite the strides made in nature education, and in better legislation for their protection the future existence of many species of predatory birds is threatened, perhaps more so than at any time in our history. Maurice Broun, an eminent authority on the status of predatory birds and Curator of the Hawk Mountain Sanctuary, says:

"I do not think that any of the so-called birds of prey are increasing. My conversations with scores of experienced observers all point to one conclusion: that they are barely holding their own, and that in most instances the cards are stacked against them. How can such large and specialized birds increase generally, except where local conditions are unusually favorable, when their habitats are constantly threatened by fire and lumbering and the ever increasing army of gunners finds hawks and owls tempting targets in lieu of legitimate (and decreasing) game?"

To maintain the numbers of the birds of prey that are left, states must have more "model laws," a constant program of education, and law enforcement that *is* law enforcement.

Predatory birds are an irreplaceable part of nature's vast plan, filling an important niche among trees and shrubs, gamebirds and mammals, and other kinds of wildlife with which their lives are intricately woven. Everyone interested in the out-of-doors and in birds of prey as economically valuable and beautiful inhabitants of woods and fields, should dedicate himself to obtaining better laws for their protection and to enforcement of those laws.

—R.S.P.

**Survey of State Laws Relating to Bird Protection**—*1955*

*Species of birds listed below are not protected by state laws. Data were furnished by state conservation departments.*

Most birds are protected by federal law. For a complete list of the species thus protected, write to the United States Fish and Wildlife Service, Washington 25, D.C., for a copy of Bulletin 327, *Birds Protected by Federal Law*. Since federal law takes precedence over state law, those birds in the following list that are federally protected, yet are not protected by the state, are marked with an asterisk. Even though specifically listed as unprotected by a state, they may not legally be killed in view of their protection by federal law. (Although blackbirds are listed as federally protected, the regulations concerning taking of them under certain conditions have been so liberalized that it seems pointless to asterisk them.) As one will note, most states extend protection to all but a few species of birds—thus legally saving from harm various hawks, owls, pelicans, ibises, and other species that unfortunately do not enjoy federal protection. "Buzzards" listed below are vultures.

*Rough-legged hawk*

*Alabama*

Chicken hawk
Cooper's hawk
Sharp-shinned hawk
Great horned owl
Blue darter
House sparrow
Crow
Starling
Buzzard

*Alaska*

Golden eagle
Hawk
Owl
Crow
Raven
Magpie
Cormorant

*Arizona*

Cooper's hawk
Goshawk
Osprey
Sharp-shinned hawk
Great horned owl
House sparrow
Crow
Raven
Starling
Magpie
Sapsucker*
Cowbird
Grackle
Kingfisher
Jay

*Arkansas*

All those not protected by federal law are unprotected

*California*

Cooper's hawk
Duck hawk
Sharp-shinned hawk
Great horned owl
Blue jay
House sparrow
House finch*
Crow
Black-billed magpie
Shrike*
White pelican
Cormorant
Blackbird in Districts 1, 2, 3, 4, and 4¾

*Colorado*

Eagle (except bald eagle)
Cooper's hawk
Duck hawk
Goshawk
Sharp-shinned hawk
Great horned owl
House sparrow
Pinyon jay
Magpie
Blue jay

*Connecticut*

All hawks and owls and eagles protected except that hawks may be killed when in the act of destroying poultry
House sparrow
Crow
Starling
Red-winged blackbird++
Crow blackbird++ (grackle)
++When in the act of destroying corn

*Delaware*

Hawks (ecxept ospreys)
Turkey buzzards
Blackbirds
Crows
House sparrows
Starling

*Florida*

Cooper's hawk
Goshawk
Sharp-shinned hawk
Great horned owl
House sparrow
Crow
Jackdaw (grackles)
Buzzard
Butcher bird* (shrikes)

*Georgia*

All those not protected by federal law are unprotected

*Hawaii*

All wild birds are protected

*Idaho*

Those species of hawks and owls that are not rodent killing.
House sparrow
Crow
Starling
Raven
Kingfisher
Cormorant
Magpie
Pelican

*Illinois*

Cooper's hawk
Sharp-shinned hawk
Great horned owl
House sparrow
Starling
Crow
Blue jay
Cowbird
Rusty blackbird
Bronzed grackle
Domestic pigeon

*Indiana*

All hawks, owls, and eagles protected except that "the owner or occupant of the land may kill hawks or owls when in the act of destroying poultry, the property of said owner or occupant, on the land owned or occupied by said owner or occupant."
House sparrow
Starling
Crow

*Iowa*

Cooper's hawk
Sharp-shinned hawk
Great horned owl
European starling
House sparrow
Blackbird
Crow

*Kansas*

Cooper's hawk
Goshawk
Sharp-shinned hawk
Great horned owl
Blue jay
Blackbird
Crow
Starling
House sparrow

*Kentucky*

Cooper's hawk
Sharp-shinned hawk
Great horned owl
Crow
Starling
House sparrow

*Louisiana*

Cooper's hawk
Duck hawk
Sharp-shinned hawk
Great horned owl

Cormorant
Vulture
Crow
Red-winged blackbird
House sparrow
Starling
Grackle++
Bobolink++
++When destructive to crops

*Maine*

Great horned owl
Kingfisher
Crow
House sparrow
Cormorant
Starling

*Maryland*

Hawk
Owl
Buzzard
Crow
Blue jay
House sparrow
Starling
Kingfisher

*Massachusetts*

Cooper's hawk
Goshawk
Sharp-shinned hawk
Great horned owl
House sparrow
Purple grackle
Crow
Jay
Starling

*Michigan*

All hawks, owls, and eagles protected except that "a farmer or landowner may destroy hawks or owls on the land he owns or occupies, which are doing real damage to poultry or other domestic animals"

House sparrow
Blackbird
Starling
Crow

*Minnesota*

Cooper's hawk
Goshawk
Sharp-shinned hawk
Great horned owl
House sparrow
Blackbird
Crow
Starling
Magpie
Cormorant

*Mississippi*

Cooper's hawk
Duck hawk
Sharp-shinned hawk
Great horned owl
House sparrow
Crow

*Missouri*

Cooper's hawk
Goshawk
Sharp-shinned hawk
Great horned owl
House sparrow
Starling
Crow

*Montana*

Eagle*
Hawk
Great gray owl
Great horned owl
Snowy owl
House sparrow
Crow
Blackbird
Kingfisher
Magpie
Jay

*Nebraska*

Cooper's hawk
Goshawk
Sharp-shinned hawk
House sparrow
Blue jay
Crow
Magpie
Starling
Bronzed grackle

*Nevada*

Prairie falcon
Cooper's hawk
Duck hawk
Pigeon hawk
Western goshawk
Great horned owl
Magpie
Crow
Raven
House sparrow
Blue jay
Starling

*New Hampshire*

Cooper's hawk
Sharp-shinned hawk
Barred owl
Great horned owl
Snowy owl
House sparrow
Starling
Crow

*New Jersey*

Cooper's hawk
Goshawk
Sharp-shinned hawk
Great horned owl
House sparrow
Starling
Blackbird
Crow

*New Mexico*

Eagle*
Hawk
Owl
Heron*
Raven
Crow
Magpie

*New York*

Cooper's hawk
Goshawk
Sharp-shinned hawk
Great horned owl
House sparrow
Starling
Crow
Purple grackle
Kingfisher

*North Carolina*

Cooper's hawk
Sharp-shinned hawk
Great horned owl
House sparrow
Crow
Jay
Blackbird
Starling
Buzzard

*North Dakota*

Sharp-shinned hawk
Cooper's hawk
Great horned owl
Snowy owl
Crow
Magpie
Blackbird

House sparrow
Starling
Cormorant

*Ohio*

Hawk++
Owl++
++When doing damage to property
Starling
House sparrow
Crow
Blackbird

*Oklahoma*

Hawk
Owl
Crow
House sparrow
Other nongame insectivorous birds not protected by federal law

*Oregon*

Duck hawk
Western goshawk
Cooper's hawk
Sharp-shinned hawk
Prairie falcon
Great horned owl
House sparrow
Cormorant
Crow
Raven
Magpie
Blue jay
American merganser
Hooded merganser
Belted kingfisher
Ringed kingfisher
Starling
Rusty blackbird

*Pennsylvania*

Goshawk
Cooper's hawk
Sharp-shinned hawk
Great horned owl
Snowy owl
Blue jay
House sparrow
Starling
Kingfisher
Crow

*Rhode Island*

Hawk (other than osprey)
Owl
House sparrow
Starling
Crow

*South Carolina*

Eagle (except bald eagle)
Cooper's hawk
Duck hawk
Sharp-shinned hawk
Great horned owl
Buzzard
Crow
House sparrow
Jaybird
Loggerhead* (shrike)

*South Dakota*

Cooper's hawk
Sharp-shinned hawk
Great horned owl
House sparrow
Starling
Purple grackle
Crow
Magpie
Camp robber
Blue crow

*Tennessee*

Cooper's hawk
Sharp-shinned hawk
Great horned owl
House sparrow
Crow
Crow blackbird
Starling
Blue jay
Turkey buzzard
Black buzzard
Cormorant

*Texas*

Cooper's hawk
Duck hawk
Goshawk
Sharp-shinned hawk
Great horned owl
Golden eagle
Blackbird
Butcher bird (shrikes)
Shrike*
Buzzard
Vulture
Crow
Jaybird
White pelican
Raven
Ricebird* (bobolink)
Roadrunner*
Sapsucker*
House sparrow
Starling
Woodpecker*

*Utah*

Cooper's hawk#
Goshawk#
Prairie falcon or bullet hawk#
Sharp-shinned hawk#
House sparrow#
Magpie#
Crow#
# When causing damage

*Vermont*

Cooper's hawk
Sharp-shinned hawk
Great horned owl
Snowy owl
House sparrow
Starling
Crow
Crow blackbird (grackle)
Kingfisher

*Virginia*

Hawk
Owl
Blackbird
Buzzard
Crow
House sparrow
Jaybird
Starling

*Washingron*

Cooper's hawk
Duck hawk
Pigeon hawk
Prairie falcon
Sharp-shinned hawk
Western goshawk
Great horned owl
Magpie
Crow
House sparrow
Raven
Starling
Cormorant

*West Virginia*

Cooper's hawk
Goshawk
Sharp-shinned hawk
Great horned owl
House sparrow
Starling
Crow
Fish crow
Cowbird

*Frequently shot as a problem bird, the magpie is now protected in many states*

*Wisconsin*

Great horned owl

Crow
Starling
Red-winged blackbird
Cowbird
House sparrow

*Wyoming*

Brown eagle
Golden eagle
Cooper's hawk
Duck hawk
Goshawk
Sharp-shinned hawk
Great horned owl

House sparrow
Magpie
Kingfisher
Blue heron*
Crow

*Alberta*

Golden eagle
House sparrow
Magpie
Starling
Crow

*British Columbia*

Goshawk
Cooper's hawk
Sharp-shinned hawk
Duck hawk
Pigeon hawk
Eagles
Great horned owl
Snowy owl

Raven
Crow
Magpie
Blue jay
Japanese starling
House sparrow

*Manitoba*

Goshawk
Sharp-shinned hawk
Arctic owl

Crow
Magpie
Cowbird
Blackbird (grackle)
House sparrow

*New Brunswick*

All birds not protected by the federal Migratory Birds Convention Act except certain game species

*Newfoundland*

Hawk
Great horned owl

Crow
Raven
Grackle

*Northwest Territories*

All species not protected by the federal Migratory Birds Convention Act or by the local Game Ordinance

*Nova Scotia*

Goshawk
Sharp-shinned hawk
Great horned owl

Crow
Starling
House sparrow

*Ontario*

Hawk
Owl

Crow
Cowbird
Blackbird
Starling
House sparrow

*Prince Edward Island*

Hawk
Owl

Crow
English sparrow
Bronzed grackle
Raven
Starling

*Quebec*

Hawk
Owl

Crow
Starling
House sparrow
Cormorant
Snow bunting
Kingfisher

*Saskatchewan*

Snowy owl
Great horned owl
Goshawk
Pigeon hawk
Duck hawk
Cooper's hawk
Sharp-shinned hawk

Crow
Magpie
Blackbird
Cowbird
Grackle
English sparrow
Cormorant

*Yukon*

Golden eagle
Baldheaded (bald) eagle
All species of hawks and falcon (no raven hawks found in Yukon)
Great horned owl

Raven
Magpie

—K.D.M.

*Model Hawk and Owl Protection Law*

The National Audubon Society has often been asked to provide a "model" hawk and owl protection law, but since each state's laws differ in so many ways, no single version is completely acceptable.

The National Audubon Society recommends, however, that a version somewhat like that of the Ohio law, given below, be adapted to local legislative practice by some qualified legislative assistant.

*Sec. 1533.07 (1408). Protection afforded nongame birds.*

"No person shall catch, kill, injure, pursue, or have in his possession, either dead or alive, or purchase, expose for sale, transport, or ship to a point within or without the state, or receive or deliver for transportation any bird other than a gamebird, or have in his possession any part of the plumage, skin, or body of any bird other than a gamebird, except as permitted in sections 1531.01 to 1531.26, inclusive, and 1533.01 to 1533.69, inclusive, of the Revised Code, or disturb or destroy the eggs, nest, or young of such a bird.

"This section does not prohibit the lawful taking, killing, pursuing, or possession of any gamebird during the open season for such bird, or the killing of any hawk or owl doing damage to property. European starlings, house sparrows, and crows may be killed at any time, except Sunday, and their nests or eggs may be destroyed at any time. Blackbirds may be killed at any time, except Sunday, when doing damage to grain or other property or when they become a nuisance.

"Each bird or any part thereof taken or had in possession contrary to this section constitutes a separate offense."

Note: A reference to blackbirds may not be needed. If an exception for blackbird control is deemed necessary, the National Audubon Society suggests the following version:

"Grackles and red-winged blackbirds may be killed at any time, except Sunday, when doing damage to grain or other property or when judged to be a nuisance, in conformity with permissive clauses of federal law."

*Status of Raptor Protection in the United States to 1963*

Although a great deal of public education about the place of hawks and owls in nature remains to be done, and the enforcement of existing laws protecting these birds is still much less than perfect, the decade 1953–1963 showed great progress toward an enlightened view of these birds. As of January 1963, records of the National Audubon Society indicated that 19 states protected all hawks and owls, 26 others protected at least some, but that 4 states still protected none.

1. States that protect all raptors (except when in the act of destroying poultry, etc.):

|  |  |
|---|---|
| Alaska | 1961 |
| California (latest legislation) | 1957 |
| Connecticut | 1951 |
| Florida (by regulation only) | 1957 |
| Georgia | 1963 |
| Idaho | 1955 |
| Illinois | 1959 |
| Indiana | 1955 |
| Massachusetts | 1958 |
| Michigan | 1954 |
| Missouri | 1962 |
| New Hampshire | 1959 |
| New Jersey | 1959 |
| New York | 1958 |
| Ohio | 1959 |
| Oregon | 1959 |
| Rhode Island | 1956 |
| South Dakota | 1961 |
| Virginia | 1958 |

2. States that protect some raptors (exceptions listed):

Alabama –, all but accipiters and great horned owl

Arizona –, all but accipiters, osprey and great horned owl

Colorado —, all but accipiters, peregrine, great horned owl
Delaware —, protects only osprey and owls
Iowa 1924, all but accipiters and great horned owl
Kansas —, all but accipiters and great horned owl
Kentucky —, all but accipiters and great horned owl
Louisiana —, all but accipiters, peregrine, great horned owl
Maine 1955, all but great horned owl
Maryland 1959, all vultures, but counties may permit killing of any hawks and owls
Minnesota 1959, all but great horned owl
Mississippi 1932, all but accipiters, peregrine, great horned owl
Nebraska 1929, all but accipiters and great horned owl
North Carolina 1935, all but accipiters, great horned owl, vulture
North Dakota 1953, allows killing of "harmful wild birds" without listing these
Oklahoma 1959, all but accipiters
Pennsylvania 1959, all but accipiters, great horned owl, but *all* species protected during September-October
South Carolina 1919, all but accipiters, great horned owl, peregrine, "eagles" and vulture
Tennessee 1937, all but accipiters and great horned owl
Texas 1939, all but accipiters, peregrine, golden eagle, great horned owl, vultures (Golden eagle protected 1962, *see under Eagle*)
Utah —, all but accipiters and prairie falcon
Vermont 1912, all but accipiters, great horned owl, and snowy owl
Washington —, all but pigeon hawk, peregrine, great horned owl
West Virginia 1947, all but accipiters and great horned owl
Wisconsin —, all but accipiters and great horned owl
Wyoming 1939, all but accipiters, pere-

*The great horned owl, unprotected in most states, and an efficient predator in helping to control rodents that destroy farm crops and gamebirds, is frequently killed by thoughtless farmers, sportsmen, and game wardens*

*Hawk hunting is a favorite sport in several midwestern states where any predatory bird is killed during hawk shoots. Here, red-tailed hawks and crows line a farm fence in Ohio—trophies of ignorance*

*Birds of prey, such as this red-tailed hawk, prefer to feed on wild animals and seldom interfere with the interests of man except where he has interfered with their food supply*

*Hunters in New Jersey shot a kestrel (left), two sharp-shinned sparrow hawks (center), and a broad-winged hawk (right) for "sport"*

grine, golden and "brown eagles," great horned owl (*See Eagle*)

3. States that protect no hawks and owls:
Arkansas, Montana, Nevada, New Mexico.

4. The protection of eagles. Although federal law extended protection to the bald eagle in 1941, and to the golden eagle in 1962, both of these birds continue to be shot.

A 1962 survey of this problem by the National Audubon Society revealed that 77 percent of 118 eagles reported dead had been shot. State laws need to be brought into accord with the new federal legislation, and education and enforcement increased to protect these great birds.

Note: The accipiters include the sharp-shinned and the Cooper's hawk, and in the northern tier of states, the goshawk also (*See Accipiter*). The peregrine is also called duck hawk. The vultures are usually called "buzzards" in the South.

Recommended Reading

**Adventures in Bird Protection**—T.Gilbert Pearson. D. Appleton-Century Company, New York.

**Fifty Years of Bird Protection in the United States**—T. Gilbert Pearson. Article in *Fifty Years' Progress of American Ornithology; 1883-1933.* American Ornithologists' Union, Lancaster, Pennsylvania.

**Hawks Aloft: The Story of Hawk Mountain**—Maurice Broun. Dodd Mead Company, New York.

**Hawks, Owls, and Wildlife**—Frank and John Craighead. The Stackpole Company, Harrisburg, Pennsylvania.

**Introduction to Ornithology**—George A. Wallace, The Macmillan Company, New York. Section titled, *Bird Protection Laws*, pp 312-315.

## PROTECTIVE COLORATION

The evolutionary process of natural selection has brought about a fascinating variety of devices by which groups of animals have become less conspicuous to predators that sometimes feed upon them. Protective coloration has increased the degree of survival value of many animals in their natural habitats. Biologists became increasingly interested in these protective adaptations after Henry Walter Bates, an English naturalist and explorer, described the myriad examples of animal camouflage that had developed in the creatures of the South American rain forests.

Protective adaptations include striking illustrations of the selective process. For example, the arctic hares *Lepus arcticus* and *L. othus*, that inhabit the barren tundra regions above the northern limit of tree growth, change from brownish-gray in summer to white in winter (*See under Hare*). This adaptation to their environment has great value for the survival of their numbers in an area where there is little ground cover to hide them from peregrine falcons, gyrfalcons, and other birds of prey. Were their coats not white, blending with their snowy background in the winter, and brownish-gray, blending with the earth-hugging lichens and cushion plants characteristic of tundra summers, their numbers would be considerably more decimated by animals that prey upon them.

It is not difficult to understand how this adaptation came about, if given a length of time adequate for its survival value to make itself felt by the process of natural selection. If, for example, one of a litter of arctic hares long ago possessed the genetic material for this seasonal change of coat, that hare would immediately have a survival advantage over the others in the litter that had not acquired the trait. Therefore, the hare with the changing coat would be genitically "superior" to those that did not, would probably live longer, and breed for a greater length of time, thus spreading the trait.

Even though the trait might not have been present for a long time *phenotypically*, (that is, visibly) but nonetheless was present in the genetic makeup of the hare, (*genotypically*) it would in time become evident. So successful is this protective device, that it is exhibited by a variety of arctic creatures. However, it is not always a defensive adaptation, but has great value offensively too. Whereas the helpless pups of some seals are white and blend with the ice on which they spend their first weeks, the polar bear that stalks seals also is white. So, too, is the winter coat of the arctic fox, the least weasel, and other predators that are thus able to stalk their winter prey without being easily detected.

The examples of protective coloration, or camouflage, are as diverse as the creatures in which they have developed. One example is *mimicry*—an adaptation whereby an animal looks like an inanimate object, or an animal, that predators have learned to avoid. One of the most ingenious mimics is the twig caterpillar. So perfect is its resemblance to twigs that, if it remains motionless, it is seldom detected by birds perching within inches of it. Katydids are remarkably leaflike in form, and, also, many moths go unnoticed on the bark of trees. One species of moth that rests characteristically on birches is pale whitish-gray with black markings. It literally disappears when at rest on a birch trunk.

In the South American rain forest a species of frog is extremely flattened in form and has markings that resemble unpalatable bird droppings. Other animals resemble a numerous variety of inedible objects. The walkingstick insects look like the slender twigs of plants, spittlebugs are often thornlike in appearance (*see Froghopper and Treehopper*), and many insects resemble pebbles.

The bright yellow- or orange-and-black markings on many wasps, hornets, lady

*With its eyes open, a screech owl is easily detected in a tree hollow*

*Eyes half closed, the screech owl blends perfectly with the bark of the tree*

beetles, butterflies, and other insects serve as warning signals to other creatures. Studies have shown that birds avoid insects with these colors, and it is assumed that they are distasteful to those that might prey on them, or, that because of their stings (in the case of hornets and wasps) the colors are ready reminders of unpleasant encounters. It is interesting that some species, particularly the syrphid flies, mimic the warning colors of wasps and hornets, and although they are perfectly palatable, are apparently avoided because of it.

Countershading is another common protective adaptation exhibited by many animals. Simply stated, countershading is the development of lighter body coloration on surfaces usually in shade and darker surfaces where light normally strikes the animal. The total effect is one of flatness. There are numerous examples of countershading in the animal kingdom. Nearly all small mammals possess it to a certain degree. Many of them are nocturnal and the value of countershading is doubtful; however, those mammals that are active during daylight hours, for example, chipmunks, squirrels, ground squirrels, pikas, rabbits, and hares probably receive some degree of protective value from countershading, especially when this is combined with a pattern of spots or lines that further breaks up the outline of the animal.

The pattern of stripes on such animals as tigers and the zebra and most of the various antelopes of the African veldt undoubtedly serve to obscure them in the grassland habitats they inhabit. Some frogs have body stripes that continue through their eyes, thus obscuring the outline of these conspicuous organs (*See under Frog*).

Many insects, especially moths, have false eyespots that can be flashed when danger threatens. These eyespots are usually located on the upper surface of the hind wings and are covered by the fore wing when the moth is at rest. When disturbed the moth pulls the fore wings quickly forward exposing the

*The yellow and black stripes on a monarch butterfly caterpillar advertise to would-be predators that it is an unpalatable species*

brightly colored dots or stripes. It is thought that this device has a startling effect on a would-be predator giving the moth a split second chance for escape.

Other spots probably are deflective, that is, they cause the predator to attack a less vulnerable part of the body. Many larvae of moths and butterflies have spots at the posterior ends of their bodies and are probably protected to an undetermined degree by being able to move forward if attacked in the rear.

Biologists have in recent years had an excellent opportunity to observe the rapidity with which these protective adaptations can develop. Studies of the phenomenon of industrial melanism in a species of moth that inhabits the industrial regions of England, have shown that the general darkening of the environment by industrial wastes in the form of soot has caused the moth to become increasingly darker in color. The evidence shows that the darker form of the moth is quickly replacing its lighter form and that the lighter variety is generally observed away from heavy industrial areas. (*See also Animal: Colors of Animals*) —G.A.B.

Recommended Reading

**Adaptive Coloration in Animals**—H.B. Cott Dover Publications, Inc., New York.

**Animal Camouflage**—Adolf Portmann. University of Michigan Press, Ann Arbor, Michigan.

**Animal Colour Changes**—G.H. Parker. Cambridge University Press, Cambridge, England.

## PROTOZOAN

The simplest of animals, those composed of only one cell, are known as protozoa. They are necessarily microscopic, of many different shapes, and of perhaps 20,000 different species. Some are without definite and regular form, while others are equipped with a variety of specialized structures, known as *organelles,* that are still within the boundaries of the single cell.

All protozoans consist of cytoplasm, the basic chemical life substance, and a nucleus. They are sensitive to a number of stimuli, such as light, temperature, and pressure, and are capable of some form of movement. They also ingest other living orgnisms or parts of them. Some forms contain chlorophyll and are also classed as plants. They reproduce by dividing, one large individual becoming two small ones. Two individuals may unite, in some protozoan groups, and then, after mingling chromosomes, split into a number of smaller individuals.

One system of classification of the phylum Protozoa divides them into five classes. The Sarcodina are generally formless, but may be covered with shells of lime or silica. Amoebas, foraminifera, and radiolarians are members of this group. The Mastigophora have a definite skin of their own, and one or more whiplike organelles called flagellae. Such protozoans as *Volvox* and *Euglena* are included in this group. The Ciliata, such as *Paramecium* and *Stentor,* have tiny hairlike organelles (cilia) that they use for locomotion or, in the species that attach themselves to solid objects, to create currents that draw food to them. The Suctoria also have cilia when young, but lose them when they become fixed on stalks. *Podophyra* and *Acineta* are typical examples. The Sporozoa are parasitic, usually with complicated life cycles and lacking in locomotor devices. Malarial parasites belong to this class.

Protozoans are believed to be the oldest, or certainly one of the oldest, forms of life on this planet. There is much evidence for the theory that all living things have evolved from one-celled forms resembling these humble animals. —G.B.S.

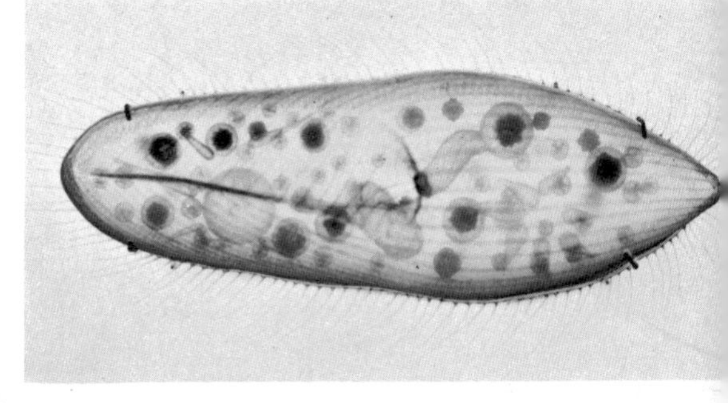

*The ciliate protozoan,* Paramecium caudatum, *is propelled through water by hairlike cilia that cover its body*

## PTARMIGAN

### Habits of the White-tailed Ptarmigan

In the lush alpine meadows of the northern Rockies, cool breezes from the snowfields flutter the showy petals of acres of brilliantly colored flowers. The sharp, birdlike chirp of the Columbian ground squirrel and the long shrill whistle of the marmot precede hikers through the meadows, warning all wild creatures that an intruder is approaching. The cony, or pika, retreats into the protection of its talus slope, but its brief nasal bleats are often heard as one passes those impregnable masses of jumbled rock fragments. Flocks of pipits wheel and turn in almost perfect flying synchrony, and high overhead an occasional hawk or eagle wheels in its persistent search for prey. Clark's nutcrackers hurl strident invectives from the scattered clusters of stunted alpine fir trees or indulge in their plaintive conversational notes. The showy little rosy finches throng over the snowfields and feast on immobilized insects that have been blown up from the valleys and numbed by the cold.

In this environment there are dozens of birds and mammals of interest to biologists, but none are more eagerly sought by visitors to Glacier National Park than the famous ptarmigan, or alpine grouse (*See Glacier National Park*). These birds are common in the frigid northern part of the continent but only come into the United States in places where high mountains create conditions suitable for their existence.

There are three species of ptarmigan in North America, but only the white-tailed ptarmigan, *Lagopus leucurus*, occurs in the United States. This species has been subdivided by ornithologists into several subspecies which occupy separate geographic areas and display minor differences in appearance.

It is natural that such interesting and scarce birds should attract wide attention and great interest on the part of biologists. Ornithologists have striven to learn the most intimate details of the feeding, mating, and nesting behavior of these grouse, and numerous observations about them have been published. Hoping to contribute something of value concerning the biology of the ptarmigan, the ranger-naturalists of Glacier National Park have searched for nests containing eggs for many years, but usually without success. Park-naturalist Lloyd Parratt joined the search for 10 summers before he finally discovered such a nest in June 1955.

Although only 100 feet from a heavily traveled trail near the Logan Pass parking area, the nest Parratt discovered would probably have escaped detection were it not for the diligent, searching, and sharp eyes of Parratt and his son, Mark. When another naturalist was shown the nest on June 30, he was warned to tread cautiously lest he step on it before seeing it. After he had halted and was told that the female was sitting on the nest on the bare ground less than 10 feet in front of him, it was still almost a full minute before he could see it. The nest was located on a very small, barren ridge surrounded by snowfields, at an elevation of 6,690 feet above sea level. In a shallow depression in the rocky soil a few bits of dried vegetation had been loosely interlaced by the female ptarmigan to form a flimsy saucer five or six inches in diameter, lined with half-a-dozen downy feathers.

As is characteristic with females of this species, the mother chose to remain motionless on the nest as the naturalists drew nearer and surrounded her. Even when one of the men slowly reached out and touched her on the head her only response was a subdued clucking. At that time they did not want to frighten the bird away from her nest, so they quietly departed, vowing to keep close watch over her in an attempt to see how the nesting activities compared with those of other species and subspecies of ptarmigan.

One of these naturalists had once seen six baby chicks with a mother bird at Iceberg Lake but had several times observed only four or five in a brood. Based upon these observations and published references, it seemed safe to state that the normal number of eggs per nest in Glacier National Park was four to six.

One may often flush ptarmigan from the bare, rocky slopes more than a thousand vertical feet above timberline (*see Arctic-Alpine*), but they are far more common near the moist alpine meadows or beside the high snowfields and glaciers. In summer they feed on flower pollen, and on seeds and their pods. Other observations of the white-tailed ptarmigan indicate that they also eat insects and leaves of pines and firs. Major Bendire, a pioneering American ornithologist in the West, saw them eating the flowers and leaves of marsh marigold, *Caltha leptosepala*, and leaf buds and catkins of dwarf birch. A.K. Fisher, a bird food-habits investigator of the federal government, examined stomach contents of two ptarmigan chicks from Mt. Rainier and found they had eaten beetles and flowers of blueberry and of heather, *Cassiope mertensiana*. Florence M. Bailey, an early woman ornithologist

*The white-tailed ptarmigan, one of three species of ptarmigan in North America, often nests near snow fields in high alpine meadows*

of the western United States, found fruiting spikes of *Polygonum viviparum* in the crop of a white-tailed ptarmigan from New Mexico, and the gizzard of the same bird contained "mainly seeds of Polygonum and a few other seeds, a few small grasshoppers, and other small insects."

In winter, white-tailed ptarmigans form flocks and usually remain in their high, frigid environment. At that time they feed mostly on the buds and twigs of willow and other small shrubs. During severe winters or when the snow is extremely deep, they descend into the mountain valleys where they find better shelter and more food.

On Friday afternoon, July 1, 1955, a violent snowstorm swept over Logan Pass in Glacier National Park, depositing five inches of snow and drifting to more than a foot deep in places. One of the park naturalists who had been periodically checking on the white-tailed ptarmigan's nest there, could not find it, even though he thought he had marked its exact location with reference to a small shrub. There was no sign of the female, but he saw a male flying about in the storm and alighting to pick seeds from plants still sticking through the fresh snow.

The blizzard continued all night and the following morning, and on July 2, the Going-to-the-Sun Highway was completely closed by fresh snow almost two feet deep, which formed deep drifts in some places. By midmorning on July 3, the road had been cleared and one of the naturalists returned to Logan Pass for his duties as an information officer in the park. At that time the covering of fresh snow extended to the floor of McDonald Valley (4,000 feet above sea level) and was knee deep above the 6,000-foot elevation. This snow covered over the four to six-foot-deep snowpack remaining from the previous winter, and persisted for about a week. On July 3, he spent considerable time searching for the nest but could find no trace of it, even though he dug through the snow in several places where he thought it might be. He assumed that the nest had not only been abandoned but also must have been destroyed and the eggs removed.

On July 4, the same naturalist and two of his friends went on another search for the nest. They were surprised to see the female bird nestled in a deep cavity in the snow, still sitting on her nest. The naturalist had missed the nest by six feet while digging for it the day before, and felt fortunate that he had not stepped on the mother where she had been sitting quietly beneath a foot of the fresh snow. Apparently as the snow melted away or was blown from the ridge by strong winds the female had eventually been able to clear away enough of it from above her to expose her to the outside world again. Apparently it is not unusual for grouse (including ptarmigan) to burrow into the snowbanks for protection during severe winter weather.

The naturalist and his friends admired the ptarmigan's perseverance and anticipated the hatching of her brood, but disaster struck just two days later. On July 6, as the naturalist waded through snow toward the nest, following the trail made on his last visit, he noticed cougar tracks ahead that had followed his previous route to the nest.

Carnivores will often follow a human trail or scent for miles, sometimes finding bits of food along the way. Knowing this, the naturalist had been careful to avoid spending much time near the nest on previous visits, and had continued to walk beyond the nest in a great circle leading back to the parking area. That precaution proved insufficient in this case, for the cougar discovered the nesting bird.

The story of what happened was clearly evident by the tracks in the snow. The mother ptarmigan had finally lost her composure and flushed from the nest with the cougar in hot pursuit. The great cat had taken two prodigious bounds through the snow after the ptarmigan, but the lack of blood or feathers on the snow proved that the bird had escaped. The cougar had then returned to the nest and crunched the eggs in its mouth, dropping portions of shell over an area about a yard square around the nest. It then retraced its steps to the main trail and continued toward Hidden Lake.

Four weeks later another of the naturalists in Glacier National Park found another ptarmigan nest near the parking area at Logan Pass. From that one the birds hatched successfully. A few days later a mother ptarmigan with four chicks nearby was seen but they were easily alarmed and were so fully developed they could not be approached in order to photograph them (*See Nature Photography*).

One day between Logan Pass and Hidden Lake View point, six adult males were feeding on a single grassy ledge beside the trail. Observers approached to within a few feet of them before they walked leisurely away.

While white-tailed ptarmigans are in their summer plumage of brown, beige, and mottled white, it is difficult to get them to stay on snowy surfaces for any length of time. They seem self-confident and unafraid while on soil or rocks, where their plumage blends with the brown,

*Feathered to the toes, the willow ptarmigan is protected from sub-zero temperatures in the barren tundra of the far North*

black, and white background, but they shun snowfields and run almost frantically when crossing snowbanks.

In winter both sexes become pure white (except for black bill and eyes) and their behavior at that time is the opposite. The summer behavior is then reversed and the birds seem unalarmed in their white plumage if they are approached on snowfields. If chased onto bare soil or rocks, however, they run rapidly back onto the snow. They actually seem to sense whether or not their background is concealing or revealing.

—J.G.E.

**Willow Ptarmigan**
**Other Common Names**—Willow grouse
**Scientific Name**—*Lagopus lagopus*
**Family**—Tetraonidae (grouse and ptarmigans)
**Order**—Galliformes
**Size**—Length, 15 inches
**Range**—Arctic Zone in both hemispheres; in North America, south to United States border.

Ptarmigans are small, arctic grouse (*see under Grouse*), with specializations that enable them to live in relatively high, cold, sparse regions. The feathers are very dense and cover even the toes of the birds. The young can run as soon as hatched, and can fly after only 10 to 12 days out of the egg.

Ptarmigans are dark brown during the summer, with nearly black tail feathers and pure white wings. A molt in the fall replaces the brown feathers with white ones, but the tail remains dark. Male birds have a tuft of reddish feathers over each eye and in spring are darker brown than the female.

*The white-tailed ptarmigan often inhabits rocky slopes above timberline*

Leaves, twigs, and buds are the main foods of the ptarmigan, although young birds feed largely on insects. The birds live on the open tundra, in the willow thickets along watercourses, and on hillsides of stunted trees. Where the snows are not too deep, they are nonmigratory, but huge flocks will travel considerable distances to find food.

Ptarmigans are prolific, laying seven or eight eggs to a clutch. Ptarmigans are eaten by Eskimos and Indians, and preyed upon by all the carnivores and predatory birds of the arctic.

The rock ptarmigan is more usually found on drier hillsides and the most exposed mountaintops. It resembles the willow ptarmigan, but males and most females have a black line through the eye in winter. The rock ptarmigan also occurs in Europe (south in the mountains to Spain); in North America it ranges south to Quebec and northern British Columbia.

The white-tailed ptarmigan has a more limited distribution, occurring from Alaska south through the peaks of the Rockies into New Mexico. It is the only ptarmigan with a white tail.

The fourth and final member of this genus is the red grouse, a famous gamebird of the British Isles. It is redder than other ptarmigans and has no white winter molt. —G.B.S.

**PUFFBALL** (*See under Fungus*)

**PUFFIN**
**Common Puffin**
**Other Common Names**—Sea parrot
**Scientific Name**—*Fratercula arctica*
**Family**—Alcidae (auks, murres, and puffins)
**Order**—Charadriiformes
**Size**—Length, 11½ to 13 inches
**Range**—North Atlantic, from Portugal north and west to Greenland, south to the coast of Maine.

No other bird in the world has the large, triangular, many-colored bill, the rounded, roly-poly shape, and the comical waddle of the common puffin. This plump, short-winged bird is a most competent fisherman, despite its ludicrous appearance, and actually swims underwater in pursuit of its prey.

The true bill is hidden beneath the colorful sheath; this structure, of no known function except show, is shed at the end of the breeding season, and replaced by a smaller and less colorful one. Young birds have a smaller, more workmanlike bill. The best way to identify these younger birds is by the large gray cheek patches.

The black-and-white plumage is worn year round, though the cheek patches darken somewhat in fall. The reddish color of the legs is constant.

Puffins build their nests at the end of burrows about four feet deep, on islands in colonies that may number up to 50,000 pairs. Only one egg is laid at a time. The chick is fed by both parents for about a month and a half, then abandoned. Shortly after that its flight feathers are strong enough and it flies to the sea.

The horned puffin, *Fratercula corniculata,* is very nearly the same as the Atlantic species. The similarly shaped bill has a large light yellow area near the base, where the common puffin has blue-gray markings. The horned puffin has a wormlike growth of flesh over

*Tufted puffins have enormous red bills and, in breeding plumage, white cheeks and long, straw-colored plumes*

*The common puffin has a large, laterally flattened bill that is banded with red, blue, and yellow*

each eye that is erected when the bird is nervous. It does not dig burrows but nests in rocky crevices.

The tufted puffin, *Lunda cirrhata,* a resident from Washington to the Santa Barbara Islands, has a red and yellow bill sheath, and yellow ear tufts. The white cheeks turn dark with winter, but the red of the bill remains. Young birds have small bills, but stouter than those of the immature rhinoceros auklet, *Cerorhinca monocerata,* which they resemble.
—G.B.S.

# Q

## QUAIL

The small, plump, nearly tailless birds of the order Galliformes are the quails. The larger members of the order, peafowls, pheasants, and chickens (jungle fowl when not domesticated) are all notable for their long tails, colorful plumage, and the presence of spurs near the hind toe.

Quails have short, rounded wings that can lift them from concealment on the ground into full flight instantly, but that are not designed for soaring. The birds feed on the ground, eating insects and seeds, and are strong runners. They nest on the ground, also, and often have 12 to 15 eggs in one clutch. The birds are monogamous, and families tend to stay together in coveys that may total more than a hundred birds.

Only the bobwhite characteristically roosts on the ground. The other North American quails spend the night on branches of low trees and shrubs.

The bobwhite, *Colinus virginianus,* is the common quail of the eastern United States. Its place is taken in the western United States by five other species.

The mountain quail, *Oreortyx pictus,* is the largest. It inhabits wooded mountainsides and scrub, from Washington to Baja California. It is the only quail with an upright plume, found in both sexes, and a reddish throat patch. The flanks are barred with nearly vertical stripes.

Both the California quail, *Lophortyx*

*californicus*, and Gambel's quail, *L. gambelii*, have short, forward-curving head plumes that look like commas. Their plumages are very similar, but the California quail has a scaled pattern on the belly, whereas the Gambel's quail has a plain belly in the female, and a black patch in the male. The California quail ranges from Oregon to Baja California, and is replaced in the dry Southwest as far east as Texas by Gambel's quail.

The scaled quail, *Callipepla squamata*, is another dry country species, occurring from Arizona to Kansas and Texas and south into Mexico. It is a light grayish-blue, with a tuft of short, upright feathers on the top of the head.

The harlequin quail, *Cyrtonyx montezumae*, a small, nine-inch bird, is a Mexican species that crosses the American border in Arizona, New Mexico, and Texas. It has a low, bushy mop of feathers on the back of the head, and a series of black and white stripes on the face.
—G.B.S.

*The bobwhite is the common quail of the eastern United States. It is a hardy bird but is dependent upon cultivated lands for its habitat*

**California Quail**
**Other Common Names**—Valley quail, California partridge
**Scientific Name**—*Lophortyx californicus*
**Family**—Phasianidae (quails, pheasants, and peacocks)
**Order**—Galliformes
**Size**—Length, 10½ inches
**Range**—Southern Oregon, western Nevada south to Baja California. Introduced in British Columbia, Washington, northern Oregon, and Utah

The California quail with its "topknot" is an unusual looking bird, full of color and pattern. It is a plump bird, small—between 9½ and 10½ inches long. Its basic color is gray, with brown and gold-red touches. The males have a black-and-white face pattern. It is the state bird of California.

The California quail has been introduced into several areas—such as Washington, Oregon, Nevada, and Hawaii—where they were not found originally. They seem to have adapted to these new regions, but attempts to introduce them into the eastern United States have not succeeded.

The little coveys of California quail roost in trees where they are safer from prowling night animals than they would be on the ground. In the early dawn they call to each other steadily—notes that, without much stretch of the im-

*California quail*

agination, sound like *"come-right-here."* A sputtering *whit-whit-whit* note is also characteristic. The flock remains together throughout most of the day, feeding and roosting. Its food consists of weed seeds.

Quail nest as early as March, but more often between late April and mid-June. In years when there is little rain, some do not nest at all. As many as 31 eggs have been found in a quail's nest, but 10 to 15 is the normal number. The nest is usually among the weeds, in a fence corner, or beside a bush or rock. It is lined with dead leaves, feathers, and grasses. Occasionally, the nest of another bird is used. Sometimes the nest is placed off the ground, in a dense bush or vine.

Incubation takes a little over three weeks. The young, like baby chickens, are well able to take care of themselves from the start. Hardly more than 15 minutes after hatching, they race about on strong legs, and follow their mother. When danger threatens they freeze—their dull colors blending with their surroundings. It is the best protection they have. The *whit-whit-whit* notes of the parents are used to call the chicks together when danger has passed.

Birds that frequent the more humid sections of the coast are called California quail. The subspecies found inland and in the dry interior is sometimes called valley quail. There is also a subspecies called Catalina quail which, of course, inhabits Catalina Island off the coast of southern California.

Quail are nonmigratory, but those that live in the higher areas may move down into the valleys during severe winter weather. —A.B., Jr.

**QUAKING BOG** (*See under Bog*)

**QUEEN ANNE'S LACE** (*See under Carrot)*

**QUIZ** (*See Nature Quiz*)

# R

**RABBIT**

Rabbit and hare are Old World terms and in Europe have the following significance: The European hare lives in a form and bears its young furred and with eyes open; the European rabbit lives in burrows and bears its young naked and blind. In this country the cottontail has badly mixed things up. It is harelike in that it does not burrow and rabbitlike in that it bears its young naked and blind. In fact, in common American usage, the words, hare and rabbit, have become so confused as to no longer have distinctive meaning (*See under Hare*). All belong to the order Lagomorpha, as distinct from the order Rodentia, of which the squirrels, mice, and rats are members and which formerly included rabbits too (*See also under Mammal*).

Although rabbits, like squirrels and mice, are animals that gnaw and have similar long curved incisor teeth for gnawing, rabbits have an extra pair of tiny cylindrical teeth behind the upper incisors. These distinguish a rabbit's skull from that of any other animal having those long gnawing teeth, with the exception of the little pika that lives in the mountains. Rabbits differ from rodents in other ways. For example, a rabbit cannot turn its forefeet inward to use them as "hands," as the squirrel and mouse can. Also, the sole of a rabbit's foot is covered with fur. This is the reason rabbit footprints so often appear blurred (*See Animal Tracks*).

Cottontails belong to the family *Leporidae* and to the genus *Sylvilagus* of which there are eight principal species:

*floridanus*—eastern cottontail
*bachmani*—brush rabbit
*idahoensis*—pygmy rabbit
*palustris*—marsh rabbit
*aquaticus*—swamp rabbit
*audubonii*—desert cottontail
*nuttallii*—Nuttall's cottontail
*transitionalis*—New England cottontail

The eastern cottontail has a wide range in the eastern United States and in central and western Mexico and inhabits parts of central New Mexico and Arizona. The brush rabbit is confined generally to the West Coast. The pygmy rabbit ranges from northern and central Nevada and western Utah to southern Idaho and southeastern Oregon. The marsh rabbit and swamp rabbit live in the southeastern United States and the desert cottontail is primarily restricted to the arid regions of the West and Southwest from central eastern Montana south to western Texas and central Mexico. It also dwells as far north as northern California, through Utah, Arizona, and New Mexico. It is absent from the northwestern United States, Idaho, extreme northern California, Nevada, and Utah. Nuttall's cottontail inhabits most of the northwestern states, and the New England cottontail dwells in New England, from Maine south to eastern Pennsylvania and south in a narrow line along the borders of the states of Maryland, West Virginia, Virginia, Tennessee, North Carolina, Alabama, and Georgia. Each species has a number of subspecies, or races. This means, of course, that cottontails show considerable variation in length, weight, and color. They may vary from 14 to 18 inches in length, and from 2 to 3 pounds in weight. Although differing in shade, all cottontails have in general the same color pattern: peppered brown backs, peppered buff flanks with a touch of black on the hips, white bellies, and white and buff legs.

All have in common a "cotton" tail and this in itself is fairly distinctive. It is nearly twice as big as the snowshoe rabbit's and though scarcely half as long as the tail of a jackrabbit, a jack's tail is usually pendant while that of the cottontail is nearly always held erect and close against the back (*See under Hare*).

The ears too, are characteristic. The cottontail's ears are relatively small, much smaller than a snowshoe rabbit's, and hardly half the length of a jackrabbit's. They are colored like the fur of the back, have no white markings, and are without the black tips of the jack and snowshoe rabbits. —W.E.S.

**Brush Rabbit**
**Other Common Names**—Pacific Coast brush cottontail
**Scientific Name**—*Sylvilagus bachmani*
**Family**—Leporidae (hares and rabbits)
**Order**—Lagomorpha
**Size**—Body length, 12 to 14½ inches; ear length, 2 to 2¾ inches; weight, 1¼ to 1¾ pounds
**Range**—The Pacific slope from the western foothills of the Sierra Nevada to the coast and from Oregon southward into southern California

**Habits of the Brush Rabbit**

The brush rabbit, as its name suggests, prefers to live in dense shrubbery and seldom ventures far away from its protective shelter, wherein it makes well-defined runways. Its breeding season is generally from January to June, and two to five young may be born in a litter.

Just as cottontails and brush rabbits are somewhat similar in appearance, so are they much alike in habits, but there are marked differences. They often feed side by side on the grass and clover of

*The brush rabbit has a white area around its eyes that is more distinct in the male*

one's lawn, and they browse alike on many shrubs, sampling a little here and a little there. Individuals will develop a habit of stopping to feed at some particular shrub at frequent intervals. After that rabbit has lived its life-span and has disappeared from one's garden, that one special shrub will not be eaten by other rabbits.

Brush rabbits have one marked dietary difference from cottontails. They are very fond of berries, a food which their larger relatives, the cottontails, never seem to eat. A brush rabbit will cut off a berry-laden twig of holly, firethorn, or privet, and carry this to the nearest rock on which it will sit while picking out the berries and eating them. Sometimes one will stand on the tips of its hind toes to reach up to a suitable branch. They are also fond of guavas and dried currants and raisins.

In their habit of perching on rocks, brush rabbits also differ from cottontails. If a cottontail happens upon a rock, it will go around it, but a brush rabbit will climb up on the rock or over it.

The nest of the brush rabbit is usually a shallow basin scooped in the earth, then lined with dry grasses and with rabbit fur. A blanket of dry grasses and fur is used by the mother to cover the babies to conceal them and keep them warm while she is away. Brush rabbit nests have much less hair in them than is usual with cottontail nests. When the mother returns to the nest, she pulls away the covering and sits over the babies to let them nurse. Such nests of young rabbits are sought by most predators, and many are raided by foxes, skunks, cats, and snakes. Each litter is small, usually just three or four young, and when one brood is taken by predatory animals, another is soon produced. By trying repeatedly from January to June, each doe may succeed in raising a few young.

Usually there are from five to seven females (or does), living in the area and two bucks. The bucks may be recognized by their shorter, broader muzzles, and by a conspicuous but broken white ring around the eye. They appear to have slightly broader ears than the females. Both does and bucks have ears that are much shorter and somewhat broader than those of the cottontails, and somewhat longer and much broader than the ears of eastern cottontails.

Brush rabbits are short and compactly built, and when fully mature are a rather evenly colored dark sepia brown, quite different from the varying shades of yellowish-gray and rufous of cottontails. The rufous patch back of the ears is brightly colored but small and not so conspicuous as in the cottontails. Young brush rabbits are dark, steel-gray in color, and in their first winter pelage retain some of this gray along the lower part of the face and across the leg and lower part of the body. Each shedding of the pelage seems to bring a browner color.

Brush rabbits molt twice each year. In May and June there is very conspicuous change with a pronounced line of demarcation between the old pelage and the new. Often the new coat first appears on the nose and then spreads back over the head and body, but it may also spread from the rump or upward from the sides at the same time. In fall, the changes can not be so clearly seen, but the coat gets longer, denser, and fluffier.

During the warm summer months, between pelage changes, the bucks seem quite uninterested in the does, and all feed together on the rolled barley one might put out for them. But after the winter coat is acquired, the bucks become more aggressive, and then most does run away whenever a buck comes near. By December in southern California, the breeding season starts, and then the bucks begin fighting. In one fight between two bucks, the animals were observed tumbling over and over, biting and raking each other with their

*Five to seven female brush rabbits usually live in an area and are accompanied by a single male*

sharp claws, when suddenly one leaped about two feet into the air, stretched out full length, with its hind feet pointing straight up.

By the first of February the young of the first litter are out of the nest. They are still very small, and the mother hunts for each one in turn to let it nurse. Now, new foes beset them, especially predatory birds, some hunting by day and some by night. Hawks and owls feed on rabbits of all sizes, and roadrunners (*see* ***Roadrunner***) catch baby rabbits at every opportunity and either eat them or carry them away to feed to their nestlings. Because of the very small size of the baby brush rabbits, even shrikes and jays are their potential enemies.

To avoid their enemies, brush rabbits lead secretive lives. Never do they go very far from the cover of dense shrubbery, and they are then quick to retreat to it at the first hint of danger. —F.G.

**Eastern Cottontail**
**Other Common Names**—Cottontail rabbit
**Scientific Name**—*Sylvilagus floridanus*
**Family**—Leporidae (hares and rabbits)
**Order**—Lagomorpha
**Size**—Body length, 14 to 17 inches; ear, 2½ to 3 inches; weight, 2 to 4 pounds
**Range**—Eastern North America, from southern New England and extreme southern Manitoba and Quebec to the eastern slope of the Rocky Mountains, south from North Dakota to southeastern Arizona, and south into central and western Mexico

A good place to meet the cottontail is in brushy open land or scrubby growth bordering woodlands. Thickets and brush piles, be they cactus and mesquite, or plain briar patch, are an essential part of rabbit habitat. They provide daytime hideouts and the surest retreats in times of danger.

The best hours to see cottontails are in the early morning or evening. Then the rabbit's salad of green grass is beaded with dew and offers drink along with nourishment. It is amusing to watch a rabbit eat. After nipping off a grass stem at its base, the rabbit will settle back, lift its head and, with a sidewise chewing motion of its jaws, slowly draw the grass in.

Grass is not only food and drink, it is home to the cottontail. In an open grass-lined depression made soft and warm with fur plucked from the mother's breast, baby rabbits are born. They are blind and naked and scarcely larger than a man's thumb. A warm blanket of fur and grass is dropped over the young when the mother rabbit leaves the nest. So perfectly does this blend with the surroundings that few persons have ever seen a rabbit's nest: This seems the more surprising when one considers that there are three or four litters a year and many of these are born almost at our doorsteps in both rural and suburban areas.

Baby cottontails grow rapidly and by the time the three to eight little rabbits are two weeks old and as big as a child's fist, they are fully furred, able to scamper through the grass and to fend for themselves to some extent.

Even at this early age the cottontail knows how to *freeze*, or turn into a statue. When motionless, these tiny rabbits are all but invisible. This is one secret of their survival, for few mammals are as relished for food as are the cottontails. In addition to man, who finds the flesh extremely palatable, the fox, wolf, coyote, lynx, weasel, mink, skunk, dog, house cat, hawk, owl, and snake all use the rabbit for food, and even the red squirrel and the crow will attack young rabbits. That the cottontail survives, and in such numbers, in the face of so formidable a list of natural enemies, is due as much to its high reproductive capacity as it is to other special adaptations.

One factor contributing to the rabbit's survival is its familiarity with the principal features of its home range. From

*The eastern cottontail rabbit feeds on a variety of herbaceous plants*

actual studies it is known that the territory covered by any one rabbit is limited for the most part to about two acres. These are more or less marked off by rabbit "signposts"—trees where rabbits have stood, scratched their chins, and so left their scent. While rabbit territories may overlap, American rabbits are not gregarious, as are Old World species. (Felix Salten's, "Fifteen Rabbits," is not a story of our cottontails.) Literally, every inch of a cottontail's range has been surveyed by its rabbit tenants. Rabbit trails, scarcely discernible except at rabbit eye-level, crisscross through it and center about a brush pile, brier patch, or a cactus thicket. The brier rose, blackberry or raspberry, and the cactus are the rabbit's "friends" and where they occur in thickets are a place of safety for the cottontail. A deserted woodchuck burrow is another snug harbor, a sort of last resort when the enemy is a dog or fox, but of no value as an escape from the weasel or mink.

Along the rabbit trails are a number of rabbit *forms*, matted grassy spots, the size of the rabbit, and used as "sitting rooms" by cottontails during periods of inactivity. In one of these forms a rabbit may spend much of the day, perhaps taking a bath, licking itself somewhat cat fashion, and rubbing its fur with its paws, or sitting relaxed with ears down resting on its back. But even so it still has a foot to the ground to receive a thumped message of danger. Rabbits, when alarmed, have a habit of stamping the ground and it is believed that these vibrations are felt by other rabbits, even some distance away, and cause them to become alert.

An alert rabbit has ears erect. The ears are extremely mobile and can be turned in various directions. Each ear can be moved independently of the other as its owner strives to get the direction of some disturbing sound. A rabbit's nose is very sensitive too and although this nose lacks the dilated nostrils of the nose of the dog or fox it is thought to more or less make up for this by being wiggled almost continuously. This motion is said to be greatly facilitated by the rabbit's split upper lip.

Once the enemy is at hand, it is the long and powerful hind legs of the rabbit that can bring about its escape. The rabbit's gait is never a run but a series of leaps. As much as eight feet can be covered by a cottontail in a single bound. A rabbit's speed for a quarter of a mile or so is as good or better than a dog's or fox's, but there is little endurance and were it not for its cleverness there would be many more rabbit dinners in the wild. By doubling, quick leaps to the side, freezing, and retreat into the brier patch, the enemy following the trail with its nose rather than its eyes is often eluded. Meanwhile, the rabbit's tiny "cotton"-lined tail held erect against its back has flashed to other cottontails the general course of the pursuit. According to Ernest Thompson Seton, an American naturalist, there is never a day in the wild that a rabbit does not need to evade its enemies more than once.

Man, however, has inadvertently done much to increase the rabbit population. For one thing he has introduced a new kind of brier, the barbed wire fence. While this is no substitute for the brier patch, the cottontail has nevertheless learned a use for it. By darting towards the fence when chased and making a sudden, quick turn, the unobserving pursuant can be led to dash headlong into the fence whose cruel barbs will give it something other than rabbits to think about.

Man has increased the rabbits in other ways. He has killed off many of its natural enemies—foxes, coyotes, wolves, owls, and hawks (*See under Predation*). Furthermore, he has increased the rabbit's food supply by raising great fields of "rabbit greens." A brief resume of the rabbit's diet will show better just how man has upset the balance of nature in the rabbit's favor. Nearly every kind of green plant is on the cottontail's bill of fare. Clover and alfalfa are especially relished by cottontails. Young grains and garden vegetables are also eaten by rabbits, although a plentiful supply of wild greens tends to minimize damage to domestic crops. Shoots, leaves, buds and bark of young trees and bushes are also consumed. Berries and cornstalks are added to the menu by rabbits in late summer and in winter they eat crops left standing in the field—dry grasses, low shrubs, evergreen leaves, and the bark of trees. Leaf buds of cactus, and leaves and twigs of mesquite, are desert fare for cottontails.

As a result, in areas under cultivation, where the rabbit's food supply has been greatly increased and its natural enemies have been cleaned out, rabbits are some-

*Seven young, eastern cottontail rabbits huddle together in a nest lined with grasses*

times so numerous as to become destructive to crops, and in winter to young orchard trees by nibbling the bark. Good protective measures in such cases are low chicken wire fences around gardens, orchards, or around the young fruit trees themselves. Spreading fresh prunings from orchard and shade trees beneath the fruit trees in winter provides the rabbits with easily accessible and tasty food and has also been found to be a practical way to protect orchard trees. The best control for rabbits, however, and for destructive numbers of mice and rats as well, is to encourage the return of the natural predators—the hawks, owls, foxes and others (*See under Hawk; Owl; and Fox*). —W.E.S.

**RABIES**

Few diseases are one hundred percent fatal, but rabies is one of them. Before the vaccine treatment, first used by Louis Pasteur in 1885, became common, there was no hope for its victims.

The agent of the disease is a virus, one of the many ultramicroscopic parasites on living tissue. The rabies virus can live only in the central nervous system and in the saliva of mammals. It is transmitted by saliva from an infected animal into an open wound. The virus travels along the nerves to the spinal cord and the brain, and then to the salivary glands of its new victim.

Although rabies can be transmitted by any mammal, more is known of its

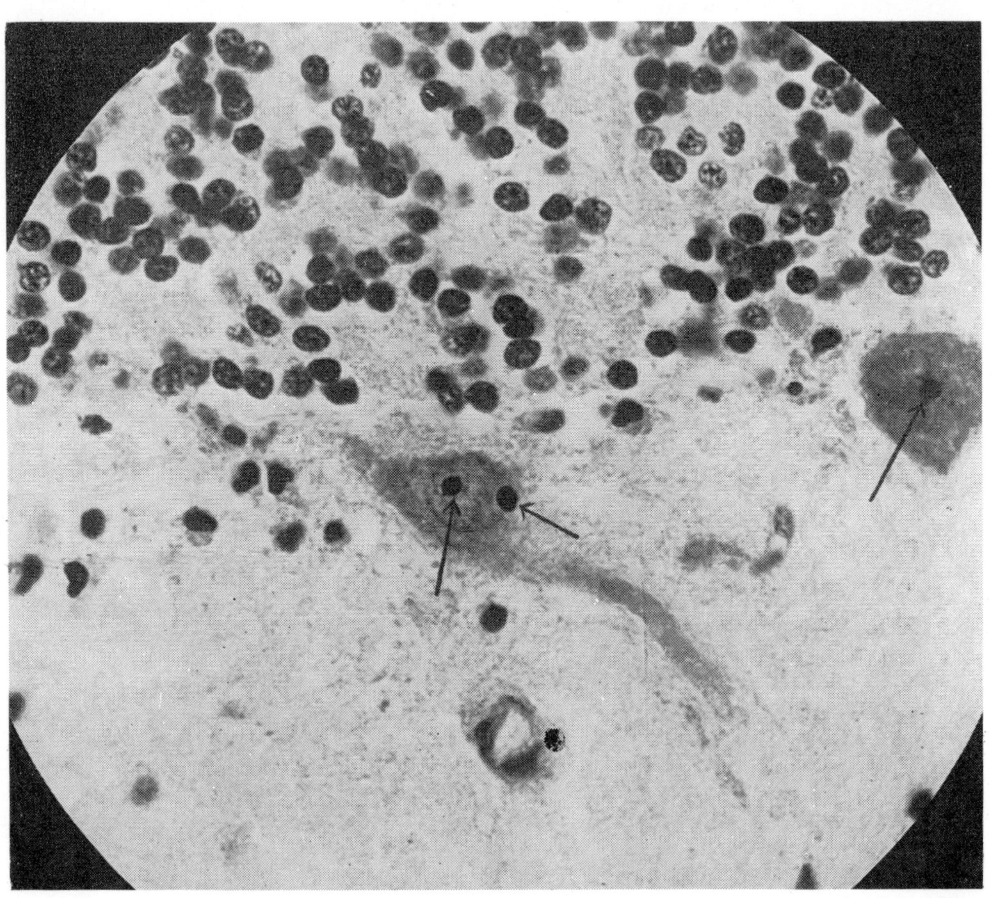

*A photomicrograph of a rabid animal reveals viral inclusions, or Negri bodies (indicated by arrows), in the large cells that are a positive indication of rabies*

effects on dogs than on any other animal except man. An infected dog may take as long as a year to develop the symptoms, but two to four weeks is more likely. A marked change in behavior in the infected animal—sudden outbursts of fury, restlessness, and a tendency in it to bite other animals without provocation—is usually followed by its paralysis and death. The animal can infect others for about two weeks before its own death.

Other members of the dog family—wolves, foxes, and jackals—are important transmitters of rabies. Cats are less so. Bats often carry the disease, but seldom infect humans; in South America, vampire bats, which do not display the symptoms in themselves, often infect cattle.

The incubation period in human beings varies from 10 days to a year or more, depending on the depth of penetration of the wound, the site of the wound, and the virulence of the virus. The vaccine is almost completely reliable in preventing the disease, but it often has serious side effects. Once the symptoms have developed, treatment is useless, and the patient becomes depressed, then convulsive, then paralyzed. The human victim's painful convulsions, even at a suggestion of drinking water, are responsible for the old name of the disease, hydrophobia, or fear of water.

Control measures consist of inoculating animals against the virus, especially dogs, and the destruction of stray dogs. Rabies has been eradicated in England and Scandinavia by strict control on the importation of dogs. Measures taken there would be difficult to apply in North America, where wildlife is also a reservoir of infection. —G.B.S.


*Recommended Reading*

**The Cyclopedia of Medicine and Surgery**—George Morris Piersol, editor. F. A. Davis Company, Philadelphia.

**Rabies**—Donald J. Dean, D.V.M. *The New York State Conservationist*, April-May, 1955.

*The raccoon is a skillful climber and spends much of its time in trees*

**RACCOON**

**Other Common Names**—Coon

**Scientific Name**—*Procyon lotor*

**Family**—Procyonidae (raccoons, coatis, and allies)

**Order**—Carnivora

**Size**—Body length, 25 to 34 inches; tail, 9½ to 10½ inches; height at shoulder, 9 to 12 inches; weight, 12 to 25 pounds (in Florida Keys, 3 to 6 pounds)

*A raccoon prowls for food in the grasses near the edge of a stream*

**Range**—Southern Canada north in Alberta and Saskatchewan south throughout United States through Mexico and Central America to South America. Absent in western Montana, Wyoming, and Utah. Locally distributed in western Colorado and eastern Utah, southern Nevada, northern Arizona and northwestern New Mexico. Also absent from most of northern Baja California

The raccoon is an abundant mammal in all of the United States except the Great Basin and northern Rocky Mountains. A clever, masked creature, it is especially abundant in swampy areas where there are watercourses and adequate den sites. The raccoon is nocturnal and wanders along stream banks at night searching for crayfishes, frogs, and other small aquatic creatures that are plucked out of the water with its long sensitive fingers. Often the food is carefully dunked and washed piece by piece before it is eaten. This is apparently done to remove sand and mud, or unpalatable secretions in the skin glands of some of its food items, particularly amphibians. Many raccoons, however, live some distance from a water source and do not wash their food before eating. The species name *lotor* refers to the habit of washing. The raccoon seems to be uninterested in the washing process and while it is busy scrubbing its food with its dexterous forefeet, it looks around in an inquiring manner, never glancing at its work. Seemingly it derives pleasure from just feeling the food under the water as it assiduously dunks each piece.

Raccoons vary greatly in size and color, the largest are medium in color and live in the eastern parts of the United States. The palest raccoons are in the Colorado River delta and in the Florida Keys. In the Keys the raccoon may weigh only three to six pounds. The largest and darkest ones inhabit the northwestern United States and many attain a length of nearly three feet.

Male raccoons are polygamous but females choose only one male each mating season. The mating season ranges from February in the North to December in the far South. The young are born nine weeks after mating and have black skins covered with a light yellowish-gray fur. In about 10 days the facial mask begins to appear and by 19 days the rings on the tail are visible. Between 18 and 25 days the eyes of the young raccoons open, and at about 50 days they are able to leave the den on their own.

Two to seven, usually four, young are reared each season—usually in a den in the hollow of an old tree, although a crevice in a rock ledge or the abandoned burrow of another mammal is sometimes utilized. The young stay with the mother through the first winter and wander about after her in search of food.

The raccoon's diet is varied and consists of such items as berries, corn, persimmons, acorns, nuts, turtle eggs, frogs, toads, earthworms, grubs, and, now and then, the eggs of ground-nesting birds. Occasionally a raid on a chicken house or a garbage can is made, but contrary to popular opinion, the raccoon is mainly a beneficial animal that more than makes up for its raids on melon patches and cornfields by the great quantities of insects it consumes.

Populations of raccoons vary from area to area; in Mississippi 8 to 10 individuals to an acre have been reported, and in Illinois some 42 per square mile have been recorded. One hundred raccoons were taken from 102 acres in Missouri in 4½ days one winter. These figures represent very high populations, and usually 1 raccoon in 10 acres is an average population.

In the North in winter, the raccoon becomes inactive and remains in its den. It does not hibernate, however, and any intruder wakes it quickly. Southern raccoons remain active all winter and wander about usually within a radius of

*The raccoon has remarkably dexterous forefeet with which it can easily pick up food items. It often washes its food if water is available*

one-half to one mile in search of food. Older males may wander considerably farther.

—G.A.B.

Recommended Reading

**The Mammal Guide**—Ralph S. Palmer. Doubleday & Company, Inc., Garden City, New York.
**Mammals of North America**—Victor H. Cahalane. The Macmillan Company, New York.
**World of the Raccoon**—Leonard Lee Rue III. J. B. Lippincott Company, Philadelphia.

## RADIOCONTAMINATION

The simplicity of the plant and animal world in the Far North, as compared to that of other latitudes, makes it of great value to scientists as an outdoor laboratory.

Biologists, who can observe more quickly and more clearly there the effects of outside factors on the environment, are concerned over the relatively large amount of radioactivity that they have discovered recently in some plants and in caribou, reindeer, and in human beings of the North.

To the biologist the ecosystem concept makes clear many aspects of life that are otherwise obscure. In attempting to take into consideration all of the facets of the environment that affect an organism, he has developed a dynamic concept for "environment," one that includes the interactions of animals, plants, soil, water, air, and sunlight. This he calls the *ecosystem.* It is a unitary view that helps the biologist to visualize and better understand what really goes on in nature (*See also under Wildlife: The Wildlife Community*).

The ecosystem itself is thrown into sharp focus in the arctic tundra and subarctic taiga. The clarity is due to an overall simplification of the system because of low levels of solar energy put into it.

A reduced energy budget, compared with the temperate zone, results in a lower *biomass,* or amount of living material per unit area. The reduced energy budget also results in the biomass being apportioned among a relatively few species.

For example, Kansas has 80 species of land mammals, while Virginia has 67 species. But northern Alaska has only 28 species; Keewatin, in North Central Canada, 20 species; and Baffin Island, 11 species.

A small number of species indicates a simple food web. A simple food web has a number of advantages over a complex one. Perhaps the greatest advantage is its efficiency. The small number of energy transformations in the food chains means fewer chances for energy to be dissipated. This is of considerable importance in the boreal ecosystems where the small amount of solar energy must be carefully husbanded (*See Food Chain*).

But simple food webs also have glaring weaknesses. Perhaps the best-known fault of a simple food web is its fragileness. It is easily thrown out of balance by changes in only one or two species. Another less-known weakness, and one based on the efficiency of the web, is the speed with which a contaminant injected into the system can spread through it.

During the 1950's and early 1960's, a number of research papers were published in Scandinavia on the ecology of radioisotope contaminants injected into the tundra and taiga ecosystems. The sources of the present contamination are nuclear explosions. The principal isotopes concerned appear to be strontium 90 and cesium 137.

These are injected into the arctic food web by means of their absorption by lichens. From lichens the contamination travels up the food chain to caribou and reindeer and thence to carnivores and man. The contaminated food chain occurs throughout the North—in Alaska, Canada, Scandinavia, and the Soviet Union.

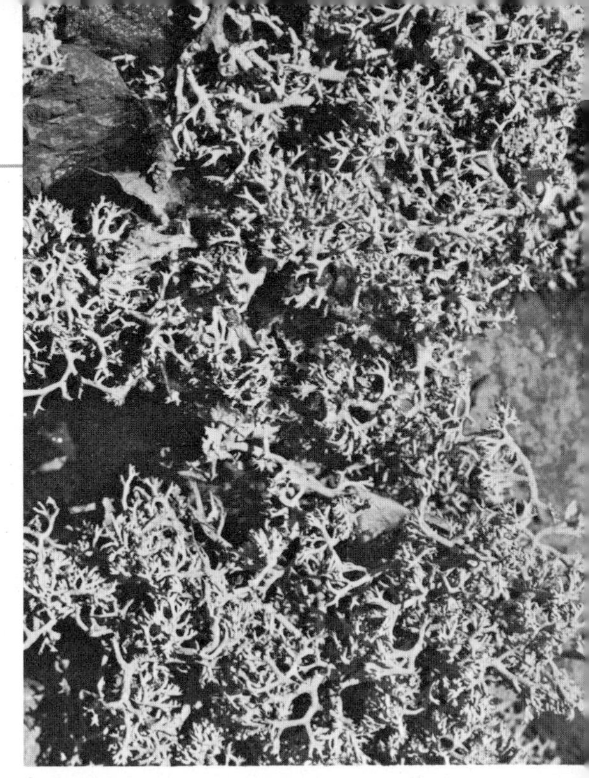

*Reindeer lichen,* Cladonia rangiferina, *retains virtually 100 percent of radioactive particles falling upon it. Biologists believe it will remain contaminated for many years*

*Caribou, a link in the radiocontaminated food chain: from lichen to caribou to man*

The accompanying chart illustrates the magnitude of the contamination in comparison with the levels of the same isotopes found in some other food chains. The areas of the circles indicate general levels only and do not express the intricacies of seasonal and annual variations. (The frequently changing units and standards found in various publications compound an already confused picture and preclude simple, direct comparison and tracking of the progress of the contamination up the chain in any one region.)

The data on which the chart is based were gleaned from several Scandinavian publications and from the few North American papers on the subject. The "hot spot" nature of the contamination is more striking when one realizes that the background radiation levels in the North are generally lower than in the temperate zone.

It is quite clear that the lichen/sedge – caribou/reindeer – carnivore/man food chain is contaminated. Parts of it are grossly contaminated. In the Scandinavian studies, sponsored by the International Atomic Energy Agency, a branch of the United Nations, the condition was well recognized as an ecological "hot spot."

Identification of the contaminants, a difficult feat, is one thing. Evaluation of its significance is quite another. In the United States this is done officially for humans by Radiation Protection Guides (RPG's). These are supposed to indicate when a detailed evaluation of possible exposure risks should be made.

Tests in Alaska have shown that people who depend on caribou or reindeer for their protein are already contaminated with strontium 90 and cesium 137 —about one-third to one-half the maximum permissible amounts for *each* isotope. To these cumulative amounts of internal radiation must be added unknown amounts of external radiation from medical sources, especially chest X rays.

It can be seen that caribou are grossly contaminated with both strontium 90 and cesium 137. These animals are in the range where, for humans, according to the RPG's "appropriate positive control measures" should have been taken. No such measures as far as is known, have been put into effect in arctic America.

We have no idea how these levels of radiocontamination affect either the genetic or somantic attributes of carbou. Moreover, it is not known whether any research has been conducted on this.

There are other aspects of the radiocontamination of the lichen/sedge – caribou/reindeer – carnivore/man food chain that have received virtually no attention. One of importance is the size of the populations concerned, both of man and of caribou.

In comparison to the total United States population of 195 million people, the number of humans dependent on caribou is quite small. (Their ecological and ethnological importance, however, is greatly all out of proportion to their total numbers.)

The RPG's were formulated on the basis of an infinitely large interbreeding human population. The Alaskan Eskimos do not fit these criteria. The Eskimos form a small population that has been virtually isolated reproductively for many generations. It is not believed the present RPG's can apply to them.

This problem in relation to the Lapps has been recognized in the Scandinavian literature. In relation to Eskimos, the problem was first recognized in 1961 by Don Charles Foote in a special report to the United States Atomic Energy Commission.

Population size in caribou has been of concern to biologists for some time and much has been written on the subject. One aspect that has been discussed is the minimum size of population necessary to maintain a reserve of genetic variation to meet environmental changes. The minimum size for a caribou population is not known.

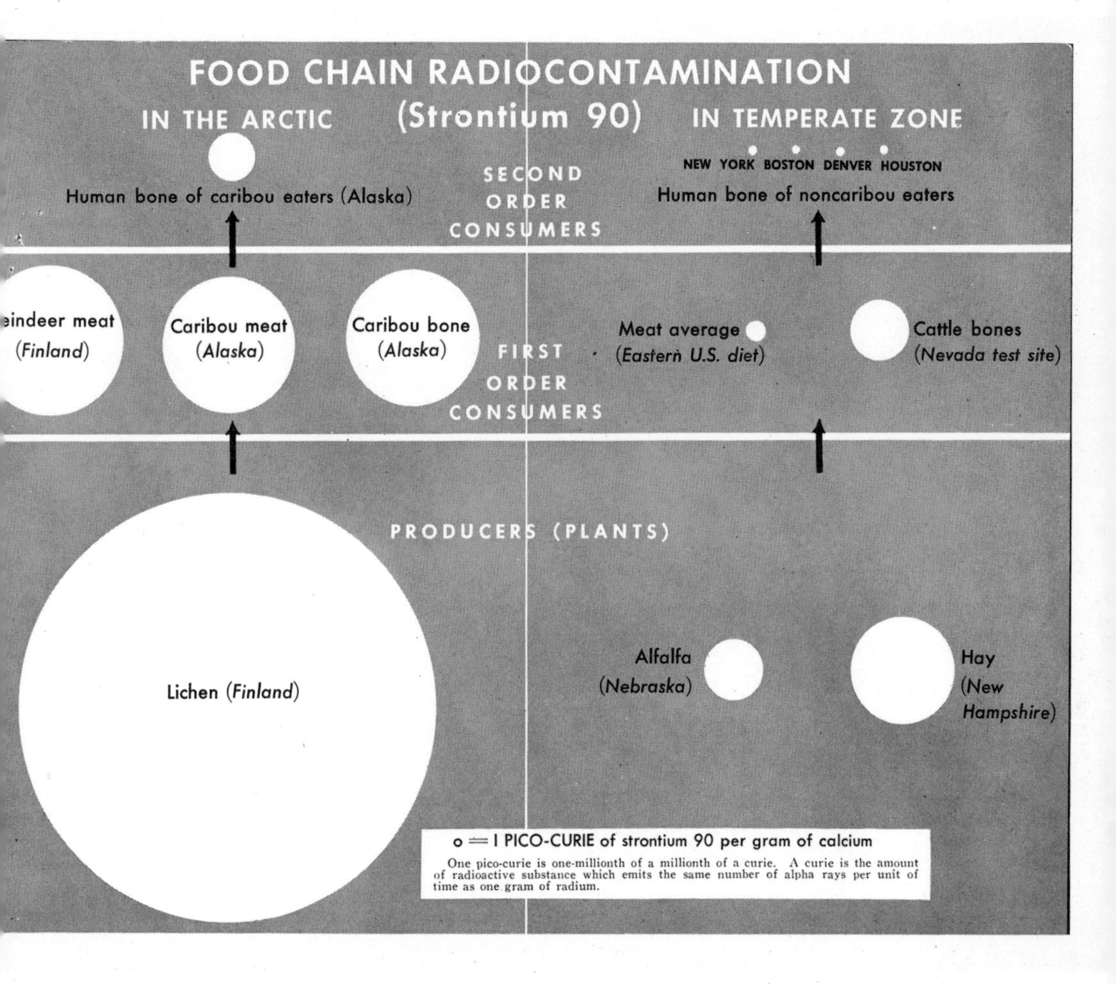


*The chart (above) was prepared from the data in Scandinavian and North American scientific papers. Variation in the data precluded the tracking of food chain radiation in any one region*

The important point to consider is that the present North American caribou population is but a small remnant of what it used to be. Estimates of original numbers vary widely, but the most reliable run about 2.5 or 3 million animals. The population on mainland North America is now less than 600,000 (300,000 or a few more in Alaska and somewhat less than 300,000 in Canada).

Thus the gene frequency evolved for a population about four or possibly five times larger than that existing today. Moreover, it is well established that the former population of caribou intermingled much more than the present one does. The present-day discrete "herds" are the result of a dwindling population shrinking into areas of optimum habitat. Thus the species today is, in effect, composed of a series of relatively small, reproductively isolated groups.

It is well known that such populations offer ideal conditions for rapid genetic changes, changes that are not necessarily adaptive or "good,"—the Sewell Wright effect, for example, under which some genetic factors are accumulated or entirely eliminated, regardless of natural selection. A.W.F. Banfield, of Canada, in his taxonomic revision of reindeer and caribou, expressed a belief that the Sewell Wright effect was one of the factors that led to the extinction of two subspecies of caribou, those on the Queen Charlotte Islands and in East Greenland (*See under Caribou*).

There appears to be no experimental data on the above situation in caribou. However, on the basis of what we know about other animals the conclusion is reasonable. We must also realize that, to date, all North American data on radiocontamination result from publication of one or a few samples. No one has yet studied the contamination levels in terms of body size, sex, and age classes or other parameters of population dynamics or in terms of range variations.

Thus we are justified in stating that the RPG's probably do not apply to the mammalian component of the contaminated lichen/sedge— caribou/reindeer— carnivore/man food chain. There is no basis for the oft-repeated statements that no danger exists. In truth, we don't know whether danger exists, but we suspect it does.

We need, in addition to detailed study of the ecology of radiocontamination, a complete reappraisal of the RPG concept for small or isolated populations. As Alaska's Senator E. L. Bartlett has so aptly expressed it, ". . . any strontium 90 is bad; more is worse; and it is foolish to deny it . . ."

So here we have another species, *Rangifer tarandus*, threatened by man's ecological ignorance. Is this situation any different from that of, say, the whooping crane or the Everglade kite? Apparently it is, because caribou are ecologically and economically the key animals of the North.

The concern expressed by Senator Bartlett regarding radiocontamination of the lichen — caribou — man food chain, has resulted in a permanent program of research on the problem. The Atomic Energy Commission contracted with the Public Health Service for an initial $100,000 grant to the Arctic Health Research Center at Anchorage, Alaska, for the work.

The Eskimos and Indians of Alaska, through their newspaper, *The Tundra Times,* have expressed appreciation to Senator Bartlett for his vigorous pursuit of the subject.

To appreciate the magnitude of the problem posed by radiocontamination of caribou and reindeer we should recall that the tundra and taiga, where the contaminated food chain exists, comprise about one-fifth of the land area of the northern hemisphere. Over most of this vast region traditional temperate-zone type agriculture is not possible because of the reduced energy budget. (In the few restricted suitable spots agriculture is highly specialized and marginal.)

Virtually the only source of terrestrial animal protein for human use is domesticated reindeer or carefully managed wild caribou. Take away this source of protein or make it unusable and vast regions of the world would then be eliminated as habitat for people dependent on the land and its products.

As has been reported elsewhere, ". . . The human population of the region is relatively sparse and, unfortunately, casts few votes in the world's halls of government. If a hot spot of similar magnitude were to develop in relation to peaches or beef or milk or tobacco it seems probable that no reason would be thought serious enough to allow the contamination to continue." (*For other types of contamination of the environment, see Air Pollution; Insecticide; and Oil Pollution.*) —W.O.P.

**RAGWEED**

What makes ragweed a weed? A weed is a plant growing where it is desired that something else shall grow. Since more than half of all the hayfever in the

United States is caused by the pollen of ragweeds, it is certainly important to make something else grow where there are now ragweeds. We have made them weeds by our mismanagement of the soil. Before the day of the white man the land was clothed with a stable and balanced society of plants. The ragweeds, native Americans, found scarcely any room, for they can flourish only in disturbed soil of which there was little. But when the land is stripped of its normal vegetation the ragweeds are among the first plants to reoccupy the denuded areas. This they do quickly and effectively, often gaining complete dominance. They flourish in almost any kind of soil, rich or poor, wet or dry. They are particular, even if the site is bare subsoil. They are pioneer plants, not invaders, and they cannot stand competition from other plants. As pioneers they perform a useful service in holding the soil against wind and water erosion and then give way to the pressure of competition from other species of plants, provided the ground is not further disturbed.

**Common Ragweed**
**Other Common Names**—Short ragweed, Roman wormwood, hogweed, bitterweed
**Scientific Name**—*Ambrosia artemisiifolia*
**Family**—Compositae (composite family)
**Range**—Newfoundland and Magdalen Islands, Quebec, Canada, to District of Columbia, frequently Northwest, local Southwest
**Habitat**—Seabeaches and cultivated or waste land
**Time of Blooming**—July to October

**Tall Ragweed**
**Other Common Names**—Giant ragweed, great ragweed, buffalo weed
**Scientific Name**— *Ambrosia trifida.*
**Family**—Compositae (composite family)
**Range**—Southwestern Quebec to British Columbia, south to Florida, Alabama, Louisiana, Texas, and Arizona

*The inconspicuous flowers of ragweed are borne in upright panicles at the top of the plant*

**Habitat**—Alluvium, rich openings, and waste places
**Time of Blooming**—Late June through September

*Kinds of Ragweed*

There are two kinds of ragweed growing in the eastern United States, the common or short ragweed, *Ambrosia artemisiifolia,* and the tall, or giant, ragweed, *Ambrosia trifida.* Both are about equally common and grow in profusion on neglected farmland and overgrazed pastures; in vacant lots, waste places, roadside ditches, and dump heaps

*Tall ragweed*

of every town and city. The common ragweed is generally a short bushy plant about three feet high, though it occasionally reaches the height of a man's head. Its leaves are lacy and fernlike in appearance and a little rough to the touch, and its stems are slightly hairy. Its flowers are borne in upright spikes at the tips of its branches. They are quite inconspicuous. They have no need to be otherwise for they do not invite the visits of insects to carry away their pollen as do showy flowers like sunflowers and daisies. Instead, their pollen is blown from flower to flower by the wind, and as pollen dispensers they have few equals (*See Pollen; and Pollination*).

One day, a scientist in a hayfever laboratory estimated the number of pollen grains coming from each flowering spike of a short ragweed plant, and arrived at the astonishing total of a little more than six million pollen grains. It has been estimated that it takes only 25 grains per cubic yard of air to give people hayfever. So each spike gives enough pollen to contaminate 240,000 cubic yards of air. And there are often hundreds of flowering spikes on each ragweed plant. When the scientist applied the same reasoning to the much larger flowering spike of the giant ragweed, he arrived at the truly amazing number of 21 million grains coming from each of them.

The tall, or giant, ragweed is in all ways much larger than the short ragweed. Often it reaches 13 or even 15 feet in height, and if growing in a fairly rich soil usually grows as high as a man's head. Its leaves are not fernlike. Instead they are broad and with only three or five segments or sometimes not divided at all. Like those of the short ragweed they are rough to the touch, and the stems are bristly. One must not jump to the conclusion that the giant ragweed, on account of its larger size and the greater amount of pollen that it produces, is more of a menace in hayfever than the short ragweed, because both ragweeds have a way of filling up all the space available to them, either by multiplying their numbers or increasing their size. Both are adaptable to an enormous diversity of soil conditions. Both are extraordinarily vigorous growers. And both will endure a great deal of abuse, which makes them difficult to eradicate.

*Eradicating Ragweeds*

Most attempts at eradication of ragweed have been by simple and direct attack, such as pulling by the roots and burning, and grubbing out the roots with a hoe. Even disking and harrowing have been advocated. Such methods only show that those who advocate them have not studied the lives and customs of the ragweeds, nor even stopped to consider how they got on a plot of ground in the first place. Always they got there on account of some man-made disturbance of the soil. They are entirely weeds of disturbed soil. If the soil had never been disturbed they would not be there. And if the soil is left undisturbed they will invariably disappear, because they cannot stand competition of other plants. But this attractive method of doing nothing at all is too slow, for it takes from three to five or more years for ragweeds to be crowded out, depending upon how capable the soil is of supporting the competing plants. But it gives us the key to the mode of attack, which is to remove the ragweed by cutting without disturbing the soil and to encourage the growth of some other plant.

If cutting is the method resorted to, it should be done in late July or early August when the plants have made their full growth but before they shed their pollen. Most of the roots will then die but some may send up fresh shoots. If so these will have to be cut again later in the season to prevent them from maturing their seeds.

A characteristic of the ragweeds which is decidedly in favor of eradicating them is that they are annuals and must come afresh each year from seeds, whereas their most serious competitors are always biennials or perennials, springing next year from the roots of the previous season where these are already established. Because of their annual habit it is quite unnecessary to pull ragweeds by their roots, or to dig or grub them out. In fact all such operations should be studiously avoided, for the slightest disturbance of the soil prepares it for a crop of ragweed next year. There are always plenty of seeds left, too, to start the new growth even if the crop is removed without a trace, because ragweed seeds can remain dormant for many years. Experiments, still incomplete, show that they can survive burying up to forty years. In cutting the weeds care should be taken to injure the competing vegetation as little as possible. If this is grass it can be cut with

*Short ragweed*

the scythe or reaper, along with the ragweed, without much injury. Then the grass has the rest of the summer to spread over the ground and thus exclude the ragweed. The following year, growing from its roots already established, the grass has a tremendous advantage over the ragweed. If there is a little grass present in a stand of ragweed, often one properly managed cutting is sufficient to control the ragweed. If not, grass or other plants that compete with ragweed should be planted.

### *Plants That Exclude Ragweed*

What shall we plant to control ragweed? This is a question that is always asked. If the soil is fairly rich and with an abundance of lime, red clover, pink clover, or white sweet clover may be planted. Of course the ragweed will come up with the clovers, but the ragweeds must be cut before they have a chance to smother their competitors. Then the following year, with their roots well established, the clovers can easily smother the ragweeds. The competitive plants chosen must always depend upon the character of the soil, its nutrient content, its acidity, its moisture, etc. so that each plot is a separate problem. But a clue to what will best grow can often be had by looking at an adjoining plot where there is no ragweed. If not, a soil expert should be consulted.

Ragweeds are not without their uses. Besides pioneering on raw soils and thus helping to prevent erosion until other plants can take over, the seeds are eaten by many species of birds—especially gamebirds, songbirds, and even by waterfowl. —R.P.W.

*Recommended Reading*

**American Wildlife and Plants**—Alexander C. Martin, et. al. Dover Publications, New York (paperback reprint).
**Pollen grains: Their Structure, Identification and Significance in Science and Medicine**—R. W. Wodehouse. McGraw-Hill, New York.
**Weeds**—W. C. Muenscher. The Macmillan Company, New York.

## RAIL

Members of the order Gruiformes, with the cranes, gallinules, coots, and others, rails are marshbirds of the deep grasses and sedges along the borders of bodies of water. All of them are short-tailed birds with long legs and short, rounded wings. Their bodies are compressed laterally, making them literally "thin as rails," an advantage to birds that slip through the dense marshy tangles to avoid pursuit, rather than to resort to their weak flying ability.

There are six species of North American rails, and the clapper rail, *Rallus longirostris,* king rail, *R. elegans,* and Virginia rail, *R. limicola,* have relatively long, thin, downcurved bills. The sora, *Porzana carolina,* the black rail, *Laterallus jamaicensis,* and yellow rail, *Coturnicops noveboracensis,* have short, chickenlike bills (*See also Sora*).

Rails are very secretive. They are somewhat gregarious, living in family groups, often calling a series of harsh cackling notes to express their alarm. They are omnivorous, eating seeds, insects, crustaceans, and worms. All of them can swim. —G.B.S.

### Clapper Rail

**Other Common Names**—Marsh clapper, marsh hen
**Scientific Name**—*Rallus longirostris*
**Family**—Rallidae (rails, gallinules, and coots)
**Order**—Gruiformes
**Size**—Length, 15 inches
**Range**—Along the west coast from San Francisco, California, south around Baja California and to Ecuador, and northwestern Peru. From Connecticut along east coast to Mexico, Central America and northern South America. Also in the West Indies, the Colorado River valley, and the Valley of Mexico

### Habits of the Clapper Rail

The clapper rail inhabits the tidal marshes from Maine to Florida, and from that great peninsula westward to the Golden Gate of California. Its continent-wide range is limited by the east-west expansion of salt meadows and the brackish creeks. The bird thrives wherever barrier islands hold off the ocean from this belt, particularly when the protected waters are crowded with rustling blades.

Such, for example, are the measureless Marshes of Glynn, so eloquently sung by the poet Sidney Lanier. As one crosses the Savannah River headed south he suddenly faces that incredible panorama. Not even the swamps of the Nile, nor those encircling the Lake of Tunis in Africa support comparable reedy seas. Our Atlantic Coast is rich in such areas, from the tip of Cape Cod to the Florida Keys and a thousand miles beyond. Nothing on earth is quite like some of these saltings, brighter than emeralds—the one and only genu-

*A clapper rail incubates its eggs in an open salt marsh*

ine sea-green. They are kept green by the tide that submerges them every 12 hours. When the tide ebbs, once more, they emerge more lustrous than ever.

No other species is better adapted for concealment in its chosen haunts than the clapper rail. The plumage of its back and shoulders, ashy gray streaked with brown, and that of its breast, russet paling into grayish on the flanks, are practically identical with typical surroundings—the floor of the marshes littered with faded reeds. For this reason one seldom sights a rail unless it moves. Even then one's eyes are so baffled by its pattern that the observer might think a bit of the marsh is slipping away. Watch a blacksnake whipping into a bush. It flows along so smoothly that the eye can scarcely record when the last inch of tail has vanished. In like manner the rail slips away into the heart of the marsh. One moment one thinks he still discerns it, but the next it is gone.

An effective auxiliary protective pattern is the array of light-bars running at right angles to the axis of the bird across its dusky flanks, crossing all its underparts except the center, which is gray. Close range study of these birds suggests that the white streaks across a blackish ground resemble the colors of the salt marsh near the bases of the reeds where the rail spends most of its life. The stripes match the stalks when the bird crouches or stoops forward, threading its way amid the tangle. This bizarre striping, totally different from the rest of the plumage is found on all rails, and may be an adaptation to background typical of this group of birds.

Clapper rails rely largely on movement when in danger. In their peculiar environment they can evade their pursuers more readily by running than by standing still or by flying. Scampering through dense rushes for ages has developed their legs at the expense of their wings. Their flight is notably weak and slow, far too slow to enable them to evade a hawk towering above the ocean of grass in the salt meadows. Such open expanses afford few shrubs or trees in which a fugitive rail might dodge pursuit.

As life spent in the marsh has developed its protective coloration and the legs of a sprinter, so it has likewise molded the form of the clapper rail to suit its chosen haunts. Its breast is sufficiently wedge-shaped to slip between close-growing rushes, from which fact originated the familiar comparison, "thin as a rail." In like manner the toes have grown long and spreading, so as to insure safe passage across quaking bogs without loss of speed. The feet resemble those of other marsh-haunting species, such as the Florida and purple gallinules and the Mexican jacana.

At low tide, clapper rails feed on the oozy flats, but when caught by rising water they sometimes find it necessary to swim. A slightly membraneous structure between the bases of their toes enables them to do so whenever the need arises. Not only do these birds swim readily, but they teach their young to do the same. Like most waterbirds they can also dive. Once in a while, when suddenly attacked, a clapper rail will plunge and avoid surfacing by allowing only the tip of its bill to protrude from the water. This is the same ruse so frequently resorted to by the pied-billed grebe (*See under Grebe*). By gripping the base of a reed the rail can hold itself submerged and remain practically invisible until peril disappears.

The clapper rail is so completely master of its environment that it usually avoids taking to the air when disturbed. Its daylight flittings are short, the rail dropping down to hide just as soon as it sees cover. But at night, during partial migrations, clapper rails fly steadily along on their short wings at no great height. They steer parallel to the water, like wildfowl, but show no traces of the feebleness so notable in their occasional flights by day.

Clapper rails have many natural enemies. Their broken nests, scattered plumage, and well-sucked eggs, together with telltale footprints in the mud, suggest that bobcats, opossums, skunks, minks, and raccoons make many a successful raid on the clapper rail. Once in a while, too, the rather slow, red-tailed and red-shouldered hawks manage to catch these birds, and swift "blue darters" (Cooper's hawks) account for a few (*See under Accipiter*). Large fishes, snakes, and sea turtles also take their toll of the clapper rail on its eggs. In the deep South a single cottonmouth moccasin has been known to swallow all the eggs in a nest and the brooding bird with them.

Far more destructive to the clapper rail than any of these living agents are the northeast storms which sometimes drive the ocean in over their extensive breeding areas. Such tempests have drowned innumerable mother rails which are so devoted to their nests and eggs that they will often perish rather than desert them. In the days of greatest rail abundance the dead bodies of the females used to strew the shore after a big storm. Nowadays the nesting areas of clapper rails have been greatly depleted, but even so the hurricanes along the Atlantic Coast in August and September 1954, and of September 1955, destroyed hundreds of these birds.

Despite all these natural dangers clapper rails multiplied exceedingly until man invaded their haunts. His coming started a notable decline in their numbers. On the high tides at the time of a full moon, gunners decimated them. Sitting in the bow of a flat-bottomed boat paddled by an assistant they would shoot great numbers of rails that had climbed to the tops of reeds to escape the water. Fortunately for the birds this kind of "sport" has declined in popularity.

Clapper rails lay large sets of eggs, and sometimes, in southern marshes, two clutches in a season. Many of the second clutches may be due to the rails' persistence after the destruction of first settings by some unusually high tide. The birds are everywhere prolific enough to overcome all handicaps if given half a chance.

The nests of this species are sometimes well concealed but not invariably so. On the south shore of Long Island, New York, they are usually grassy platforms raised in the rushes just sufficiently to keep the eggs safe from the tides. Some are screened by canopies woven of dead reeds, and all are somewhat hollowed. Flotsam conceals some nests, but others may be sighted from a rod or so away. Even the eggs show protective hues—glossy buff spotted with reddish-brown, lavender, and gray, closely matching the nest cavity itself.

Similar nests may be seen on such places as Cobbs and Wreck islands off the coast of Virginia immediately south of the eastern shore of Maryland, where small colonies of clapper rails persist. Wreck Island is an ideal refuge for these birds. On the ocean side, sandbanks, anchored by beach grass, form a barrier—low but adequate to protect the isle. The inland parts are largely meadows, veined by creeks and subject to partial inundation at high tide. Adjacent higher stretches are shaggy with bushes in which a colony of little green

*Clapper rail*

herons build their stick nests, sometimes as many as two or three in a single blueberry thicket. There, too, the common grackle nests in large numbers.

Clapper rails frequently build several nests but lay eggs in only one. Although none of the grassy cradles may look old, many are empty. A partial explanation may be in the nesting of fish crows nearby (*see under Crow*); however clapper rails are usually pugnacious in defense of their nests and eggs. They often jump up and strike savagely at marsh hawks that happen to skim low over their reedy homes.

However, fish crows are very crafty and contrive to get eggs from rookeries

*Virginia rail*

whenever brooding birds leave them unprotected. On Devilfish Key off the southwest coast of Florida an observer frequently saw cormorants chasing fish crows among the mangroves.

The safest nests seem to be mere depressions in the tall grass, located several rods inland from high water on the seaward side of an island.

These are well concealed by weeds and flotsam. An observer was once attracted to a clapper rail's nest upon seeing two clapper rails fighting fiercely —jumping and striking at each other's throats like gamecocks. They proved to be a mother bird guarding three eggs against an intruding clapper rail which scampered away at the observer's approach. The intruding rail showed extraordinary fleetness of foot but did not attempt to fly. The mother bird threw herself on the grass at the observer's feet—not on her breast but on her side—and lay there motionless, as if hoping to escape notice.

The instant the observer stooped to touch her, the rail sprang up and dashed into a patch of tall grass about three rods distant. About a hundred paces from the first nest the observer discovered another which contained 16 eggs, almost a record number for the species. —H.M.H.

**Virginia Rail**
**Other Common Names**—Little red-breasted rail, small mud hen
**Scientific Name**—*Rallus limicola*
**Family**—Rallidae (rails, gallinules, and coots)
**Order**—Gruiformes
**Size**—Length, 9½ inches
**Range**—North America. Breeds from British Columbia, southern Saskatchewan, Ontario and New Brunswick south to southern California, Utah, Kansas, Missouri, Illinois, New Jersey, and North Carolina. Winters from Oregon, Utah, and Colorado to Baja California and Guatemala, also in lower Mississippi Valley states, and from North Carolina to Florida

This shy and secretive bird is almost an exact duplication in miniature of the king rail, and like its larger relative is an inhabitant of marshlands. Its favorite haunts are freshwater marshes. It is especially fond of cattail marshes and river meadows, and often inhabits oozy, sodden areas where button bushes and other marsh-loving shrubbery grow. It threads with stealthy grace all the intricate windings and runways of the marsh, its slender body slipping and squeezing between the stems of reeds and rushes. Where cover is available it seldom takes wing, preferring to hide among the tussocks or in the grasses.

The Virginia rail, in addition to its

exploits on the ground and underwater, is a good climber, now and then clambering about rushes, shrubs, and vines in search of insects, seeds, and berries. It is very fond of grasshoppers and beetles, small crustaceans, and many small forms of aquatic life.

The nest is built of grasses, in tussocks or on the ground in marshes. The eggs are six to twelve, pale creamy white, speckled with brown (*See also under Sora*).

**RAT**

The New World rats are assigned to the family Cricetidae that, in addition, includes many of the New World mice, the voles, and the lemmings (*See also Lemming; Mouse; and Vole*). Within North America north of Mexico, three genera of rats occur—*Oryzomys* (rice rats), *Sigmodon* (cotton rats), and *Neotoma* (wood rats). In common with the other genera of cricetids, the three genera of rats have compressed lower incisors, no premolar teeth, and tails that are usually naked, sparsely haired, or scaly. These mammals are generally differentiated from mice on the basis of their larger size, the term rat having little, if any, biological significance.

The rice rats, of which some 18 species occur in Central America, Mexico, and North America, have only one representative north of Mexico, the marsh rice rat, *Oryzomys palustris,* of the southeastern United States.

The genus *Sigmodon,* or cotton rats, is represented in Central America, Mexico, and North America by some 13 species, of which 3 inhabit North America north of Mexico. The hispid cotton rat group, *Sigmodon hispidus,* contains some 33 described subspecies of which 17 occur north of Mexico, primarily in the southeastern and south-central United States, but also locally in southern New Mexico, Arizona, and California.

Three subspecies of the least cotton rat, *Sigmodon minimus,* occur in the desert regions of southeastern Arizona and southwestern New Mexico. In the same area, but more restricted to the southeastern corner of Arizona and the southwestern corner of New Mexico, with an extension into southern Texas, is the yellow-nosed cotton rat, *Sigmodon ochrognathus.* These two species of cotton rats have adapted to a desert environment in much the same way as other desert-dwelling rodents (*See under Desert: Animal Life in the Desert*). They are inactive during the daytime and produce most of their water requirements through metabolic processes rather than drinking. They have also been observed to seal off their burrow entrances to prevent the escape of cool moist air in much the same way as the kangaroo rat (*See Kangaroo Rat*).

The 22 named species of wood rats (*Neotoma*) are represented by 7 species in North America north of Mexico. These rodents have adapted to a variety of swampy, semiarid, and arid environments in the southern United States. One species, the bushy-tailed wood rat, *Neotoma cinera,* that lives from northern Arizona and New Mexico north to southern Yukon Territory in Canada, west to the Pacific Coast in British Columbia, Washington, Oregon, and northern and central California, and east to central Colorado, eastern Nebraska, North Dakota, and South Dakota, is the only New World rat with a heavily furred tail.

Other species include the eastern wood rat, *Neotoma floridana,* the southern plains wood rat, *N. micropus,* the white-footed wood rat, *N. albigula,* the desert wood rat, *N. lepida,* the Mexican wood rat, *N. mexicana,* and the dusky-footed wood rat, *N. fuscipes.* All of these species build rather bulky houses that resemble beaver lodges. These are built on dry land, sometimes in crevices or under overhangs of cliffs, and, in some species, in trees. The nest is added to as long as it is occupied and sometimes attains great size. The habit of collecting things, particularly shiny objects such as tin foil or coins has given the wood

*The eastern wood rat builds a lodge of sticks in the shelter of a cliff or thicket, and is continually adding material to it*

rat the common names of pack rat, or trade rat.

The Old World rats—family Muridae—are also represented in the New World by the black, ship, or roof rat, *Rattus rattus*, and the brown, house, or Norway rat, *Rattus norvegicus*. These species have reached the New World on ships from Europe and Asia, and have established themselves successfully wherever man lives. The black rat probably came to the New World with the earliest explorers and the brown rat, about 1775. The range of the black rat has been literally pushed to the edge of the sea by the introduction of the second species. Unlike the other murids (the brown rat and the house mouse, *Mus musculus*), the black rat inhabits areas that have not been heavily populated by man. Its range is restricted to parts of the southeastern United States and along the North American and Mexican coasts.

The brown rat ranges from southern Canada and the Alaskan coasts throughout the United States and Mexico to Central and South America. It is particularly concentrated in areas inhabited by man, and is responsible for several diseases that attack man and livestock, among which are rabies, tularemia, typhus, trichinosis, and bubonic plague. The brown rat is the major contributor to an estimated quarter of a billion dollars damage annually by the three Old World rodents. —G.A.B.

**Eastern Wood Rat**
**Other Common Names**—Pack rat, trade rat
**Scientific Name**—*Neotoma floridana*
**Family**—Cricetidae (mice, rats, voles, and lemmings)
**Order**—Rodentia
**Size**—Body length, 14 to 17 inches; tail, 6 to 8 inches; weight, 7 to 12 ounces
**Range**—Eastern United States, as far north as the southeastern tip of New York and southern Pennsylvania, southern Missouri and extreme southwestern South Dakota; south to eastern Colorado, central Oklahoma, and eastern Texas. Also south in the mountains to northern Alabama, southern Georgia, and South Carolina to southern Florida

The eastern wood rat sometimes collects such useless objects as old shotgun shells and empty tobacco tins that it

*The hispid cotton rat lives in moist places where it burrows in the soft soil, often doing much damage to earthen dams and levees*

merely drops in and around its lodge This lodge, usually located in the shelter of a rocky cliff or thicket, looks like a pile of sticks and twigs. It never seems to be completed, for the rat is constantly adding new sticks. Each additional layer may make it more waterproof. Inside are many hallways, some leading to a nest of dry grass and fibers. Several broods of blind, helpless young are born between the spring and fall. When they are about three weeks old their eyes open, and a week or so later they are out on their own. Wood rats feed on juicy plants, nuts, berries, and seeds. They usually live in mountain rockslides or lowland swamps, and their presence conflicts little with man's interests. Bobcats, foxes, weasels, and owls help keep their numbers in check.

**Hispid Cotton Rat**
**Other Common Names** – Common cotton rat
**Scientific Name** – *Sigmodon hispidus*
**Family** – Cricetidae (mice, rats, voles, and lemmings)
**Order** – Rodentia
**Size** – Body length, 9 to 13 inches; tail, 3¼ to 5¼ inches; weight, 4 to 8½ ounces
**Range** – Southern United States, from North Carolina, southern Missouri, Kansas, southern New Mexico and Arizona, west to Colorado River; south through Central America

One of the worst agricultural pests in the South is the cotton rat. These rodents often feed on sweet potatoes, alfalfa, or sugarcane, and sometimes destroy the eggs and young of bobwhites. They may dig burrows that riddle banks and levees. They inhabit swamps, forest glades, ditches or any location where weeds and grass will provide good cover for their innumerable runways. Their grass and fiber nests are located in these tunnels or in burrows underground. Here, many litters of 6 to 11 young are born each year. Unlike most newborn rats, they are covered with hair at birth, their eyes open in less than three days, and they are weaned at the age of two weeks. Before they leave the nest their mother may be raising her next litter.

The removal of weeds and other cover discourages the presence of cotton rats. Without shelter, they are easy prey for hawks and snakes by day, and at night they are eaten by owls, foxes, coyotes, weasels, raccoons, and even alligators.

**RATTLEWEED**
**Menzie's Rattleweed**
**Other Common Names**—Locoweed
**Scientific Name**—*Astragalus menziesii*
**Family**—Leguminosae (pulse family)
**Range**—Coastal species ranging from Monterey to southern California
**Habitat**—Dunes and bluffs along the ocean, 10 to 300 feet altitude
**Time of Blooming**—April through September

On sandy slopes as far south as Serf the long trailing stems of the Menzie's rattleweed furnish much interest. The soft green leaves composed of many leaflets are from three to six inches long. The panicle of yellowish cream flowers set close together on the stem and the six-inch clusters of iridescent pods combine to make an admirable picture. Each individual pod, from 1½ to 2 inches long, is strongly inflated and contains the seeds that produce the "rattle" when the parchmentlike pods are shaken.

Other species—up to five feet high, their flowers varying from white to purple and yellow, and the pods, from short, inflated ones to those that are long and beanlike—are found from early spring until late fall in almost all sections of the state. In high desert ranges appears a beautiful scarlet flowered species, *Astragalus coccineus,* with white and very silky leaves. Locoweed is a common name for this plant since some species are poisonous to livestock.

*Rattleweed*

**RAVEN**
**Common Raven**
**Other Common Names**—Mexican raven
**Scientific Name**—*Corvus corax*
**Family**—Corvidae (jays, magpies, and crows)
**Order**—Passeriformes
**Size**—Length, 26 inches
**Range**—Alaska and northern Canada, south through western United States and Mexico to Nicaragua; in central and eastern North America to Minnesota, Wisconsin, northern Michigan, central Ontario, southern Quebec, and Maine, south in the Appalachian Mountains to Georgia

The largest and the heaviest of the passerines, or perching birds, the common raven, has been driven from many of its former haunts by encroaching humanity. In North America it is uncommon except in northern Canada, parts of the Appalachians, and the Far West.

Nearly twice as large as its relative, the crow, the common raven differs from it in possessing a wedge-shaped tail and a thick ruff of feathers on the front of the throat. Its call is more of a croak than a caw. In soaring, the wings are held flat, in eagle fashion, while the crow

*The common raven is the largest North American perching bird*

holds its wings at an angle. Ravens fly by alternating power strokes with short glides; crows have a direct flight.

Like crows, ravens are scavengers, eating carrion, the eggs and nestlings of smaller birds, and even taking small mammals. Nests are usually built on cliffsides, and four or five eggs is the normal clutch. Besides the common raven, the white-necked raven, *Corvus cryptoleucus,* is a resident bird in southeastern Arizona, southern New Mexico, north-central Colorado, south-central Nebraska, and western Kansas, and south into Mexico. —G.B.S.

**Return of the Raven in the Southeast**

There is probably not a bird in history that has figured so directly in legend, superstition, and folklore as has the raven. The result of this has been its persecution, almost to the verge of extinction in some places throughout its wide range, including much of the eastern part of the United States. A generation ago our northern raven, *Corvus corax principalis,* a subspecies of the common raven, had all but disappeared in the eastern United States, except along the coast of Maine. And its local extirpation was largely caused by superstitious ignorance.

An amazing number of people go about under a constant dread of incurring "bad luck" by breaking mirrors, walking under ladders, raising umbrellas indoors, or in crossing the path of a black cat. All these and many other similar puerile superstitions have a stronger hold on people even today, than one might think. When such unreasoning attitudes extend toward and embrace any living creature, *woe betide it!* Such was the raven's fate, and so it has been for centuries, both in the Old World and in the New.

Innumerable legends, stories, and beliefs have been built around the bird from early times, and thousands of people have lived in dread of ravens. An example or two will be illustrative. Charles Waterton in his *Essays* (London, 1870) indicates this general feeling of dread:

> That raven on the left-hand oak,
> Curse on his ill-betiding croak,
> Bodes me no good!

Again, Grower's *Confessio Amantis* contains the following:

> A raven by whom yet men maie
> Take evidence, when he crieth,
> That some mishap it signifieth.

Last, the fear with which many regarded the somber bird as a spreader of disease is vividly described in *Jew of Malta* (Marlowe) in this verse—

> Like the sad presaging raven that tolls
> The sick man's passport in her hollow
> beak,
> And, in the shadow of the silent night,
> Does shake contagion from her sable
> wing.

So it went. Even the sight of the bird was an evil omen, and if one alighted on church or dwelling it was taken as a certain sign of death or disaster. Should a sick person be in any such dwelling, quick death was sure to follow. Many of these superstitions of Europe and elsewhere were brought here by the early settlers. The occasional predatory habits of the raven did nothing to alleviate the ill will against the bird. Its attacks on young domestic animals—kids, lambs, and poultry—evoked the wrath of farmers and overcame superstitious dread to the extent of frequent shooting of ravens. This grew to be a confirmed habit. It seems certain that some animosity toward the raven, and superstition about it persists in remote areas such as the coves and valleys of the Blue Ridge Mountains, whose early settlers and many present-day residents are of Anglo-Saxon stock. Undoubtedly, their attitude toward the bird has been handed down for generations.

In recent years, however, the common raven has reappeared in the Southeast to a gratifying degree and has been staging a definite "comeback." In the use of this expression one thinks almost automatically of our egrets, but though the egrets have increased greatly, neither of the "plume birds"—the American egret and the snowy egret—even at their lowest ebb, ever had any onus attached to them, as did the raven. The egrets were killed because of their beautiful feathers; ravens were often killed because of superstitious fear of them. Both white birds and black, are, happily now, reaping the harvest of enlightened public opinion.

While it is not possible to give any population figures of the decline, scarcity, and eventual increase of the common raven in the Southeast, something may be visualized of its rarity 30 years ago from one ornithologist's experience as a bird student in a favored part of the raven's original eastern range. As a boy, a youth, and an adult he spent each summer, or a great part thereof, from 1914 to 1934, in the high Blue Ridge Mountains of western North Carolina and Virginia. He made several visits to these areas afterward from 1942 to 1945. This country is dominated by two peaks of some fame—Mt. Mitchell of 6,684 feet altitude, and Grandfather Mountain, 5,964 feet above sea level. Mt. Mitchell is the highest mountain east of the Mississippi River, and was about the heart of the raven's range in the old days.

Each summer, camping trips to then very remote areas allowed a constant watch for birds, always with the consuming desire to see a raven. In the summers of the 1920's this ornithologist had a kindred spirit as field companion, James J. Murray of Lexington, Virginia. Near his home in the famed Valley of Virginia, a few occurred, and while on a visit there, this observer saw his first raven on August 15, 1931.

The Blowing Rock-Linville, North Carolina, resort region, over which towers Grandfather Mountain, has shown a gradual but steady increase in opportunities to see ravens, for that great mountain has tremendous rocks, cliffs, and ledges of which the bird is so fond. Extending westward into the Great Smokies the same thing is true. Mt. Mitchell is the culminating peak of a short but high range of the Blue Ridge known as the Black Mountains (by reason of the spruce-balsam growth) and though cliffs are not abundant there, there are enough of them to attract ravens.

The greatest factor that has favored the comeback of the common raven in that whole eastern region has been the establishment of the Great Smoky Mountains National Park. Protection of wildlife there is absolute. Exactly the type of habitat preferred by the raven is present, and the area is a source from which increasing raven populations may extend outward. Nesting sites of ravens in mountainous country are notoriously difficult to reach, which is another factor favorable to their increase.

However, the whole southern mountain country forms good raven habitat, and today, travelers along that great scenic motor route called the Blue Ridge Parkway (beginning in Virginia, at the end of the Skyline Drive), have excellent chances of seeing and watching ravens. Certain it is that the sight of the big black bird does much to enhance the wild natural beauty of that spectacular region. Any reasonably good look will reveal the raven's identity. It is twice the size of a crow, and its flight is hawklike, in that it alternately flaps and soars on *horizontal* wings and the conspicuously large tail is wedge-shaped.

Never a frequent coastal species in the middle and southern Atlantic region, the common raven has even appeared there in recent years. South Carolina may be taken as the area as far down in the Southeast where such records have transpired, or are likely to. Though the species is, and has been an uncommon permanent resident in the extreme northwestern corner in the mountains of South Carolina, it has been practically unknown within the coastal plain since colonial times. Arthur T. Wayne, the veteran ornithologist who lived near Charleston, South Carolina, all his life, never saw a raven in his 45 years in the field there. None the less, in later years, the raven has appeared in that area. Two were seen in 1936, three in 1928, and two in 1943, one of the latter being captured with a broken wing and taken to the Charleston Zoo. The bird lived there until 1950. Not only has the raven made a very definite return to its upland haunts in the last decade, but it has appeared in areas where it had not been seen in far longer periods of time.

As this century passed its halfway mark, it seemed clear that conservation endeavor had made its mark in many ways. The increased protection of wildlife and the growing knowledge of its important relation to human welfare had arisen to ward off ignorance, bias, and thoughtless destruction of animals and of their habitats (*See Protection of Birds*).

The present status of the common raven may well be taken as an indication and example of what education and the setting aside of great national parks may do for threatened species of wildlife (*See under National Park*). The birdwatcher of the early part of this century, who was all but denied sight of a raven in the East, today has an excellent chance of thrilling to the observation of the black dweller of the mountain crags, and even in the lower levels. There are many who look for it today as they come southward over highways through the high country. Certainly, there is vivid contrast in the witnessing of its occurrence now to that of the day when Matthew Lewis wrote his sea-faring ballad "Bill Jones":

*The raven lives throughout much of North America in forests, prairies, and deserts*

Ah, well-a-day, the sailor said,
Some danger must impend,
Three ravens sit in yonder glade
And evil will happen, I'm sore afraid
'Ere we reach our journey's end.

And what have the ravens with us to do?
Does their sight betoken us evil?
To see one raven 'tis luck, its true,
But it's certain misfortune to light upon
two,
And meeting with *three* is the devil.

Anyone today "meeting with three," soaring majestically over the peaks of the Great Smokies of North Carolina and Tennessee, or over a wide valley there stretching away from the slopes of Mt. Mitchell or Grandfather Mountain, would be far from thinking of such encounter as anything but great good fortune and the blessings of a red-letter day. —A.S., Jr.

**RAY** (*See under Sharks, Rays, and Chimeras*)

**REDBUD** (*See with Pecan*)

**REDPOLL**

**Common Redpoll**

**Other Common Names**—Redpoll linnet, lintie, little meadowlark

**Scientific Name**—*Acanthis flammea*

**Family**—Fringillidae (grosbeaks, finches, sparrows, and buntings)

**Order**—Passeriformes

**Size**—Length, 5¼ inches

**Range**—Circumpolar in arctic and subarctic regions south to British Columbia, Alberta, Saskatchewan, Manitoba, and Ontario, southeastern Quebec and Newfoundland, Winters south to northern California, Utah, and Nevada, central Labrador, Kansas, southern Indiana, and Ohio, northern West Virginia and North Carolina. In Old World south to central and southern Europe, the Caucasus, China, and Japan

The common redpoll is an irregular winter visitor to the more northerly portions of the United States. Sometimes it comes in flocks when driven southward by unusual cold or lack of food. It closely resembles the goldfinch in its general habits. The nest is in a low tree or grass tuft and is made of moss and grasses, and lined with hair, feathers, or other soft materials. The eggs are from four to six and are white, tinged with bluish-green and spotted with reddish-brown.

*The common redpoll is a bird of the circumpolar region and only visits the United States irregularly*

**RED TIDE**

A dinoflagellate named *Gymnodinium breve*, a microscopic protozoan classed with other one-celled animals with whip-like structures called flagellae in the class Mastigophora, causes the phenomenon known as red tide (*See also Protozoa*).

Normally an unimportant part of the drifting fauna (plankton) of warm oceans, under certain conditions this dinoflagellate increases its numbers to such an extent that patches of water turn reddish or brown. The waste products of masses of red-tide organisms are fatal to many species of fish and marine invertebrates.

Red tide occurs chiefly in the Gulf of Mexico. A similar dinoflagellate in the Pacific, *Gonyaulax*, is responsible for producing a substance toxic to humans—one that becomes concentrated in mussels that have fed upon this dinoflagellate. (*See also Plant Kingdom*) —G.B.S.

*American redstarts, female (above); male (below)*

**REDSTART**
**American Redstart**
**Other Common Names**—Redstart warbler, redstart flycatcher, firetail, yellow-tailed warbler
**Scientific Name**— *Setophaga ruticilla*
**Family**—Parulidae (wood warblers)
**Order**—Passeriformes
**Size**—Length, 4½ to 5½ inches
**Range**—Breeds from southern Alaska, central Manitoba, northern Ontario, central Quebec, and Newfoundland south to Oregon, northern Utah, Colorado, Louisiana, southern Alabama, and Georgia. Winters in the West Indies, and from central Mexico to northern South America

Like many other North American birds, the redstart's name was taken from a similar European species. The English redstart is a small thrush but the American redstart is a wood warbler, one of a large family of birds peculiar to this hemisphere. Ornithologists refer to the wood warblers as the "butterflies of the bird world." None of them is more butterflylike than the redstart. It flits from tree to tree, and its habit of spreading its tail and drooping its wings, thus displaying the gaudy black-and-orange flash pattern, adds to the illusion. The Cubans call the redstart *candelita* which means *little torch.*

The American redstart is one of the most abundant birds in eastern North America. It is not improbable that there are as many redstarts as there are robins. Robins are birds of towns, farms, and roadsides, and are seen very often. On the other hand, the redstart is not seen as often because it is found in the thick foliage of second-growth woodland trees.

The American redstart does not reach its nesting territory until the trees have leafed out. Its voice is rather colorless. Like most warblers it has at least two distinct songs. One sounds like *tse-tse-tse-tse-a;* the other sounds like *wee-see, wee-see, wee-see-wee.* On the nesting grounds, the male's song is his way of proclaiming territory. He claims a small piece of woodland for his own and then sings out its boundaries to the other males. Where redstarts are numerous, they must do a great amount of singing and chasing other males. The closer the territories are to each other, the more constantly the male redstarts sing.

The nest of the American redstart is usually 5 to 35 feet up in a sapling, placed in an upright crotch, or where a branch shoots off from the main trunk. It is a silvery-looking, firm-walled cup, made of plant down, cobwebs, plant fibers, and often birch bark. The three to five eggs are cream-white or gray-white, spotted with lilac and brown. Incubation takes about 12 days. When the young are ready to leave the nest (another 10 days) they are plain gray, but later in the season they look much like their mother—brown with yellow patches. The young males, the following spring, are still much like their mother, except that the yellow patches have assumed a more orange tone; sometimes there are a few black feathers showing, but the adult male plumage usually takes two years to develop.

Few birds are more active in their search for insects. Caterpillars—both smooth and hairy ones—bugs, moths, flies, beetles, and many other insects are eaten. Some are picked from the underside of the leaves where they have been hiding, some from the crevices in the branches, and others are snatched out of the air.

American redstarts move southward by September, and late in the month, only a few stragglers are left in the more northern parts of the bird's range. A few linger into October, and an occasional one is found even later. The redstart hordes sweep southward on a front 2,000 miles wide that extends from the Atlantic to the Rocky Mountains. In leaving the United States, unlike some of the other warblers that depart by a narrow lane, the redstart uses at least three or four of the main bird flyways. Many of them go through Florida and hop over to Cuba and Haiti, in the West Indies. Many more fly across the Gulf of Mexico, making the crossing in a single night. Some follow the Gulf shore down into the tropics; others wander down the Rocky Mountains into Mexico.

Although a great many American redstarts spend the winter in the West Indies, large numbers of them go to South America, where they remain from November to March. Travelers in the tropics get some idea of just how abundant they are, for often they may see a half a dozen, or more, in a single bush or tree. —A.B., Jr.

## REDWOOD

**Other Common Names**—Coast redwood, California redwood
**Scientific Name**—*Sequoia sempervirens*
**Family**—Taxodiaceae (taxodium family)
**Range**—A coastal strip about 30 miles wide; from Monterey County, California, north to extreme southwestern Oregon, a distance of about 450 miles
**Habitat**—Humid coastal forests
**Leaves**—Needles, one-half to one inch long, in double ranks around the stems but bending outward at the sides to form flat sprays at the twig ends
**Bark**—Deeply grooved and fluted, often a foot thick, bright cinnamon-red underneath but weathering to grayish, tan, or chestnut brown
**Flower**—Male and female flowers on different parts of the tree in late winter
**Fruit**—The oval, woody cones are about one inch long, compact and dark green at first, ripening the first season

The coast redwood, *Sequoia sempervirens*, grows in the more favorable parts of an area that forms a narrow coastal belt some 20 to 30 miles wide from extreme southwestern Oregon to the Santa Lucia Mountains of Monterey County, California, a distance of 450 miles. It seldom ranges to an altitude above 1,000 feet and is averse to the boggy soil of stream mouths, and to windy headlands. The tallest and densest forests grow along the river benches of Humboldt and Del Norte counties, where long tongues of summer sea fog extend far up the ocean-facing canyons, and temperature and humidity vary least. These river benches are said to support the tallest and heaviest stands of timber in the world.

Fossil redwoods date back many millions of years to a time when climatic conditions were favorable to their growth in regions where they no longer grow. Fossil specimens have been found in Alaska, Greenland, Connecticut, New Jersey, Montana, North Dakota, Arizona, and in France, Germany, and Siberia. A closely related genus, the dawn redwood (*Metasequoia*) was known only from fossils until its discovery as a living tree in Central China in 1944. The dawn redwood, unlike the redwoods of the West Coast of North America, is a deciduous tree, shedding its leaves each year.

The coast redwoods were first discovered by a group of Spanish explorers of the Portola Expedition that traveled overland from San Diego to a point near the present town of Watsonville on the shores of Monterey Bay in the year 1769. Father Crespi, the expedition's recorder, noted in his notebook on October 10th of that year that the coastal plains and low hills were "well-forested with very high trees of a red color, not known to us."

Impressive circles of tall redwood trees grow in virgin forests, as well as in cutover land, and in their symmetry resemble the "fairy circles" of mushrooms on a lawn (*See under Fungus*). The sprouts grow very rapidly and form fine trees, ready to be lumbered 40 years after the original cutting of a tract. A redwood tree, known as the "Founder's Tree," after the three founders of the Save-the-Redwood League, growing in the virgin forest of the Bull Creek Flat area of Humboldt County, stands 364 feet in height and for many years was reputed to be the tallest tree in the world. However, in the winter of 1963, the National

*Ninety percent of the coast redwood forests are now owned by the public*

*Two cross-sections of redwood trees show their growth rings and age*

Geographic Society sponsored an ecological study of the redwood forests, and three trees measuring 367.8 feet, 367.4 feet, and 364.3 feet feet were discovered in the Redwood Creek Woods near Orick, California. In virgin redwood forests the ground beneath the trees is densely shaded, for, although the trunks are clear of branches from 50 to 100 feet above their bases, the tips of the crown branches weave such a close canopy overhead that only filtered light reaches the forest floor beneath. The late John C. Merriam has said of these tree trunks, "like pillars of a temple, the giant columns space themselves with mutual support, producing unity and not mere symmetry." It is this unity, together with the silence of the forest, which has caused many authors to write of the cathedral-like quality of these groves. For this reason a tract in Del Norte County has been appropriately dedicated as the "National Tribute Grove," a memorial honoring the men and women who served in the armed forces of the United States during World War II.

In 1901, largely because of the efforts of the Sempervirens Club of San Jose, California, the first state park in the coast redwoods was established at Big Basin in Santa Cruz County. Seventeen years later, the Save-the-Redwoods League was organized by Dr. John C. Merriam, Madison Grant, and Dr. Henry Fairfield Osborn to raise funds for the acquisition and preservation of coast redwood stands that were threatened by increasing logging activity in Humboldt County.

The dedicated members of the League have been responsible for the creation of several state parks, among them Humboldt Redwoods State Park, Prairie Creek Redwoods State Park, Del Norte Coast Redwoods State Park, and Jedediah Smith Redwoods State Park. The funds raised by the Save-the-Redwoods League to purchase outstanding redwood forest areas have come from private donations that the State of California has matched dollar for dollar. About 85,000 acres of forest of which 50,000 are covered with virgin trees are now owned by the State of California. Another 250,000 acres are owned privately. The League is still actively raising funds for the purchase of these areas.

At present, plans are underway to create a national park of 30,000 to 35,000 acres that will include 10,000 acres of California's Prairie Creek Grove and an 150 acre forest owned by the National Geographic Society.

*Recommended Reading*

**A Living Link in History**—John C. Merriam. Save-the-Redwoods League, 114 Sansome Street, San Francisco.

**Animal Life in the Yosemite**—Joseph Grinnell and Tracey I. Storer. University of California Press, Berkeley, California.

**Giant Sequoia, Useful Trees of the United States, No. 16**—United States Department of Agriculture, Forest Service. United States Government Printing Office, Washington, D.C.

## REPTILE

### The Wonderful Variety of Reptiles

Virtually every modern zoological garden displays giant tortoises, pythons, and cobras. A zoo without reptiles would be as incomplete as a circus without elephants. Tropical jungles are no longer the only places where large reptiles can be seen. Without exposing themselves to hazards more disconcerting than crowds, intrepid explorers can watch mambas, tegus, or boa constructors in San Diego, Chicago, or New York. And, of course, large reptiles can be watched in the excellent zoos in other parts of the United States. People may regard snakes with revulsion, suspicion, awe, or admiration. If one may judge by the crowds that hover around the snakes exhibited, however, they are as irresistible as the penguins, gibbons, and seals.

Millions of Americans know less about native reptiles than they know about Nile monitors, king cobras, or green iguanas of other countries. Numerous visitors at the zoo can watch a big python in a well-planned exhibit. Small reptiles, however, are likely to interest the visitor only if he can examine them closely. Consequently, the diminutive reptiles must be housed in small cages, where they can be seen by only one or two visitors at a time. Curators and keepers in zoological gardens encounter further handicaps if they attempt to display small secretive reptiles that avoid exposing themselves to bright light. Moreover, the highly specialized burrowers, particularly the blind snakes and lizards with subterranean proclivities, seldom thrive if they are forced to expose themselves to view.

To meet the demands of the visitor, therefore, zoological gardens try to obtain the lizards, snakes, and tortoises that attain the greatest size. Nearly all are natives of tropical environments. The warm lowlands bordering the equator are also the great centers of reptile abundance and diversification. It does not follow, however, that all reptiles in the tropics are larger or more picturesque than those inhabiting other parts of the world. The attributes, appearance, or habits of several reptiles in the United States are as colorful, or in some instances even as bizarre, as those of the exotic species.

There are approximately 20 species of reptiles that live outside the United States for every one that occurs within. Reptiles do not live in Alaska, although the distributions of one lizard and one viper in Europe extend slightly beyond the Arctic Circle. Virtually all the reptiles in Hawaii—including but one tiny snake, a blind burrower—were introduced there. Of the four orders or the principal groups of reptiles with living representatives, only the order Rhynchocephalia with a lone survivor, the superficially lizardlike Tuatara, *Sphenodon,* of New Zealand, is missing from the United States. Turtles (Testudines), crocodilians (Crocodilia), and the lizards, amphisbaenians, and snakes grouped in one order (Squamata) are all represented within the United States.

The crocodilians are—or were, prior to their decimation—the greatest in length of the 240 species of reptiles known to inhabit the United States. The leatherback turtles, *Dermochelys,* that sporadically visit American shores are doubtless the heaviest. The alligator snapping turtle, *Macroclemys,* may be the heaviest freshwater turtle now living, but sheer bulk is not the most distinctive feature of many North American reptiles. The external appearance and feeding habits of the horned lizards, *Phrynosoma,* that inhabit the United States and Mexico are closely paralleled by those of the Australian thorny devil, *Moloch horridus.* The horned lizards, however, have the additional outlandish trait of being able to spurt blood from the corner of one or both eyes (*See under Lizard*).

Less outlandish, but certainly not commonplace, are the limbless lizards, *Anniella,* of California, that propel themselves through the sand, sporadically

*The western coachwhip snake is essentially uniformly colored, but the pattern of dark crosslines is one of many moderately distinctive regional ones*

*The reptiles flourished in great numbers and variety during the Mesozoic Era, some 280 to 135 million years ago. They filled virtually every ecological niche in a temperate climate when inland seas and marshes covered much of the present land mass. Reptiles roamed the land on two feet and on four, swam in the sea, and soared in the air. Then the great dinosaurs, ichthyosaurs, pterodactyls, and others, having given rise to the first birds and mammals, vanished, and the Age of Reptiles ended*

*The large fourth tooth in the lower jaw of the American crocodile fits into a groove in its upper jaw and remains visible when its mouth is closed*

*When alarmed, the collared lizard bolts away on all fours until it gains speed, then it runs on its hind legs like a small dinosaur*

*Today, only four orders of reptiles remain of all that great and varied group. One of these, the tuatara, clings to life on a few islands off the coast of New Zealand. A little time, and it too will join the impressive list of extinct species. Only the turtles, snakes and lizards, and alligators and crocodiles have survived the millions of years since they first appeared on earth. Protection of some of these animals is needed, for they too, are becoming dangerously few in numbers and may soon become museum pieces*

*The northern diamondback terrapin lives in coastal marshes and tidal flats, or wherever it can find a sheltered body of salt or brackish water*

*A Sonora kingsnake emerges from its leathery egg*

thrusting the head above the surface to seize their insect prey. Though far from being identical, the habits of the Florida sand skink, *Neoseps reynoldsi,* a sand-dwelling lizard, are amazingly similar. It literally swims through the sand but comes to the surface to feed. With only one toe on the forelimbs, and two toes on the hind limbs, the remnants of its legs play no part in its locomotion. Whether on the surface or beneath it, the tiny skink propels itself by flexing its body. Its movements are much less snakelike, however, than those of the much larger glass lizards, *Ophisaurus.* These limbless, partly subterranean reptiles are better adapted to crawl through tall grass or dense vegetation than to burrow.

The fossorial adaptations of the sand skink and three species of glass lizards in Florida, however, are surpassed by those of an amphisbaenian restricted to that state. This odd creature, *Rhineura floridana,* though known as the Florida worm-lizard, possesses features that are not characteristic of lizards. It shares many of its distinctive traits with other subterrestrial, vestigial-eyed reptiles largely concentrated in the tropical environments of Africa and South America. The amphisbaenians, like the snakes, have evolved separately and independently from the lizards from which they were derived. The chisel-snouted, completely limbless and almost eyeless "worm-lizard," though neither a worm nor a lizard, has stout jaws and other features that point to remote affinities with the lizards. Superficially it is a reptile in earthworm's clothing.

Florida has its lone amphisbaenian and more than its share of limbless lizards, but the arid Southwest also has its "sand swimmers." Other reptiles occasionally enter the desert dunes, but only a few specialists actually live in such extreme habitats. Such specialists as the shovel-nosed ground snake, *Chionactis occipitalis,* progress almost as rapidly in the sand as they do on the surface. On the other hand, the sidewinder, *Crotalus cerastes,* the only rattlesnake that invades the larger dunes, restricts its activities to the surface. It almost literally rolls along on the sand. Leaving behind parallel imprints of its belly, it progressively carries each segment of its body through an S-shaped arc between the points of contact on the sand.

The reptiles best fitted for life in dunes, however, are the fringe-footed sand lizards of the genus *Uma.* They feed on the surface, but if pursued they often launch themselves headfirst into the loose sand. They move only a short distance below the surface, usually little beyond the disrupted sand that reveals the point of entry. They avoid excessive heat as well as predators by submerging themselves in the sand. When they are not pursued, however, these dune-dwellers enter the sand slowly but efficiently. After they thrust the head beneath the surface, they cause the rest of the body to sink into the sand by rapidly vibrating the forelimbs, the hind limbs, and finally the tail.

A lizard, *Aporosaura,* that lives in the dunes of the Kalahari Desert in Africa, is adaptively modified in much the same way as the fringe-footed lizards, although it belongs to a distantly related family. Nothing comparable to the chameleons of Africa occurs in North America, where the name "American Chameleon" is erroneously applied to the American anole, *Anolis carolinensis.* (*See under Lizard*). This lizard can change from green to brown, but it lacks the prehensile tail, or the extraordinary tongue, eyes, and feet that put the true chameleons in a category by themselves. Arboreal (tree-dwelling) lizards, *Corythophanes* and *Laemanctus,* in the American tropics resemble chameleons to the extent of having casques, or crests, on the head, but they have long, relatively stiff tails more befitting relatives of the iguana.

Spines, crests, dewlaps, and similar structures characteristic of arboreal lizards cause them to blend into the vegetation of their native habitats. Predators and prey alike are baffled by the obscurity of the body outline. For similar reasons the head and neck of the bizarre, aquatic turtle, the matamata, *Chelys fimbriata,* is decked with flaps and fringes. Small fishes fail to become aware of the creature as it lies in wait on the bottom of muddy pools until they are confronted abruptly by gaping jaws. The huge alligator snapping turtle in the United States has evolved a different but equally effective way to trap small fishes. It lies in wait on the bottom with its mouth widely opened and its tongue exposed. Attached to the tongue there is a reddish appendage so constantly in motion that fishes readily mistake it for a squirming worm. For the majority of the fishes lured into the mouth, however, it is their last mistake.

Not all of the startling modifications in the structure or the behavior of modern reptiles enhance their effectiveness as predators. The survival of modern reptiles, whether they live in the United

*A young alligator*

States or elsewhere, is not simply a matter of food getting. Survival also depends upon the ability of reptiles to avoid predators as well as intolerable conditions that sometimes arise in the physical environment. Not every adaptive modification in the behavioral or structural traits of the reptiles in the United States is unique. Many, however, are adapted in ways that are unusual if not strikingly different. Snakes in other parts of the world "play 'possum" or feign death as a means of discouraging attack. The western hognosed snake, *Heterodon nasicus*, like some of its relatives east of the Mississippi, manages to look dead by rolling over on its back, and remaining motionless, with its jaws askew and its tongue distended.

The cobras, *Naja*, of Africa and Asia are world-famous, not so much because of the threat they pose but because of the posture they assume when they are threatened. A hissing cobra with its head raised and hood distended presumably intimidates, alarms, or confuses—and quite possibly discourages animals that intend to attack it. Slightly longer ribs support the hood of the cobra, but no extensive structural changes are associated with its defensive posture and behavior.

In contrast, the amazing mechanism that adds noise to the threatening display of the rattlesnakes is singularly complex. Thirty species of rattlesnakes, 15 of which inhabit the United States, are so widely distributed between Canada and Argentina, that Americans seldom regard such snakes with awe unless they are exceptionally large. The rattle is a truly unique structure, however, that readily distinguishes rattlers from all other snakes. It has excited the admiration of naturalists ever since explorers and colonists in the New World first encountered rattlesnakes.

Americans may not know that the eastern diamondback rattlesnake, *Crotalus adamanteus*, is among the most formidable and dangerous of snakes now living. Also, they may not know that the United States is inhabited by lizards that run on their hind legs or that some attain speeds of 20 miles per hour, although these are obvious things that these reptiles do. Many people may not know, as those who study reptiles do, that rattlesnakes and other pit-vipers are equipped with infrared receptors that permit them to discriminate between objects with temperatures that differ by a fraction of a degree. Students of reptiles also know that marine turtles orient their movements with sufficient precision to reach destinations as remote as Ascension Island in the middle of the Atlantic. Thus far, however, no one knows how turtles perform such feats, although A. F. Carr, the foremost American student of turtles, may yet find the explanation.

The majority of reptiles are aware of sounds, but vision and the sense of smell are more often used by them in locating their prey. The sounds (vocalizations) uttered by geckos are apparently important in their mating activities. Thus far, however, no one has undertaken a thorough investigation of the mating activities of these nocturnal lizards. Male crocodilians (alligators and crocodiles) advertise their presence by bellowing and seemingly discourage other males from venturing into their territories. The croaking sounds uttered by the tuatara at night may also be manifestations of territorial behavior, but this has not been ascertained. Experiments suggest that snakes hear airborne sounds of low frequency, even though it was long believed that vibrations of the substratum accounted for their reactions to sound.

Lizards and snakes that are habitually underground are ill-equipped to see, particularly when their eyes are covered by opaque or translucent scales. Reptiles, particularly those in aquatic or arboreal habitats, seem to depend more on vision than their sense of smell in locating their prey. In such reptiles the eyes have shifted to positions that permit binocular vision (*See also under Bird: Senses*). The resulting overlap in the individual fields of vision may afford better depth perception. The evidence is not wholly conclusive, but some reptiles appear to have color vision (*See under Animal: Color Vision of Animals*).

The forked tongue that all snakes and many lizards thrust beyond their jaws picks up odorous particles that are carried to organs of smell in the roof of the mouth. The senses of smell and taste are not distinguishable, however, for aquatic turtles become aware of substances in the water by drawing samples into the mouth through the nostrils. Marine turtles, and possibly others, close the nostrils and cease sampling the water while they are asleep. Turtles searching for food on land may depend less on the sense of smell than vision. Field observations suggest that this is true of the whipsnakes, *Masticophis*, and some other diurnal snakes. Bullsnakes, *Pituophis*, apparently use their vision as well as their sense of smell in locating their prey; the sense of smell is perhaps of greater importance to nocturnal snakes.

Detailed investigations of the senses of reptiles have not been sufficiently extensive, however, to account for many of their activities. Barely enough has been learned about the behavior of reptiles to pose all the questions that remain to be answered. It is evident, nevertheless, that many sensory mechanisms come into play, whether reptiles are searching for food, engaged in mating activities, or avoiding predators. Almost nothing is known about the habits or the behavior of the most secretive reptiles.

### *Dispersal and Distribution*

The abundance and diversification of reptiles in warm environments suggest that this group of backboned animals evolved in the tropics. Reptiles cannot tolerate prolonged exposure to freezing temperatures or the seasonal heat of dry deserts. Conditions intolerable to reptiles are virtually never encountered in the tropical lowlands, where reptiles are active almost the year around. It is reasonable to infer that the early reptiles could not tolerate temperatures much above or below the extremes encountered today in the tropics. They could adjust their activities, however, in ways that permitted them to avoid exposing themselves to excessively hot or cold conditions on the surface. This in turn depended upon their being aware of changes in the environment.

In order for reptiles to survive in regions subject to seasonal changes, they must seek protective cover before they are incapacitated. Green iguanas, *Iguana iguana*, and other reptiles shifted from their native habitats in the tropics to outdoor cages in the United States fail to move into shade or sun when temperatures rise and fall beyond compatible limits. They survive, however, if they are kept under conditions where temperatures can be artificially controlled. Reptiles native to temperate climates ordinarily find shelter before they become inactivated by low temperatures or overheated when temperatures rise. It seems probable, therefore, that their initial spread from the tropics into the temperate zone was accompanied by modifications in behavioral traits. Physiological adjustments were also necessary before reptiles endured climatic conditions that imposed prolonged periods of inactivity during the winter.

Lizards that absorb heat directly from the sun are often warmer than human beings. But the lizards remain warm only while they are active. During the night, or when direct sunlight is unavailable, they become cooler and seek protective cover. As a rule snakes and turtles can tolerate fewer days of sunshine and cooler environments than lizards. Such tolerances are reflected in the distributions of the various groups of reptiles. Approximately 240 species of reptiles occur within the borders of the United States, but the number dwindles to fewer than 40 in Canada. Turtles fare much better in the north than lizards, however, for nearly one-fourth of the turtles in the United States also occur in Canada. In contrast, there are 80 species of lizards in the United States, but the distributions of only 5 extend as far north as Canada. Of the 115 snakes in the United States, only 22 are in Canada.

The southern part of Florida is semitropical rather than tropical, but the state is inhabited by nearly as many kinds of reptiles (twice as many turtles) as the whole of Europe. There are many fewer lizards in Florida, however, partly because lizards are less diversified in humid regions than in warm, dry deserts. Lizards thrive in the Southwest, particularly in the arid regions where they can avail themselves of direct sunlight more often than they can in humid regions.

Because reptiles avail themselves of heat from sources outside the body, they consume less food than birds or mammals of similar size. Without basking, many of these "warm-blooded" creatures can maintain the body at temperatures much above those prevailing outside the body. Consequently birds and mammals are abroad and active at times when reptiles retreat to shelter. "Warm-blooded" animals, whether they are insulated by fur or feathers, however, lose heat. Energy is required to compensate for this heat loss, and this is costly in terms of fuel consumption. The food that sustains one mammal for a year might contain enough energy to support 20 to 30 reptiles of comparable size and weight for a similar period of time.

Reptiles must, nevertheless, regulate their intake of heat. Except in some aquatic environments or the relatively stable conditions that prevail in tropical lowlands, great bulk is disadvantageous. The time required for a reptile to raise or lower its temperature depends upon its size and to some extent upon its shape. Other things being equal (which they seldom are) a large reptile might bask for hours to heat its body to the same level reached by a tiny lizard in a matter of minutes. In part, this explains why so few of the 240 reptiles in the United States are large, but the duration of the growing season may also impose limits on bulk.

*Origins and Ancestries*

Reptiles appeared when their progenitors were sufficiently advanced (or adapted) not merely to *be* on land but to begin life on land. Before reptiles evolved well over 200 million years ago, the only backboned animals on land were amphibians (*See Amphibian*). They hatched from small eggs deposited in the water, and began life as fishlike creatures with gills. As hatchlings they were little more than animated digestive tracts. Flimsy muscles attached to tails propelled their fragile bodies. They had eyes and a mouth, and if they encountered food, nibbled often enough, and evaded predators, they eventually developed limbs. Lungs had evolved as a substitute for gills at about the time these creatures shifted their activities to land. Their lungs were primitive, but amphibians augmented their intake of oxygen by absorbing it through their mucus-covered skin. They thrived, largely perhaps, in the humid atmosphere of the swamp.

Dry environments were unsuitable for amphibian eggs, or skins that were continuously losing moisture. Millions of years elapsed before a few exceptional amphibians, those destined to give rise to the reptiles, overcame these shortcomings. Their eggs became progressively larger and covered with hard shells or tough membranes. Each egg, in essence, was an individual natal pool that contained nearly everything the offspring needed during its development. It emerged fully formed, with limbs, lungs, and a skin that remained dry and curtailed the loss of moisture. Such near-replicas of their parents could seek food on land from the moment they escaped from the egg.

The evolutionary transition from amphibian to reptile entailed more than the changes that led to larger, well-protected eggs, and a skin resistant to moisture

*Two of the poisonous snakes in North America are the cottonmouth, or water moccasin (above), and the western diamondback rattlesnake (below). They are both extremely dangerous reptiles but prefer to live away from man, the diamondback in the arid Southwest, the cottonmouth in swamplands*

loss. These were important features of the transition, however. Later on a few salamanders, frogs, and caecilians also omitted the free-swimming larval stage as they became better adapted for life on land. All amphibians now living nevertheless continue to be handicapped by losing water from their moist skins. Such restrictions no longer beset the reptiles. Lizards in particular thrive in warm, arid environments that amphibians, except for a few specialized frogs, cannot tolerate. Although dependence on heat from sources outside the body imposes limitations on the reptiles, the modifications in the skin and the egg that signalized their origin, opened the door to a wider distribution, far beyond the confines of the swamp.

An evolutionary innovation in the reptile egg includes a saclike structure, richly supplied with blood vessels. It arises at the rear end of the embryo and comes to lie immediately under the hard but porous outer shell of the egg. Thereafter this sac serves as a lung during the embryo's development. In other words, it takes in oxygen and gives off carbon dioxide. A few adult lizards, snakes, and amphisbaenians retain the eggs within the body until their offspring are fully developed. Oxygen reaches their eggs through their blood, which also carries off waste products.

It follows that a reptile's egg cannot be submerged in the water without drowning the occupant. Ironically, crocodilians and aquatic turtles, including those otherwise highly adapted for life in the oceans, return to the shore when they lay their eggs. Such monsters as the pelagic leatherback turtle, *Dermochelys*, propel themselves efficiently enough with their flipperlike limbs in the water. Their travels on land, however, are laborious. Nevertheless, the female drags her body onto the beach when the time comes for her to lay her eggs.

Evolution is irreversible in the sense that a reptile may be amphibious, but can never become an amphibian. Once their hatchlings were prepared to meet the rigors of life on land, reptiles were on their way to becoming widespread land-dwelling animals. The Age of Reptiles saw the rise of the dinosaurs, their spread and diversification, and finally their triumph as the largest animals that ever lived on earth. For millions of years they were the dominant creatures on land. Curiously and inexplicably, however, the reptiles destined for survival were not the dinosaurs but the relatively inconspicuous reptiles on the sidelines during the dominance of the dinosaurs. Whether they were large or small, carnivorous or herbivorous, aquatic or terrestrial, the dinosaurs left no descendants.

The reptiles on the sidelines, the turtles, crocodilians, beakheads, and lizards, nevertheless, went right on producing descendants. Turtles, the oldest group of reptiles still extant, can be traced to ancestors that antedate the dinosaurs. The beakheads, or rhynchocephalians, also preceded the dinosaurs. If the lone survivor, New Zealand's tuatara, *Sphenodon*, had not reached this distant outpost, the beakheads too would probably be extinct. Crocodilians and lizards, however, arose from separate branches of the same stock that led to the dinosaurs. The few crocodiles, alligators, caimans, and gavials now living retain traits of the ancient crocodilians that restrict them to aquatic habitats, largely in the tropics. Lizards, although they were once overshadowed by the dinosaurs, proved to be far better fitted for survival.

The diversification of the lizards reflects their adaptability. Today they are 10 times as numerous as the reptiles that adhere more closely to ancestral traits, namely the turtles, the tuatara, and the crocodilians. Lizards have been less successful than the crocodilians and some of the turtles in adapting to life in the water. On land, however, they have been evolutionary innovators—they scale cliffs, run on the water, swim, or climb trees. Lizards have not managed to fly, but some of them glide. Not all lizards were equally successful, to be sure, for some evolutionary trends among them led to extinction.

Even before the dinosaurs were gone lizards had become burrowers. If this trend was advantageous, it proved to have drawbacks as well. For subterrestrial (underground) specializations led to the evolution of snakes, and hence also to an increase of the animals that prey on lizards, for some snakes eat lizards. Snakes, the most recently evolved of all reptiles, made their appearance before the dinosaurs were gone. Evolutionists are uncertain, but it is probable that snakes arose as relatively small descendants of fossorial (burrowing) lizards. Burrowing imposes limits on size, but after becoming limbless or nearly so, snakes evolved habits that led them to return to the surface. Free of the restrictions imposed by subterrestrial habits, snakes proceeded to enter numerous habitats on the surface. Giant snakes at least 30 and possibly 40 feet in length appear in the fossil record at an early date.

*Reptiles Widely Represented in the United States*

As noted in the preceding discussions, one reptile, the tuatara of New Zealand, is the sole surviving rhynchocephalian in the world. Crocodilians, with scarcely more than a score of species now living, are confined largely to tropical and semitropical regions. The American crocodile, *Crocodylus acutus,* is all but exterminated in Florida where it was never so abundant as the American alligator (*See under Alligator*). Most of the amphisbaenians, perhaps 130 species, are superficially wormlike creatures confined to their centers of abundance in Africa and South America. The one species indigenous to the United States, the Florida worm-lizard, *Rhineura floridana,* is briefly described in an earlier section of this account.

The other reptiles, in the order of their appearance in the fossil record—the turtles, the lizards, and snakes—are those most widely known in the United States. They all share the reptilian features of backbones, dry, usually scaly skins, and the "cold-blooded" condition that restricts their activities to warm weather. In their habits, locomotion, and other aspects of their behavior, however, they differ in so many ways that there are advantages in discussing each group separately. The species native to the United States are emphasized in the ensuing discussions.

## TURTLES

Almost from the time of their origin turtles have been conservatives. They cling to the ways of their ancestors. Unlike the reptiles of the more adaptable groups that invaded habitats at various levels, from the subsoil to the treetops, turtles scarcely got off the ground. Several other reptiles walked or ran on their hind legs, but Lewis Carroll's Mock Turtle was the only one that ever stood erect—and sang. Pond turtles often bask on stumps, or projecting limbs a few feet above the water, but none ever became arboreal. Protected, but also burdened with their armor, turtles either trudged about on land or lightened their burden by becoming aquatic. A few turtles dig burrows, usually to escape extreme temperatures rather than to forage, although some fossorial snakes, lizards, and amphisbaenians feed below the surface.

Lizards were ancestral to snakes, amphisbaenians, and modern lizards, but turtles were the only reptiles that evolved from turtles. The turtle's acquisition of armor, however, accompanied even more amazing changes in its internal structure. Modifications in its mode of development resulted in the shift of the hips and shoulder girdles to positions inside the ribs. The limbs could then be drawn inside a stout shell that consisted largely of broadened ribs, and some additional bone covered by horny plates. Turtles have adhered closely to the ancestral architecture, although shells have been modified in their evolution or reduced in various ways.

The soft-shelled turtles, represented by the genus *Amyda* in the United States, have lost most of the hard outer armor. The bony shell of most turtles, like that of their ancestors, is protected by horny plates. The smooth skin covering the leatherback, *Dermochelys*, however, contains osteoderms, a veritable mosaic of small bones that serve as a substitute for the shell. Aside from such departures from the ordinary or the typical, and modifications in the limbs that converted them into paddle or oarlike flippers characteristic of marine forms, few evolutionary innovations can be attributed to the turtles. Those now living on land, in streams, ponds, lakes, and oceans can be assigned to somewhat more than 200 species. Without doubt the number has fluctuated during the last 200 million years, but it is questionable whether turtles were ever much more numerous in species. Perhaps their formidable ancestry and their limited diversification are both attributable to their evolutionary acquisition of armor.

The rankest amateur naturalist could scarcely fail to recognize a turtle. Superficially turtles remotely resemble armadillos, but the shell-covered mammals retain enough hairs on the body to be identified readily as creatures that suckle their young (*See under Mammal*). The extraordinarily flat bodies of the aquatic soft-shelled turtles represent a marked departure from the normal condition. Despite the reduction of the bone underlying the flexible, leathery covering on the body, however, the soft-shells are readily recognized as turtles. They are more conspicuously different, however, than one of the African tortoises on which the shell is also flat but reduced. This odd animal, *Malachochersus tornieri*, seeks safety in close-fitting crevices in solid rock, inflates its lungs, and thus expands a shell that is pliable despite the presence of horny plates. This greatly augments its protection, for most predators find it nearly impossible to extricate it from crevices that may be bordered by several feet of rock.

As a group the shell-covered reptiles are lumped under the name "turtles" in ordinary usage. Other terms have, or originally had, more specialized connotations. Many people may, for example, apply the American Indian name *terrapin* to any edible freshwater species. Preferably the name should be reserved for the diamondback terrapins, *Malaclemys*. Innumerable local names have arisen. In Florida, for example, names for turtles such as *sliders, cooters, Suwanee chicken,* and *canal pullet* are heard as often as turtle.

Terrestrial species, including only those of the genus *Gopherus* in the United States, are correctly called tortoises. In Florida, however, natives virtually always refer to the gopher tortoise, *Gopherus polyphemus*, simply as a "gopher." This can be perplexing to outsiders, since in the Middle West a gopher is a ground squirrel (*See under Classification of Animals and Plants*). Any Californian, however, would assume that a Floridian who mentioned gophers was referring to the pouched burrowing rodents that leave small heaps of earth at the entrance to their burrows (*See Gopher*). The application of one name to such a variety of creatures may be a nuisance, but it is not illogical. Settlers found it expedient to apply the name *gopher* to any animal that honeycombs the ground with its burrows. The name is derived from *gaufre*, which any Frenchman recognizes as a *honeycomb*.

Presumably the gopher tortoises in the United States descended from a single stock that began to diverge millions of years ago. Today there are four species, one in the Southeast, one in Texas, and adjacent parts of Mexico, and one farther south in the Mexican Plateau. The fourth is an inhabitant of the arid Southwest, the desert tortoise, *Gopherus agassizii*, a narrow-headed, elephant-footed creature, often seen in dry, sandy terrain.

*The desert tortoise, a gopher tortoise, feeds on the tender fruits of prickly pear and other vegetation*

It is known from Utah to southern Sonora, but near the southern extremity of its range in Mexico it tolerates the relatively dense vegetation of the *barrancas* as well as the arid terrain of the deserts. Berlandier's tortoise, *G. berlandieri,* lives in regions nearly as arid as those inhabited by its western congener, but its feet are narrower. In contrast to both, the head of the Floridian gopher tortoise, *G. polyphemus,* is relatively broad, but its feet are proportionately small, scarcely more than half the diameter of those seen on desert tortoises the same size.

Few American turtles other than these tortoises are quite so restricted to land, or so inclined to excavate long burrows. In Florida "gopher holes" may extend 30 feet beneath the surface. In addition to the tortoise, these burrows are often inhabited by numerous other animals, including the gopher frog, *Rana capito,* and the diamondback rattlesnake, *Crotalus adamanteus.* The desert tortoise both hibernates and estivates in burrows similar to, but not so deep as, those of its Floridian relative. In southwestern Utah several individuals often spend the winter in the same "den." During the hotter part of the day and at night they do not invariably retire underground. Instead they select the shade of some convenient bush, draw in the head and feet and presumably sleep.

*Feeding Habits*

Tortoises are almost completely herbivorous. Rarely, those in Florida nibble halfheartedly at a grasshopper, and those in the desert may try to eat the dried flesh of a dead jackrabbit. By and large tortoises are vegetarians, but other turtles have less restricted diets. Those with aquatic habits (water turtles) commonly feed on water plants, fishes, clams, snails, and other small creatures they can most easily catch in streams, ponds, or rivers. Studies of the snapping turtle, *Chelydra serpentina,* reveal that approximately equal quantities of water plants and game fishes account for two-thirds of its diet. The remainder is carrion, insects, crayfishes, snails, and clams.

The diets of other aquatic turtles are comprised of similar assortments of plants and animals. Musk turtles, *Sternotherus odoratus,* inhabitants of quiet waters in lakes, ponds, and streams in the eastern states, devour several kinds of insects, worms, crayfishes, and fishes, but nearly half of the food they consume is carrion. Fishes and plants comprise a relatively small percentage of the total. In contrast, the spiny soft-shelled turtles, *Amyda spinifera,* more often prey on crayfishes, but they also eat a good many insects. Plant materials are more abundant than animals in the diet of the painted turtle, *Chrysemys picta.* Therefore nearly all the aquatic turtles appear to compete with fishes more often than they prey upon them.

The wood turtle, *Clemmys insculpta,* is exceptional in that it lives mostly on land but enters the water to mate and to hibernate. It eats plants and small animals, whether it forages in one habitat or the other. The feeding habits of eastern box turtles, *Terrapene carolina,* differ little from those of wood turtles, although box turtles neither mate nor hibernate in the water. Nevertheless they sometimes enter pools during periods of abnormally warm weather.

*Mating*

Whether turtles live on land or in the water, the union of the sexes is invariably preceded by some sort of courtship. The female is nearly always larger than the male, and in most instances she behaves as though she were unaware of his courtship antics. For example, during the courtship of the spotted turtle, *Clemmys guttata,* the male pursues the female as she swims in the shallow water. He manages to outdistance her time after time, and then pauses in front of her. The female, however, merely detours around the male as though he were a rock on the bottom. In contrast, painted trutles, *Chrysemys picta,* usually carry on their courtship near the surface in deeper water. The male painted turtle is equipped with exceptionally long claws on the fore feet, twice the length of those of the female. When courting he swims toward her and strokes her cheeks with his outstretched claws.

The gopher tortoises do their courting on land. The male desert tortoise approaches the female with his neck outstretched and rapidly bobs his head up and down. The female usually responds by withdrawing her feet and head into her shell. Thereupon the male commonly withdraws his head, approaches her from the front and bumps her with a projection at the front of his carapace. Or he may attempt to bite at the edges of her shell. If another male approaches the female, the courting male immediately turns his attention to the intruder. If he proves to be larger, a battle may ensue. The contending males, their heads safely withdrawn, bump each other vigorously. Often they engage the front ends of their shells, and, with a deft twist of his body, the larger male usually manages to overturn his opponent. The overturned tortoise eventually rights himself, but meanwhile the victor may have completed his courting, or moved out of sight with the female.

Most turtles in the United States mate in the spring, but some also mate during the summer and fall. Nearly all species, however, deposit their eggs during the early summer. The female commonly selects a sunny spot, usually on sand, but occasionally on dirt or decaying vegetation, where she excavates a flask-shaped hole. Invariably she digs this with her hind legs, whether they are modified for swimming or for land travel. Frequently the female, while digging the nest and laying her eggs in the pit,

*The ornate box turtle (above) often appears in incredible numbers after rainstorms. An adult Texas tortoise (below) has a rounded carapace that is nearly as long as it is broad*

is faced away from it. Thus she sees neither the pit she digs nor the eggs she deposits in it.

Box turtles lay as few as three or four eggs, but snapping turtles may deposit 40, rarely more. Marine turtles produce many more eggs than other turtles. The normal clutch of the green turtle, *Chelonia mydas*, for example, consists of approximately 100 eggs. Furthermore, the female, after laying one clutch, ordinarily deposits additional clutches, usually two, at intervals of 12 days. The same female does not produce eggs every year; usually it is every third year.

As the eggs are expelled from her vent the female often employs her hind feet to ease them into the excavation. After the nesting site has been carefully covered, the female departs. She gives no further attention to the nest, and when the young turtles dig their way to the surface, they shift for themselves.

Most turtles emerge from the egg under the ground surface within two or three months. In the colder portions of the United States young snapping turtles, though fully formed, sometimes fail to hatch or to leave the nest until the following spring. After hatchlings emerge from the eggs, they dig upward through the loose sand or dirt that covers the nest. Once they reach the surface they promptly head for a body of water.

Juvenile turtles, just emerged from the nest, encounter the greatest hazards of their lives at this time when their protective armor has not yet hardened. Marine turtles are preyed upon by a formidable array of creatures ranging from crabs to shorebirds, sharks, and other fishes. On land, hatchling turtles are seized by crows, ravens, and a host of mammalian enemies, including skunks, raccoons, coyotes, and domestic pigs. The shells of medium-sized desert tortoises sometimes display the unmistakable tooth marks of mammalian predators that failed to penetrate the shell. These examples show that the protective covering of the turtle has served its purpose. But the shell of the mud turtle, *Kinosternon*, affords little protection if it happens to be seized in the powerful, crushing jaws of an alligator or a crocodile. These enemies, however, are considerably reduced in numbers, owing to the persecution of that other destroyer of turtles—man.

In addition to man, hosts of other mammals, a few reptiles, and some birds dig into the nests of turtles and eat the eggs. Depredations by man account for the destruction of many turtle eggs in the United States, not because men eat the eggs, but because they afford the best source of young turtles for which a ready market exists. Thousands of red-eared turtles, *Pseudemys scripta*, are sold annually, many of them juveniles with paint applied to their shells. Such turtles eventually die unless the paint is removed to permit normal growth of the shell and of the imprisoned animal. Tons of adult turtles are converted into the soup consumed by gourmets in the restaurants of the larger cities, and the edible pond turtles, *Pseudemys*, are known in Florida as *Suwannee chicken*, or *canal pullet*. The snapper also affords a source of meat suitable for soup, but epicures prefer the diamondback terrapins, *Malaclemys*. Efforts to raise for the market these once sought-after turtles met with discouraging results. Fortunately diamondback terrapins are increasing in numbers, largely because restaurants find it excessively expensive to prepare turtle soup.

### *Growth*

During the early part of their lives large tortoises increase in weight rapidly, even though years are required for them to attain maximum size. Within a period of seven years the weight of a Galapagos tortoise reared in California increased from 29 to 350 pounds. Smaller turtles reach average adult proportions within 5 to 10 years, but rates of growth vary from species to species. Some, but not all, turtles shed the outer coverings of the plates covering their horny shells.

Tortoises shed only the skin covering their soft parts, not the covering of the horny plates. Periodic accretions to the edges of each horny plate, however, accompany growth. The ridges that parallel the edges of the plates on tortoises, as well as box turtles, are the result of the periodic additions that accompany increases in size. On old individuals the ridges may be worn, and the plates may be almost smooth.

*Longevity*

The maximum authenticated age record for any backboned (vertebrate) animal is currently held by a tortoise. Unfortunately information concerning the longevity of such animals is drawn largely from animals under abnormal conditions in captivity. The tortoise that survived 152 years on the island of Mauritius may not actually hold the longevity record. Furthermore, this oldster was killed accidentally. Otherwise it might have reached the two century mark. An eastern box turtle, *Terrapene carolina,* reportedly attained an age of 125 years. So many box turtles are run over by careless motorists in some areas, however, that the life expectancy of box turtles can scarcely be what it was in the horse-and-buggy days.

## LIZARDS

The most diversified reptiles now living are the lizards. Nearly 4,000 species are distributed from tropical to temperate climates, and from oceans to elevations of at least 14,000 feet above sea level. Pterosaurs, the flying reptiles of an earlier era, disappeared with the dinosaurs, but Asiatic lizards known as flying dragons, *Draco,* are efficient gliders. One West Indian lizard, *Deiroptyx,* that inhabits streams is a sort of counterfeit crocodilian, a diminutive imitator of the alligator.

Innumerable lizards are efficient climbers, and many of them spend most of their lives in trees or bushes. Others climb on rocks or they may be specialized as crevice dwellers. The Galapagos marine iguana, *Amblyrhynchus cristatus,* dives beneath the surface or swims out beyond the breakers to graze on seaweed. These are exceptions, however, for the majority of the lizards are terrestrial; they inhabit sand or rocks on the desert, or the litter on the forest floor in humid regions.

Limbs become disadvantageous when lizards live underground. They can, in fact, propel themselves through soil or humus, or "swim" through the sand more efficiently without limbs, which are often reduced or wholly lacking in the subterranean lizards. There are limbless lizards, moreover, that progress in much the same fashion as the snakes that employ lateral undulations of the body. Of more than 20 families of lizards now recognized, four are comprised of burrowers, and several other families contain subterrestrial species.

Lizards in other parts of the world include species representing virtually all stages of limb reduction. Similar changes, coupled with the loss of ear openings, movable eyelids, and partial loss of the eye itself, accompanied the evolutionary transition from the lizard to the snake at a much earlier date. Because several modifications in burrowing lizards duplicate those found in snakes, it is difficult to define the two groups. The lack of movable eyelids characterizes snakes, but the eyes of night lizards, *Xantusia,* of the Southwest, most geckos, and some other lizards are also protected by a transparent scale or *spectacle.* Snakes lack an external ear opening, but several fossorial lizards, as well as the superficially wormlike reptiles, the amphisbaenians, also lack ear openings. In fact burrowing lizards tend to become snakelike in so many ways that structures largely peculiar to snakes also occur in one or more lizards.

On the whole, lizards differ from snakes in having jaw bones united at the front. Snakes, in contrast, have only an elastic ligament connecting the lower jaws anteriorly. The bones on one side of a snake's jaws can be moved independently of those on the other.

*Predator Avoidance*

The fastest reptiles in North America are perhaps the zebra-tailed lizards, *Callisaurus draconoides*. They move so rapidly that in parts of their range they are called lightning lizards. The short-legged forms, including skinks, *Eumeces*, adeptly escape predators by scrambling into crevices. The slow-moving, partly nocturnal Gila monster, *Heloderma suspectum*, depends less on speed than its obliterative markings and venomous bite to protect itself (*See Gila Monster*). Bipedal locomotion (running upright on the two hind legs) perhaps helps some lizards to run faster. The leopard lizard, *Crotaphytus wislizenii*, and the desert iguana, *Dipsosaurus dorsalis*, as well as another inhabitant of the arid Southwest, the collared lizard, *Crotaphytus collaris*, commonly run on their hind legs. Such lizards usually begin their sprint on all four feet, but as they gain momentum they raise the front limbs and become bipedal.

Adhesive pads on the toes of most geckos, as well as the American anole, *Anolis carolinensis*, and its relatives, enable these lizards to move about on smooth surfaces. The pads consist of numerous microscopic hairs that impinge on minute irregularities of the surface. Lizards that lack such pads employ their claws with amazing efficiency on rough surfaces. The banded rock lizard, *Petrosaurus mearnsi*, races up overhanging surfaces on granite boulders with astonishing rapidity. On smooth glass surfaces, however, lizards lacking the adhesive pads cannot compete with the geckos or anoles, on which claws are supplemented by pads.

Boulder-strewn slopes or outcrops of granite afford suitable habitats for the banded rock lizard as well as the granite night lizard, *Xantusia henshawi*. This latter, a diminutive nocturnal creature, hides beneath the exfoliations on granite boulders. The flattened body of the night lizard enables it to creep into narrow crevices from which it emerges to feed during the hours of darkness. A smaller relative, the yucca night lizard, *Xantusia vigilis*,

*The large, fat chuckwalla lizard was once eaten by the Southwestern Indians*

which is not flattened, feeds surreptitiously during the day working its way through vegetable debris to find small insects. Its habitat is often, but not invariably, associated with Joshua trees and other yuccas that afford cover (*See Joshua Tree*).

Crevice dwelling is not monopolized by the granite night lizard. Rocky situations in the deserts of the extreme Southwest are inhabited by a large herbivorous lizard with an Indian name, chuckawalla, *Sauromalus obesus*. Normally the chuckawalla selects a relatively tight-fitting crack into which it timidly retreats upon the slightest provocation. If it is disturbed by attempts to remove it from a crevice the Chuckawalla inflates its lungs. Its skin, like an ill-fitting shirt, hangs in wrinkles and folds when the chuckawalla's lungs are deflated. When air is drawn into the lungs, however, the skin balloons out and wedges the creature securely in the crevice. Three times as much air than the chuckawalla normally inhales can be taken into its lungs under these conditions.

*Predators and Protective Devices*

Even the most active lizards fail to escape all of their predators. Lizards themselves may be lizard-eaters, as they so often demonstrate when large and small lizards are kept in the same cage. Numerous birds, including hawks, shrikes, jays, and even domestic fowl, catch small lizards. The prairie falcon has been known to carry lizards as large as the chuckawalla to its nest. The bizarre roadrunner (*see Roadrunner*), though famed as a killer of rattlesnakes, more often eats lizards. However swift-mov ing the whiptail lizards, *Cnemidophorus,* may be, they constitute a significant percentage of the roadrunner's diet. Skunks and other mammals occasionally dig lizards from their hideouts in the sand, and snakes are ubiquitous and effective predators upon lizards. Seven species of patch-nosed snakes, *Salvadora,* in the United States and Mexico, all manifest a definite preference for lizards, particularly the whiptails, *Cnemidophorus.*

Such spinose creatures as the horned lizards, *Phrynosoma,* must constitute rough meals for snakes. Snakes occassionally die from eating them. The desiccated carcasses of such lizard-eaters as the glossy snake, *Arizona elegans,* have been found with the spines of the head of a horned lizard projecting from their skins. Even after being engulfed by the snake, the horned lizard had evidently retaliated by twisting its head from side to side. It thereby managed to thrust one or more of its "horns" through the body wall of the snake that had swallowed it. This belated retaliation by the lizard did not save it from its dead captor, which nevertheless would never again attack a horned lizard. The lizard's use of its horns under such circumstances affords protection against snakes for the species as a whole, rather than for the individual.

The spines on the head of the horned lizard, along with the smaller spines on its back, and the small scales that fringe its body and tail, serve another purpose. They tend to obscure the outline of the body, which is broad, flat, and so nearly flush with the ground that it produces virtually no telltale shadow. Horned lizards, with one species or another occupying regions with sparse vegetation from southwestern Canada to the Isthmus of Tehuantepec, are largely inhabitants of open country. Regardless of the species or the color of the soil, however, horned lizards conform closely to the color of the substratum. Few lizards have so fully exploited cryptic coloration as a means of eluding predators as have the horned lizards

Unlike iguanas and most other members of the same family, horned lizards do not readily lose their tails when seized. There are breakage planes on vertebrae near the base of the tail of iguanas and their relatives, as there are in many other lizards. The tail is less easily broken between the vertebrae than at the breakage planes that actually provide for tail loss. This is so widespread among lizards that it seems safe to assume that it is an effective means of defense. A predator that seizes a lizard by its brittle tail rarely gets a grip on the rest of the body. More often the predator, distracted by the squirming tail, is unaware that its former owner is making its getaway.

The loss of the tail, which is readily regenerated, is no serious handicap to most lizards. The regrown tail is not a perfect replica of the original, however. The bony vertebrae are replaced by a cartilaginous rod, the scales covering the tail are usually irregular, and it may be shorter than the original. Occasionally a tail that is partly fractured but not separated may induce the regeneration of a second tail. Lizards with paired tails are not rare, and lizards with as many as five tails have been discovered.

*Reproduction*

A species is in trouble, but not necessarily destined for extinction, whenever the survival rate of its members drops below their rate of increase. Populations of animals are relatively stable in number only when rates of reproduction counterbalance their death rates. It is costly, but plainly advantageous, for animals to devote time and energy to perpetuating their kind. Lizards are no exception, regardless of how exceptional some species may be in other respects.

At widely separated times and places, perhaps for similar reasons, though rarely in the same way, distantly related lizards without limbs, functional eyes, or ear openings have evolved. All these structures are lacking in a few subterrestrial species. Whatever they may have lost, however, these lizards retain the ancestral trait of internal fertilization and the senses and behavior that bring

*The Texas horned lizard can run when danger threatens. When frightened it sometimes squirts blood from the corners of its eyes*

it about. Males or females can more readily dispense with limbs than the senses they employ in finding each other. Internal fertilization, and the pairing and courtship that precede it, are all cooperative activities.

It is questionable whether subterrestrial lizards carry out such activities while underground. Observations on record for a few blind lizards suggest that during the breeding season burrowers of both sexes emerge from their burrows at night. Reliable information is lacking, but the female perhaps emits a distinctive odor that is attractive to the male. If so, the male's sense of smell would enable him to find the female. The chances of a male finding a female beneath the ground surface appear to be remote, but this is conjectural.

Virgin birth, the production of offspring from unfertilized eggs, would nevertheless seem to be particularly advantageous to lizards in subterranean habitats. Contrary to this assumption, the only lizards in which this mode of reproduction (known as *parthenogenesis*) has been discovered are agile lizards living in terrestrial habitats. Studies of the Armenian lizard, *Lacerta saxicola,* revealed that females in areas where no males of the species were ever encountered could produce eggs that developed young without being fertilized. In other regions, however, the same species was represented by both sexes, and their eggs were fertilized.

Investigations in the United States have failed to discover males in some species of whiptailed lizards, *Cnemidophorus.* A sample consisting of more than a hundred checkered whiptails, *Cnemidophorus tesselatus,* from Texas, proved to be comprised entirely of females. Apparently a similar situation prevails in other members of the genus. Even though both sexes were present in some populations, the females greatly outnumbered the males. Further study of these lizards may reveal that females are active at one time of the year and males at another.

Whiptail males tend to be slightly larger, but otherwise similar to females. In other groups of lizards, however, the males are appreciably larger, and often brighter in color. Consequently they are more conspicuous than the females, and hence more often seen or captured. This is true of collared lizards, *Crotaphytus collaris,* in many areas. The male of this species commonly establishes and defends a territory surrounding one large rock, boulder, or even a pile of rocks. It retreats from larger predators to the shelter of a crevice or a burrow that it digs or enlarges beneath the small promontory that becomes the center of its activities. It spends most of its day on top of the rock, however, where it basks while scanning the surrounding terrain. From its vantage ground, often two or three feet above the ground, it is in a suitable position to detect the large insects or the small lizards that it pursues for food. But it is also on the lookout for predators or intruding males of its own species.

The female seldom climbs far above the ground, and she is less frequently seen. She can enter the male's territory, which may be particularly attractive to her during the spring mating season. If another male collared lizard approaches, however, the resident male arches his back, raises his tail, and waits with his mouth agape. The intruding male may be intimidated by this threatening display. If not the resident male moves closer and chases or bites it. This active defense of his territory is nearly always effective, and intruding males commonly flee. Many, perhaps most, diurnal lizards maintain some sort of territory, at least during the breeding season. When lizards of the same species are found in the same shrub or tree, they virtually always prove to be male and female. Not only during the breeding season, but at other times of the year, two males of the same species rarely occupy the same tree. Males of other species of lizards are, however, tolerated.

The courtships of few lizards have been investigated in detail. The evidence derived from such studies suggests that vision plays a prominent role in the courtship of diurnal lizards. One lizard responds to the presence of another in ways suggesting that it can discriminate between sexes. Females respond only to males of their own species, whereas males commonly "challenge" members of their own sex, but stage a different sort of display when a female approaches. The behavior of closely related species may be similar in many respects, but distinctive in others. Male spiny lizards, *Sceloporus*, for example, rapidly raise and lower their heads in the presence of females. This head bobbing, however, follows a different pattern in each species, but females behave in a receptive fashion only when approached by males of their own species.

Nocturnal lizards perhaps depend more on their sense of smell to locate mates or to distinguish them from lizards of other species. Many geckos, however, issue sounds that in at least some instances not only reveal their location but serve to attract mates. A female Oriental gecko, *Gekko gekko*, that escaped from its cage in a zoological garden in Germany was later retrieved. It appeared one night near a cage where a male of the same species had been issuing its call. The sense of hearing, therefore, may prove to be more important during the courtship of geckos than either vision or the sense of smell.

Throat fans, dewlaps, crests, or similar structures that can be elevated are largely limited to lizards that carry out their courtship antics during the day. Males of several species, whether they mate during the day or at night use their jaws to restrain the females by seizing them by the neck. The male may retain his grip for prolonged periods, perhaps until both members of the pair are ready for the copulation that follows. Courtships are initiated only when both male and female are physiologically prepared, but complete readiness apparently depends upon the courtship.

The eggs of most lizards are laid shortly after they are fertilized. Extremely small geckos largely restricted to the West Indies lay only one egg, but most other geckos produce two. Large horned lizards lay as many as 30 eggs, but the green iguana, *Iguana iguana*, of the American tropics deposits twice as many in a single clutch. It may, however, produce only one clutch annually, whereas some lizards in the United States produce three or four clutches during one summer. The eggs of some geckos are laid in crevices or even attached to walls or rocks in exposed positions.

Eggs laid in the open are protected by hard shells; the eggs of most lizards, covered by leathery shells, are deposited in holes excavated in the ground. Some of the African chameleons give birth to living young, but others that virtually never leave their arboreal habitats at other times descend to the ground to deposit their eggs. The green iguana is reported to spend several days digging a burrow, sometimes more than three feet deep, in which to lay her eggs.

Not only some African chameleons, but lizards in many other families produce living young. The yucca night lizard, *Xantusia vigilis*, of the United States ordinarily gives birth to two offspring annually. Horned lizards of some species lay eggs, but others, particularly those in habitats at higher elevations, produce living young. A similar situation prevails in the alligator lizards, *Gerrhonotus*, and their relatives. The live-bearing lizards are not restricted to cool habitats, but a larger percentage of them inhabit mountains or areas with cold climates. The distribution of the viviparous lizard, *Lacerta vivipara*, of Europe extends farther north, and also farther from the equator, than that of any reptile now living. This lizard and the European viper, *Vipera berus,* both of which bear living young, are the only reptiles known within the Arctic Circle.

SNAKES

Secretive habits, and nearly silent locomotion, coupled with lethal means of defense, have endowed snakes with an aura of mystery not wholly deserved. No other animals are so widely feared, misunderstood, or misrepresented. Do people cherish so many fallacious beliefs or egregious notions concerning snakes solely because some of them are venomous?

*An Essay Toward a Natural History of Serpents,* a veritable compendium of misinformation concerning snakes that was published in 1742, recounts myths as prevalent today as they were more than two centuries ago when the book was written. The author, Reverend Charles Owen, sought to discredit such yarns as that told about the glass snake "which breaks into pieces, which some say, and nobody believes, are capable of reunion." However improbable it may have seemed to the Reverend Owen, this fanciful belief is widely entertained wherever the fragile-tailed glass lizards, *Ophisaurus,* are encountered. Even educated people who ought to know better are loath to reject the idea that the disconnected portions of the limbless lizard reunite. Almost invariably the same people quite as earnestly believe that the hoop snake puts its tail in its mouth and rolls downhill.

A snake that moved about in such outlandish fashion could scarcely be expected to live long enough to perpetuate its kind. It must be admitted, however, that snakes do progress in ways far removed from those of other backboned animals. The elongate body, whether it advances in a straight line, follows a sinuous route, sidewinds, or alternately

*The Arizona vine snake is a back-fanged species but is not considered dangerous*

straightens and draws its coils together, is a thoroughly complex mechanism. The snake's virtually noiseless mode of progression inspired the name *snake*, derived from an Anglo-Saxon word meaning *sneak*, according to those who should know. It is tempting to suspect that the word snake was coined first, since a treacherous, underhanded person is sometimes called a "serpent,"—with unwarranted reflections on the reptile. For the snake's stealthy method of creeping up on its prey is more properly regarded as a trait adaptively advantageous to such reptiles.

A snake can easily ingest prey of greater diameter than its head because the two halves of the lower jaw are separated by an elastic ligament. The motility of the jaws is further enhanced by two movable joints between each jaw and the back end of the head. Snakes lack an external ear opening, as well as an eardrum. They also lack movable eyelids, and when the skin is shed the transparent outer covering of the eyes is cast off with the outer layer of the epidermis. Roughly one-fifth of the snakes of the world are venomous, that is, equipped with tubular fangs used primarily to inject venom into their prey. These, and many other highly developed attributes peculiar to snakes, are not encountered in all members of the group.

The snakes are represented by nearly 3,000 species. The 115 species in the United States range in length from slightly less than eight inches to slightly more than eight feet. A good many snakes in the Southwest, including the long-nosed snakes, *Rhinocheilus*, the leaf-nosed snakes, *Phyllorhynchus;* and the western glossy snake, *Arizona*, to cite only a few examples, are partly subterrestrial in habits. Most of them find their food on the surface. Whipsnakes, *Masticophis;* kingsnakes, *Lampropeltis;* bullsnakes, *Pituophis;* rattlesnakes, *Crotalus* and *Sistrurus;* and many others largely are terrestrial, but whipsnakes and kingsnakes occasionally climb trees. The species in two other genera, the garter snakes, *Thamnophis*, and the water snakes, *Natrix*, are largely but not wholly aquatic. Most species grouped in these two genera spend considerable time in the water and secure much of their food in ponds, lakes, and streams. A few garter snakes, however, are terrestrial.

The Pacific and Indian oceans, but not the Atlantic, are inhabited by sea snakes, Hydrophiidae, all species of which are aquatic and largely marine. The European viper, *Vipera berus*, penetrates the Arctic Circle on the Scandinavian Peninsula, but it occurs only in the areas where the subsoil is not permanently frozen. Within the United States the Pacific rattlesnake, *Crotalus viridis oreganus*, is encountered as high above sea level as 12,000 feet, in the Sierra Nevada of California. Diversified habits and habitats, like their diversity in structure, point to the adaptability of snakes, an attribute that characterizes all widely distributed groups of animals. It is instructive to note, however, that the various snakes have overcome many of the handicaps that arise from their limbless condition.

Animals without efficient cooling systems or ways of generating appreciable amounts of internal heat can avoid intolerable conditions on the surface by burrowing. In part, this accounts for the prevalence of subterrestrial snakes, particularly in deserts where surface temperatures often are so high that snakes exposed to so much heat would be killed. During winter it is warmer beneath the surface than on it, whereas during the summer the reverse is true.

It is not unusual during hot weather for sand surfaces to exceed 145° F. at midday in deserts. Temperatures are appreciably lower only a few inches beneath the ground. But snakes crawling on the ground, with their slender bodies flush with it, can rapidly become overheated. They can avoid overheating by descending to cooler depths during the

*The leaf-nosed snake of the arid Southwest (above) is a pugnacious species, but harmless. The eastern diamondback rattlesnake (below) inhabits the dry pinelands of the South and occasionally swims in salt water to the Florida Keys*

day and emerging at night, after the surface cools. Snakes that cannot burrow avoid the heat by crawling into the burrows of desert-dwelling rodents (*See under Kangaroo Rat; and under Prairie Dog*).

The sidewinder, *Crotalus cerastes,* often emerges shortly after dusk and prowls for hours, sometimes traveling two or three hundred yards before it settles down in a compact coil. It may come to rest in open sand, but when the sun reappears, the sidewinder retreats to the shade of a bush, or a rodent burrow. If the ground temperature rises, the snake descends to cooler, deeper recesses. While studying sidewinders, Raymond B. Cowles discovered that these peculiar little rattlers while at rest in burrows shifted often enough to maintain their bodies almost precisely at 92° F.

In the hot, arid wastes of the Southwest, snakes not wholly dependent upon vision while foraging readily become nocturnal. They retreat below the surface when it becomes excessively hot during the day, or remain below ground when temperatures are high both day and night. The red racer, *Masticophis flagellum piceus,* among more than a score of snakes that inhabit warm deserts in the Southwest, is the only snake commonly abroad at midday. Apparently it moves swiftly enough to find shelter and cool its body at frequent intervals.

The red racer's movements are rapid only in comparison with other serpents. The great speed in snakes is largely an illusion. On a rough terrain a frightened racer can easily move faster than a man in pursuit, and can change its direction without greatly diminishing its speed. Nevertheless, the speed a snake attains may not greatly exceed four miles per hour. Bushes, rocks, or other obstacles that impede or block human beings are not disadvantageous to a snake. When pursued in open country devoid of vegetation or other obstacles the snake loses this advantage, *and* the race.

*Modes of Progression*

Snakes in search of their prey, especially the thick-bodied venomous snakes, including rattlesnakes, move slowly, almost at a snail's pace, when they employ "caterpillar locomotion." They advance the body in a nearly straight line, with virtually no movement of the spine or ribs. Movement is largely restricted to the broad, overlapping plates on the snake's belly. These plates are shifted in waves by means of an intricate system of muscles that extend from the skin to the bony skeleton. Smoothly coordinated action of this complex array of muscles causes the broadened scales on the belly to be lifted consecutively in alternate parts of the body. Each plate is carried forward for a short distance, and then returned to the surface on which the snake is crawling. Once the plates are in frictional contact with the ground, muscles come into play that draw the snake's body forward within this part of its tubular skin.

In simpler terms, the snake's distensible skin is moved forward in sections and then the body is drawn forward inside it, much as though it were a stick inside a rubber tube. The snake "keeps a inchin' along," though not quite in the manner of the "po' inch worm," which alternately advances the front and hind parts of its body. The snake, in contrast, leaves a relatively straight track, much as though it had dragged its body along the surface.

The majority of the rattlesnakes use caterpillar movement, more aptly called rectilinear locomotion. Hence their telltale tracks are often identifiable in areas where other snakes leave sinuous tracks. But at times, seemingly when there is need for haste, a rattlesnake also adopts the swifter lateral undulatory mode of progression. When this is employed by a rattler or any other snake, it launches the body forward in a series of S-shaped curves, each of which pushes against projections on the substratum. Such propulsion is dependent upon an irregular surface, or the snake's ability to dig the edges of its body into the sand in order to secure the necessary pivots.

The extraordinary locomotion of the small rattlesnake known as the sidewinder, *Crotalus cerastes,* though mentioned earlier, warrants further attention here. The sidewinder moves with only two sections of its body resting on the surface at any one time. Its "rolling" movement endows it with many of the advantages of the caterpillar tread now widely used on tractors, bulldozers, and tanks. Where such motorized vehicles leave two continuous parallel tracks, however, the sidewinder leaves a series of oblique, disconnected tracks that are, however, parallel. This comes about because the snake, with but one "tread" on its body, manages to transfer it from one track to the next.

In order to do this, the sidewinder shifts its body, not as a whole, but segment by segment. Without touching with its head the surface on which it is traveling, the snake lifts the head along with the anterior (forward) part of the body, carries it forward, and brings it down on the sand. The head, pointed forward, momentarily remains in this position, but the body is drawn sharply to one side of the head as it is progressively rolled onto the track now being formed. Once the head is lowered, the rest of the body follows, lifted from the substratum in an S-shaped wave that progresses toward the tail. The belly plates one after another are lifted on the wave that carries them from one position to the next. Consequently the sidewinder neither slips nor loses traction, even in loose sand.

The locomotion of this small rattlesnake, like that of vipers inhabiting the deserts of Asia and Africa, is admirably suited for travel on smooth, flat surfaces where other snakes are unable to move efficiently. Other rattlesnakes inhabit the Colorado and Mojave deserts, but the sidewinder is the one most often encountered in dunes or sandy areas where the vegetation is sparse. While prowling, the sidewinder avoids passing through shrubs. In contrast, the larger rattlers almost invariably go from bush to bush, and often crawl through the branching base.

On smooth terrain snakes, other than those that sidewind, usually extend the front part of the body, and then draw up the rest of the body in sinuous coils. This crude, relatively ineffective way of traveling has been called *telescoping locomotion.* Such slender snakes as the American racers and whipsnakes invariably propel themselves with lateral undulatory movements. Other snakes, however, are less restricted. Sidewinders sometimes switch to caterpillar movement. Garter snakes and small boas, that normally use undulatory locomotion, resort to a crude, imperfect mode of progression that resembles sidewinding when they encounter flat surfaces.

*Means of Subduing Prey*

Snakes kill their prey by various means. All snakes have teeth, but not necessarily in both upper and lower jaws. Both jaws of the common nonvenomous snakes, however, are thickly set with recurved, needlelike teeth. Garter snakes, *Thamnophis;* whipsnakes, *Masticophis;* and racers, *Coluber,* are well equipped to seize small animals, but they do not necessarily kill their prey before they swallow it. When a snake seizes a backboned animal near the middle of its body, the snake usually shifts its grip to the head of the prey. Nearly all snakes ordinarily begin at the head when they start to swallow their prey, but occasionally a snake swallows an animal tail first. Usually this proves to be difficult because the fins, scales or legs of animals are almost invariably angled toward the rear.

Some snakes do not coil around their prey. They simply press it against the ground where it is held until its head can be drawn into the mouth. But the kingsnakes, *Lampropeltis;* bullsnakes, *Pituophis;* the two boas, *Lichanura* and *Charina,* living in the western states, and some of the large burrowers kill their prey by constriction. They usually seize rodents, lizards, or birds, either by the head or immediately behind it, and quickly coil around the body. By tightening their coils and taking up the slack when the victim allows air to escape from its lungs, these snakes eventually throttle their prey.

Snakes rarely crush the bones of their prey, contrary to widespread belief. Small animals die after their circulation and breathing are stopped or impaired by the pressure of the snake's coils. A six-foot bullsnake, *Pituophis melanoleucus,* can dispatch a rodent within two or three minutes. The western ringneck snake, *Diadophis amabilis,* may simply seize a salamander by the head and engulf it. When offered a small lizard, however, the same snake will use its coils and kill by constriction. Other snakes behave in ways that suggest that they distinguish one kind of animal from another.

The elaborate venom apparatus characteristic of vipers, pit-vipers, and cobras, mambas, and their allies enables them to kill their prey by injecting it with powerful secretions of their modified salivary glands. Muscles force venom from the glands and into the prey through tubular teeth, or fangs, the prototypes of the modern hypodermic needle. Cobras, with beautifully adapted fangs closely resembling those in the upper jaws of venomous snakes now living, inhabited Europe at least 20 million years ago. In all probability fangs were undergoing their evolution shortly after snakes began to flourish.

Venomous snakes of three families live in the United States. The family Colubridae includes a few rear-fanged snakes, but these are neither dangerous nor abundant. Relatively small grooved, rather than tubular, fangs are present in the lyre snakes, *Trimorphodon;* the cat-eyed snake, *Leptodeira septentrionalis;* the Arizona vine snake, *Oxybelis aeneus aeneus;* the black-banded snake, *Coniophanes i. imperialis;* and the black-headed snakes, *Tantilla.* Because grooved teeth are situated at the back of the mouth, rear-fanged snakes rarely engage their fangs unless they can chew. Because such snakes cannot effectively drive their fangs into the flesh of an aggressor, they use them largely to subdue their small prey.

Venomous snakes related to the cobras, mambas, and kraits are assigned to one family, the Elapidae. The only members of this family in the United States are the eastern coral snake, *Micrurus fulvius,* and the Sonora coral snake, *Micruroides euryxanthus.* These snakes, like others in the group, possess permanently erect fangs at the front of each upper jaw. Fangs in this position may be driven into the prey by a strike, but the snakes of this family more often engage their fangs by means of a chewing action.

The fangs of an adult, eastern coral snake, 32 inches long, are but a tenth of an inch long. In contrast, the fangs of rattlesnakes approximately the same length are more than three times as long. The Gaboon viper, *Bitis gabonicus,* of the African rain forests holds the record for fang size. The curved fangs of a six-foot individual are nearly two inches long.

The pit-vipers, or snakes of the family Crotalidae, are represented in the United States by 15 rattlesnakes, the moccasin, and the copperhead. The facial pits that mark the location of infrared receptors distinguish pit-vipers from their relatives, the true vipers of the family Viperidae, found only in the Old World. All viperine snakes are alike to the extent of having very short upper jaws that permit them to rotate their elongate, tubular fangs to a resting position flush with the roof of the mouth. In coral snakes and cobras a sheathlike pocket outside each lower jaw receives the tip ends of the fangs when the mouth is closed. The

*The plains garter snake is an abundant species; it is sometimes seen around cities*

fang-tilting mechanism peculiar to the vipers and pit-vipers permits them to have the largest fangs.

*Size and Longevity*

Fossils representing large snakes have been recovered from Eocene deposits in Patagonia and Egypt. These snakes, however, may have been no more gigantic than the largest snakes now extant. The snake that now attains the greatest length is probably the reticulated python, *Python reticulatus,* of Asia. A reputable naturalist, H. C. Raven, reported one 33 feet in length. This length may be surpassed, however, by exceptionally large anacondas, *Eunectes murinus,* in South America. Monsters nearly 40 feet long have been reported, although it is noteworthy that large adults are seldom much more than 20 feet long. Without better evidence to the contrary, a length of 28 feet is the maximum that can be accepted. North of Panama, the boa constrictor, *Boa constrictor,* is the largest snake in the Americas. The largest individual known, however, one 18.5 feet in length, was killed on the island of Trinidad.

Only five snakes, all of them tropical representatives of the family Boidae, attain lengths in excess of 20 feet. The anaconda is a boa, but the other four are pythons, two in Asia and one each in Africa and Australia. In addition to holding the record for size in the Western Hemisphere, the anaconda once held the longevity record for snakes. One lived for 28 years in the National Zoological Park in Washington, D.C. The record was surpassed by three months, however, by a Java python, *Python molurus bivittatus,* exhibited in the zoological garden in San Diego, California. Not only boas and pythons, but bullsnakes, and at least one copperhead and one rattlesnake, have lived for 20 years or more in the San Diego Zoo, where two men, Mr. Charles E. Shaw and his predecessor, Mr. C. B. Perkins, have established longevity records for several snakes. No snake is known to have lived longer than an African cobra, *Naja melanoleuca,* that Perkins and Shaw kept alive for slightly more than 29 years.

Most of the snakes in the United States reach maturity within two to three years. In the tropics, where growth continues during most of the year, some snakes are sexually mature, or large enough to reproduce, within a year or two years following their birth. Growth does not cease, however, although rates of growth commonly diminish after snakes are sexually mature.

*Reproduction*

Elaborate courtships by snakes commonly precede the fertilization of the eggs. The male garter snake, *Thamnophis,* for example, rubs the back

*The slender blind snake is strictly insectivorous, having a small mouth*

of the female with the sensitive tubercles on its chin, and the males of several nonvenomous snakes sporadically bite the female during their courtship. Whether the male bites the female or rubs her with his coils, the female is thus stimulated and prepared for the actual mating.

Either one, but only one, of the paired copulatory organs located in the base of the tail of a snake is extruded from the vent at the time of mating. The tubular copulatory organs are everted by being turned inside out. They may, however, be forced out by injury or pain, sometimes revealing curved spines that remotely resemble claws. To the uneducated, they *are* claws, and hence it is assumed that the everted organs are legs. Such assumptions readily explain the stories of "snakes with legs" that occasionally appear in newspapers.

After snakes have mated, usually in the spring in the United States, the females lay their eggs in rotting logs or cavities underground. The eggs of some snakes hatch nearly three months after they are laid, but those of other species require little more than a month. When fully formed, the young snake slits the leathery shell, using the egg-tooth attached below its snout. The egg-tooth drops off the hatchling a few days after it emerges. Egg-teeth occur on the snouts of the offspring of some live-bearing species, including rattlesnakes and most other pit-vipers.

The pit-vipers, as well as water snakes, garter snakes, boas, many vipers and other snakes, retain the embryos within the body of the mother until they are fully developed. At birth the young are encased in thin, transparent membranes, from which they normally emerge without difficulty. These near-replicas of their parents may nevertheless differ from them in their markings or color. For example, the young of the common uncolored black racer, *Coluber constrictor,* are blotched.

*Predators and Prey*

It is axiomatic that only large snakes can devour large prey. The diet of the juvenile often differs, therefore, from that of adults of the same species. The hatchlings of small species can readily devour insects or other small animals. Young garter snakes are big enough to tackle earthworms as well as insects. Relatively few snakes restrict themselves to one kind of prey. No snake, however, is herbivorous. Larger species rely heavily on rabbits or rodents, including squirrels, mice, and rats. Many snakes, however, are too small to eat rodents. Small-mouthed forms, such as the slender blind snakes, *Leptotyphlops,* are strictly insectivorous. Such specialists as the hook-nosed snakes, *Ficimia,* of Texas, New Mexico and Arizona manifest a decided preference for spiders. The shovel-nosed ground snake, *Chionactis occipitalis,* eats both centipedes and scorpions, but it will also eat insects or their larvae.

The leaf-nosed snakes, *Phyllorhynchus,* often have the eggs of lizards or the tails of geckos in their stomachs. Lizards become the prey of a number of snakes, particularly the whipsnakes and racers, which also eat rodents or birds. The small species of rattlesnakes, as well as the juveniles of the large species, subsist largely on lizards. As they mature, however, the big rattlesnakes shift to rodents or rabbits and rarely take lizards, although rattlers of moderate size occasionally eat birds or amphibians. Frogs and salamanders become the prey of many snakes. In Mexico the cat-eyed snakes, *Leptodeira,* find and devour the eggs that some arboreal frogs attach to the vegetation. The eastern hognosed snake, *Heterdon contortrix,* rarely eats anything except toads, but the western hognose, *Heterodon nasicus,* also eats lizards.

A snake, by virtue of its shape, is an ideal meal for another snake. The kingsnakes, *Lampropeltis getulus,* though famed for their attacks on rattlesnakes, also eat virtually any snake they can subdue; they also devour lizards, rodents, and birds. The prey of the Sonora coral snake, *Micruroides,* seems to consist entirely of smaller snakes, notably the slender blind snake, *Leptophyphlops,* a subterrestrial termite-eater.

*Protective Devices*

The snake's secretive habits enable it to avoid many predators, but in the open it has few protective devices. Swift-moving snakes often escape predators by seeking cover, but the slow-moving species depend more on devices that intimidate the enemy. Rattlers not only vibrate the tail, they hiss and assume threatening postures, and distend the forked tongue. The loud hissing, and the inflation of the body by the hognosed snake, have led to its being called puff-adder, a name preferably restricted to a large African viper. The hognosed snake may also flatten its body, and in Florida it mimics the cottonmouth by distending its jaws to display the white lining of its mouth. The ringneck snake, *Diadophis,* curls the tail and displays the brilliant vermilion of the underside.

Rattlesnakes react to the kingsnakes in distinctive fashion, by arching the body but keeping the head flush with the ground. When a kingsnake approaches the rattler administers a blow with the arched coil of its body, slapping it downward toward the head of the oncoming kingsnake. This unusual behavior, which is not accompanied by rattling, suggests that rattlesnakes discriminate between mammalian and ophidian enemies. The odor of the kingsnake elicits the characteristic defense posture of the rattlesnake—even when no kingsnake is present.

Because most harmless snakes enjoy a high degree of immunity to rattlesnake venom, the fangs of the pit-vipers offer little protection against larger snakes, especially the constrictors. Mammals and birds native to North America may, however, react to the sound of the rattle. Nevertheless some birds capture small rattlers and skillfully avoid being bitten. The agile roadrunner, by carefully waiting for the opportunity, delivers death-dealing pecks on the serpent's head. Deer and other hoofed animals kill rattlesnakes by trampling on them.

### INFLUENCE ON MANKIND

*Venomous Reptiles*

There are valid reasons for exterminating venomous snakes in densely populated areas. Vipers, pit-vipers, cobras, and similar snakes can be potential hazards, particularly in warm regions where people consider clothing a nuisance. It is senseless, however, to kill snakes indiscriminately merely because some of them are dangerous. Removal of the harmless snakes can, in fact, result in an increase in the rodents or other animals that attract the venomous predators. In some areas rodents, rabbits, and other small mammals are not only pests, but carriers of fleas, mites, ticks, or other parasites that transmit diseases including bubonic plague, tularemia, and Rocky Mountain fever. Snakes are not invariably important in checking the increase or dispersal of disease-bearing mammals. Under some conditions, nevertheless, the potential value of venomous snakes in the control of rodents may offset the danger of snake bite.

It is pertinent to note that reptiles may be equipped with fangs and endowed with extremely potent venoms without being either obnoxious or particularly dangerous. In the United States the Arizona coral snake, *Micruroides euryxanthus,* illustrates this situation. People rarely encounter this gaudy little reptile, though it is widely distributed in southern Arizona, New Mexico, and northwestern Mexico. Like its larger relatives, this coral snake restricts its diet largely to smaller snakes that it subdues with its venom. When encountered on the surface, however, the Arizona coral snake attempts to defend itself by seeking shelter rather than by biting. It makes noises by expelling air from its cloaca when it is molested. But it neither coils as though threatening to strike an intruder nor attempts to bite with its fangs.

Notwithstanding this unaggressive demeanor, this coral snake's venom kills small animals quickly. The effects of its bite might be extremely serious or even fatal to human beings. The fangs are relatively small, but those of a fully grown snake could undoubtedly penetrate human skin. If people are bitten, physicians practicing in areas inhabited by the Arizona coral snake must occasionally be called upon to treat the victim. But fatalities or even descriptions of the symptoms of patients bitten by this coral snake remain unmentioned in the literature dealing with venomous snakes and snake bite in Arizona. Numerous accounts refer to the species, but only as being potentially dangerous.

The same cannot be said for the eastern coral snake, *Micrurus fulvius,* a larger, more widely distributed species. Its range extends from northeastern Mexico through the lowlands bordering the Gulf and northward on the coastal plain through the Carolinas. Bites from coral snakes seldom qualify as "legitimate accidents." Usually they result from ignorance or carelessness in handling such snakes. In view of these circumstances, it is astonishing that quite so many bites and fatalities have been reported. But events as rare, unusual, or as improbable invariably attract attention.

Mishandling coupled with ignorance

more often accounts for bites inflicted by the Gila monster, *Heloderma suspectum*. This venomous, but slow-moving, secretive, and largely nocturnal lizard of the deserts in the Southwest, can scarcely be considered a menace. It cannot strike for it lacks the flexible body that permits the pit-vipers to drive their fangs into the victim. But the Gila monster can bite, of course, and it does when disturbed by an aggressor incautious enough to come within reach of its jaws.

Despite its relatively crude venom apparatus, the Gila monster can force enough venom into a wound to kill a person. Nearly all of those who died from bites, however, were intoxicated men who were mistreating captive Gila monsters. Only one death resulted from a bite that occurred under conditions not wholly ascribable to carelessness. As reported in 1893, a hunter, said to have been sleeping in a cave, was disturbed by a Gila monster as it clambered over his chest. Without seeing what he was doing the man seized the reptile by the tail. Thereupon the lizard turned and clamped its jaws on the man's wrist.

Accounts of the disastrous aftermath of this improbable accident were published as far away from Arizona as Philadelphia and Paris. Fortunately, the lurid details had been forgotten a half century later when conservationists were disturbed by the excessive commercialization of Gila monsters in Arizona. Prompted by the fear that the venomous lizard was being exterminated, the state of Arizona actually protected it by law. Both dealers and amateurs were forbidden to capture Gila monsters or have them in their possession. Without a permit, therefore, anyone who keeps a captive Gila monster in Arizona not only risks being bitten, but fined as well. Those individuals who lack the foresight to consider the effects of the bite might worry about the fine. The law may therefore be equally effective in protecting human beings and venomous lizards.

*Reptiles and Man*

People and reptiles live side by side in many parts of the world. Wherever this situation prevails, however, reptiles seldom fare as well as people. Venomous snakes that ordinarily employ their fangs to kill their prey may also use their fangs as weapons of defense. They are, of course, responsible for human casualties. Infrequently and nearly always in tropical jungles, a crocodile, a python, or an anaconda searching for a suitably large morsel, finds, attacks, and perhaps even subdues and devours a human being.

Far more often, however, people are the predators or the killers. Crocodilians have been exterminated by hide hunters in many parts of the tropics. Whether they are after eggs, hatchlings, flesh, shells, or even the oil rendered from the fat the large tortoises contain, human beings have decimated populations. Giant tortoises are gone from islands where they were once abundant. As human populations expand, the large reptiles in particular will be threatened with extinction. Despite laws protecting it, the American alligator is rapidly becoming scarce outside a few preserves. Crocodiles and caimans formerly thrived in places in the tropics where they are seldom seen today. Crocodilians have diminished in numbers in regions that were looked upon as being remote prior to the advent of the airplane.

Lizards, some of them almost ten feet long, inhabit four small inslands between Borneo and Australia in the Lesser Sundas. For reasons partially explicable, the world's largest lizards, giant monitors, *Varanus komodoensis*, are confined to Komodo, Rintja, Flores, and Padar. Such tiny islands cannot support unlimited numbers of carnivorous lizards as large as giant monitors. One estimate places the total at approximately a thousand individuals. Large animals slow to reach maturity, too bulky to be secretive, and neither prolific nor widely distributed might easily be exterminated. Zoological gardens could readily exhaust the supply of these magnificent "Dragon Lizards of Komodo" if dealers met the demand. Average-sized dragons already bring several hundred dollars apiece. The species might face extinction if the Indonesian Government had not set aside Rintja and Padar as a dragon reserve. Even with hunting prohibited, it is costly to curb the activities of poachers, and insular populations are subject to other hazards. Rats and dogs often gain access to islands visited by man, with catastrophic effects on native animals ill-adapted to cope with them.

Not many reptiles are protected by statutes, but a few states have prohibited capturing or killing some kinds of turtles and lizards. Efforts are belatedly being made in various parts of the world to protect crocodilians and marine turtles. Fortunately, snakes and a good many lizards are sufficiently secretive to survive without the meager protection laws afford, but the large turtles and lizards seemingly cannot escape detection and decimation. Human disruption or destruction of natural habitats in many parts of the world threatens many species with extinction. It is imperative, therefore, that governments in all parts of the world do more than consider setting aside wildlife areas. The time for action is today, not tomorrow, when perhaps too little will be left. Preserves in which both plants and animals are undisturbed do not solve all of the problems, to be sure. In many situations, however, there are no better alternatives.

Reptiles were preying on smaller creatures, and in turn becoming a prey of other, usually larger animals, long before man invaded their habitats. No other predator has been quite so destructive as man, however. If venomous snakes take their toll in human lives, be it recalled that people annually kill millions of reptiles. People inhabiting coastal areas frequented by nesting turtles consume or sell turtle eggs literally by the ton. The flesh of the green turtle, *Chelonia mydas,* was once a mainstay in the diets of millions of people inhabiting islands in coastal areas in many portions of the tropics.

Assumptions that the supply of green turtles was inexhaustible led to the decimation or near-extermination of populations in many areas. Nothing short of a concerted campaign to reestablish and protect breeding colonies will bring green turtles back to levels of abundance that permit hunters to harvest a crop. Worldwide regulation of traffic in turtles, not only the all-too-edible green turtles, but those sought for their shells, will be necessary if the marine species are to reattain importance as natural resources.

—C.M.B.

*Recommended Reading*

**Amphibians and Reptiles of Western North America**—Robert C. Stebbins. McGraw-Hill Book Company, New York.

**Field Book of Snakes of the United States and Canada**—K. P. Schmidt and D. D. Davis. G. P. Putnam's Sons, New York.

**A Field Guide to Reptiles and Amphibians**—Roger Conant. Houghton Mifflin Company, Boston.

**Handbook of Lizards of the United States and of Canada**—Hobart M. Smith. Comstock Publishing Company, Ithaca, New York.

**Handbook of Turtles: The Turtles of the United States, Canada, and Baja California**—Archie F. Carr, Jr. Comstock Publishing Company, Ithaca, New York.

**Living Reptiles of the World**—K. P. Schmidt and R. F. Inger. Hanover House, Garden City, New York.

**The Natural History of North American Amphibians and Reptiles**—James A. Oliver. D. Van Nostrand Company, Princeton, New Jersey.

**The Poisonous Snakes of the New World**—C. H. Pope. New York Zoological Society, New York.

**Rattlesnakes: Their Habits, Life Histories, and Influence on Mankind**—Laurence M. Klauber. University of California Press, Berkeley, California.

**The Reptile World**—C. H. Pope. Alfred A. Knopf, New York.

**Reptiles**—Angus d'A. Bellairs. Hutchinson's University Library, London.

**Snakes Alive and How They Live**—C. H. Pope. The Viking Press, New York.

**Snakes in Fact and Fiction**—James A. Oliver. The MacMillan Company, New York.

**Turtles of the United States and Canada**—C. H. Pope. Alfred A. Knopf, New York.

*The flowers of the rhododendron are borne in clusters at the tips of the branches*

**RHODODENDRON**

Pink to rose-colored flowers, borne in clusters (umbels) at the tips of the branches, contrast strongly with the deep green leaves of the rhododendron. The plant is a shrub, usually evergreen, growing in woodlands from Nova Scotia south through the mountains to Georgia. There are several species, all noted for the flowers that appear in spring or summer.

Azaleas are really rhododendrons, at least to the botanists, although horticulturalists have popularized the name azalea for some of the more showy varieties.

Five species of mountain laurel, no close kin to the true laurels of Europe, are found in North America. Most are easterners, from Canada to the southern states, but the pale laurel spreads down the west coast from Alaska to California, and is also found in the Northeast. In the southern Appalachians, the mountain laurel may become a small tree. It has pink or white flowers, while other mountain laurels are crimson or purple.

Rhododendrons, azaleas, and mountain laurels are in the very large heath family, the Ericaceae. Within that group all the plants have flowers of four or five petals, either one or two stamens to each petal, and with small seeds in a five-parted capsule. The leaves are always simple and are usually alternate.

The heaths are widespread, found on all the continents. Very few become trees; most are shrubby, while a few that grow above the timberline are stunted.

Other members of the heath family of economic importance as well as general interest are blueberries, huckleberries, whortleberries, cranberries, and the aromatic wintergreen, or checkerberry. The bog-loving Labrador tea and bog rosemary are also in this group, as is the saprophytic Indian pipe. —G.B.S.

*California rhododendron*

**California Rhododendron**
**Other Common Names**—California rose bay
**Scientific Name**—*Rhododendron macrophyllum*
**Family**—Ericaceae (heath family)
**Range**—Western British Columbia, south through western Oregon to the Santa Cruz Mountains, California
**Habitat**—Ravines and flats, humid Transition Zone
**Time of Blooming**—April through July

The California rose bay is a shrub from four to eight feet high. In northern woods it is sometimes a tree over 25 feet high. The leaves are leathery and evergreen. Groups of deep rose colored flowers are at the ends of the branches. The upper petals have greenish dots. The name rhododendron comes from the Greek *rhodos*, rose, and *dendron*, a tree, and the shrub really looks like a large tree-rose. This shrub is the state flower of Washington but it grows from Washington to northern California.

**RIME** (*See under Frost*)

**RINGTAIL**
**Other Common Names**—Ringtailed cat, civet cat, miner's cat, cacomistle
**Scientific Name**—*Bassariscus astutus*
**Family**—Procyonidae (raccoons, coatis, and allies)
**Order**—Carnivora
**Size**—Body length, 25 to 30 inches; tail, 13 to 15 inches; height at shoulder, 6 inches; weight, 2 to 2½ pounds
**Range**—Southern Oregon south along coast through California and Baja California, west through southern Nevada, and Utah to western Colorado and central Kansas. South through Arizona, New Mexico, Oklahoma (except extreme eastern part), and Texas south through Mexico to Costa Rica

The ringtail is named for its long, bushy tail that has seven black-and-white bars across it. Considered by many the most appealing of all the furry mammals, the ringtail has the face of a fox and the body of a buffy-gray marten. Its tail is the approximate length of the head and body, and the broad, black bands give the ringtail a conspicuous and fascinating appearance shared by no other North American animal.

Although the ringtail is common over a great part of the southwestern United States and southward to Costa Rica, few persons have ever seen it. It is exceedingly shy and keeps to dark crevices and caves. Miners and ranchers of the Southwest frequently capture the ringtail when it is young. It quickly

*Ringt*

becomes a useful pet, destroying rats and mice. It also eats insects, some birds, and occasionally fruit. It is an excellent climber.

The ringtail's young are born in May or June, usually two to four in number. The den site is almost always in some crevice high upon the face of a bluff, but occasionally its dens have been found in hollow trees. The ringtail, with its semiretractable claws and the springy, curved, hind legs of a cat, is as much at home in the trees as in the bluffs. Its thick fur is golden brown on the back to light gray on the underparts, and is used by some furriers. Economically, it is much more valuable in rodent control than as a furbearer, and its unique and appealing ways make it a highly desirable pet.

Owls are probably the most serious of the ringtail's natural enemies, the chief reason being that the ringtail hunts only at night. It never strays far from its natural habitat of bluffs and trees. Snakes, too, probably take young ringtails during the ringtail's denning season.

The presence of the ringtail in southwestern areas of the United States always is a source of deep interest to the naturalist who is fortunate enough to see this shy and handsome furbearer as it streaks up and over the bluffs and cliffs in the bright moonlight. —N.G.W.

**ROACH** (*See Golden Shiner under Fish: Some Common Freshwater Fishes of North America*)

**ROADRUNNER**

**Other Common Names**—Ground cuckoo, lizard bird

**Scientific Name**—*Geococcyx californianus*

**Family**—Cuculidae (cuckoos, roadrunners, and anis)

**Order**—Cuculiformes

**Size**—Length, 23 inches

**Range**—From the head of the Sacramento Valley in California, to Nevada, southern Utah, Colorado, southwestern Kansas, central and eastern Oklahoma, western Arkansas, and northern Louisiana south to Baja California and central eastern Mexico

A lizard-eating, ground-dwelling cuckoo, the roadrunner inhabits the arid and semiarid desert lands in the Southwest, chiefly from California to Texas and in Mexico. The legs are long and heavily muscled, and the wings short, rounded, and comparatively weak. Like all cuckoos, two toes on each foot turn forward, and two backward. Roadrunners and the other North American cuckoos are not brood parasitic (*see under Parasite, and under Cowbird*), but build nests of their own. —G.B.S.

**On the Trail of the Roadrunner**

The deserts of the southwestern United States (*see Desert*), with their sterile, sun-baked hillsides and flats grown with mesquite and cacti, are the most inhospitable lands of the United States—to the casual observer. To those who have visited them through the seasons and have been afield at dawn and after sunset, and have tried to learn something of the hardy wild folk living in the dense, thorny growth, it is a different story.

One learns to like the deserts through the seasons—even the hot days of summer when scarcely a breath of air seems to stir across the parched earth, and all animal life has taken refuge in the dense shadows. Then one enjoys the cool nights when the desert animals, large and small, start their nocturnal activities. At these times the naturalist goes afield with search light to look for the desert wildlife. The eyes of insects, spiders, birds, mammals, and reptiles glow in the rays of one's lantern, and reveal the hiding places of the ordinarily inconspicuous creatures of the rock-strewn, cacti-covered lands.

Summer merges into fall almost im-

*A roadrunner incubates its eggs in a nest of sticks and roots fixed to the low branches of a pine tree. It also nests in bushes and cacti*

perceptibly; the vegetation is a little drier, the thorny growths are dust-covered, and the dried stalks of the annuals have gradually disappeared. The great cumulus clouds of midsummer begin to give way to wind streamers, and it is not long before chill breezes usher in the short days of winter. Then rains fall, to be quickly absorbed in the parched earth, or to rush in torrents down the ordinarily dry gulches.

If the winter season is moist, the desert is a place of beauty when spring comes. The flowering belt extending from east to west is narrow—acre after acre of solid bloom seems to move northward with spring. On the northern edge are green plants breaking into bloom, while on the southern they have reached maturity. The flowers fade, the seed is formed, and the brown vegetation soon crumbles and is inconspicuous against the desert floor.

Spring is the joyous time in this arid region. The voices of birds will be heard before sunup, and many of the feathered songsters are accustomed to perch on the topmost limbs to greet the golden glow of sunrise. Some are brilliantly colored, especially the male orioles and the flaming vermilion flycatchers, but the majority are in somber dress to match their usual surroundings. All are fitted to make a living in a world where much of the vegetation is dagger-pointed; they are hardy creatures well able to care for themselves (*See Cactus*).

Among the voices of early morning, one is apt to hear a throaty *coo-coo-oo* of a roadrunner; the notes are hoarse and resonant and seem to come from all directions, but a little patient stalking may reveal the musician perched upon a boulder or the top of some thorny tree, as the bird bathes in the warm light. These large birds of the desert are generally brownish, streaked with brown and green, and during the nesting season they erect their iridescent crests and have blue-and-orange bare patches back of the eyes that can be expanded or closed at will.

Roadrunners are usually shy in their natural habitat, and the perching bird will take flight when disturbed, its wide-spread tail and short wings reminding one of pictures of the ancient reptilelike creature, Archaeopteryx (*See under Bird*). The speed with which these roadrunners move when they drop to the ground is amazing, for they dart in and out among the thorny growth, literally disappearing in a flash.

They are well named the roadrunners, for in the cool hours of morning or evening, they are apt to go along the highways, where, no doubt, they find an abundance of food. When motor cars pass they are likely to race parallel for a short distance, their necks outstretched and legs working like pistons—then, suddenly, they turn at right angles and disappear from view. Unless sorely pressed, they seem to prefer to escape by running, instead of taking flight.

It is hard to realize these birds are cuckoos, for they are so much larger than their secretive relatives the black-billed and the yellow-billed cuckoos of the woodlands. They are pugnacious fellows and attack dangerous and timid prey alike, but, as with the majority of wild creatures, their killing is for the purpose of securing food. The fast moving desert lizards make up a good percentage of the roadrunners' bill-of-fare with insects, spiders and scorpions, birds, mammals, and snakes making welcome additions.

As killers of poisonous reptiles, these ground cuckoos are unique, for they have no hesitation in making an attack; they feint to make the snake strike, and then dart in with rapierlike thrusts before the animal is able to recover its balance. By repeated onslaughts, the snake is finally pecked to death.

Probably the characteristic view of this cuckoo is to see it running along with great strides, its head held high and a large lizard dangling from its beak. On every trip to the desert, one looks forward to seeing these birds, and the nature photographer always

*The roadrunner has a tail that is longer than the rest of its body*

hopes to film them catching fast-moving lizards, but the action has always been too rapid. With incredible speed a roadrunner will grab an unfortunate lizard and with quick blows upon the ground, quickly beat it to death; then with an upward thrust of the beak, the reptile is juggled around and downed by the roadrunner with a convulsive gulp.

Usually, visits in the Southwest have been too early or too late to coincide with the nesting period, but during one season a wildlife photographer's timing was perfect. It was late May when he bumped over the rough terrain down Laredo, Texas way—and among the prickly pears and mesquite bordering the Rio Grande, were many roadrunners. Whenever one of the birds crossed the photographer's trail, he would stop his car and inspect all the great clumps of prickly pear growing in the near vicinity, hoping to find a nest with small young. At first he was discouraged, for although several nests were located, the young had already left. Then he found a sturdy nest, head high in a mesquite, in which there were two large dark fellows nearly grown and two much smaller. When he passed through the tangle of vines the older ones gave startled cries, dived headfirst from their platform, and ran off into a cluster of nearby cacti, disappearing from view.

A little later, the photographer discovered the nest he had long been looking for—it was in a prickly pear three feet off the ground, just right for taking pictures without bending over or looking up. Spread on the nest was a brooding female with the heads of two medium-sized young sticking out from under her sides. As the photographer moved close, the old bird crouched lower on the nest, but held her place. She allowed him to extend his hand within a foot of her before she jumped from the nest and disappeared with a note of protest.

In addition to the two young, about one-third grown, there were two chalky white eggs—one just hatching. The photographer had been told by friends that roadrunners were "touchy" about their nests, that rarely would one come back to a photographer's blind, or remain near when a camera was started. Consequently, it was with considerable misgiving that a little canvas tent was erected by the photographer to serve as a photographic blind. He cleared away one or two blades of cactus so that light might illuminate the nest, and then climbed into his hiding place.

Within fifteen minutes the *coo-coo-oo* could be heard as the anxious parent circled twenty or thirty feet away. Gradually the sound worked nearer, and then the photographer began to catch glimpses of the brown bird as she crossed little open areas in the desert tangle.

The photographer's camera was on a tripod, aimed at the nest. Finally, after many minutes, the roadrunner seemed satisfied that all was well, and her head disappeared only to be thrust into sight again as she climbed upon the nest. She half straddled the two panting young, sheltering them with drooping wings, and again took up the patient task of watching the photographer's blind, trying to out-stare the camera's eye.

Soon the roadrunner gave a throaty *whoo-oo*, swelling out her throat and making a convulsive movement of her head. An immediate answer came from the cacti thicket near at hand, and after a considerable interchange of conversation, the brooding bird stepped off the nest to reappear in a few moments with a large lizard dangling from her beak. It seemed evident that her mate had approached with food, was alarmed at the photographer's blind, and had requested the female to come and get the food. Later, the larger bird, which the photographer believed was the male, took his turn on the nest; hence he was able to note that there was a considerable difference in the size in the two adults.

Trips were made with food about every half hour, one of the parents remaining on the nest to shelter the young and the eggs, while the other foraged afield. For the most part, the roadrunners carried small lizards to the nest, but, occasionally they brought a large one in, which required some negotiating in order to feed it to the young.

The photographer remained with the roadrunner family throughout the afternoon, although light conditions were not suitable for his photographic work. The blind had become a natural part of the roadrunner's habitat, and consequently they came to and from their nest in a normal manner; the wheezy young demanded food constantly, and both of them mobbed the incoming old one to secure the food brought to them. As the evening shadows grew long, other roadrunners scuttled across open areas, indicating there were many nests in that cacti jungle.

Finally, when the photographer backed out of his blind to leave, he expected the bird on the nest to flush wildly. Instead, she slowly raised her crest, displaying the colored bare patches back of the eyes, and froze, watching every movement of the photographer. Slowly he pulled the tent pegs, and took down the blind—yet the roadrunner held her place. Then cautiously he approached within an arm's length of the nest, and without flushing his photographic subject, carefully replaced the cacti he had removed until she was completely concealed. It seemed to him a suitable ending for an afternoon spent with the roadrunner—swift-moving phantom of the desert (*See Nature Photography*). —A.M.B.

*A male robin feeds on an earthworm that it has pulled from the moist soil*

**ROBIN**
**Other Common Names**—American robin, fieldfare, redbreast, migratory thrush
**Scientific Name**—*Turdus migratorius*
**Family**—Turdidae (thrushes, solitaires, and bluebirds)
**Order**—Passeriformes
**Size**—Length, 8½ to 10½ inches
**Range**—Breeds from the tree limit in Alaska and northern Canada south to southern United States and into Mexico. Winters from New England, the Ohio Valley, and Oregon south to Central America

Without question, the best known and best loved bird in America is the red-breasted thrush that the early settlers insisted on calling a robin. Similar to the smaller European robin of the Old World, the American robin is colorful and returns year after year to the same gardens to sing its beautiful flutelike song. It is the state bird of Connecticut, Michigan, and Wisconsin.

To many Americans the robin is the true bird of spring. Although a few robins stay as far north as southern Canada all winter, the vast majority winter in the South. In spring, hordes fly northward just as the ice begins to thaw. After a series of daytime flights, the bright-breasted males arrive and sing their territorial songs. The females, slightly duller and with grayer heads, usually arrive a few days later. Often the females return to mate with the same males of the year before.

The days that follow mating are full of activity. Passing flocks, moving on to more northern localities, do not disturb the resident pairs, but there is an almost constant conflict with local home-hunting males, especially young birds that have not established territories. While the black-headed males buffet each other, the female stands by. The newcomer seldom, if ever, succeeds in displacing the rightful owner.

By late April the half-finished nests and completed nests are seen everywhere. Usually they are on the lower limbs of trees, but also on window ledges, beams, bridges, and even stumps. Anywhere from slightly above ground level to 70 feet up is a potential nesting place for a robin. Probably the female selects the site. Although the male helps, most of the work of constructing the mud-walled nest is done by the female.

The blue-green eggs are laid, one a day, until there are four. In a few rare instances, five eggs are laid. When the clutch is complete, the female starts brooding. Some males share in the incubation of the eggs, but most female robins will do it by themselves. Within two weeks, between 11 and 14 days, the naked, skinny young hatch. They are sunburned-looking, with cavernous mouths that look like strange orange flowers.

Earthworms form a large part of the diet fed to the young birds, especially after rains when the ground is moist and the adult robins find worms near the surface. Worms very often rest with just the tips of their bodies showing at the mouths of their burrows. Robins also eat insects, cherries, mulberries, and many kinds of fruits.

When, after 10 or 12 days, the fledglings feather out, they have big speckles on their breasts. These spots reveal their relationship to the other members of the thrush family. The first flight is usually a short one—a flutter of a few feet to the nearest branch. The male robin takes full charge of the brood at this time, and stays with it for another week or two. Meanwhile, the female prepares for a second brood, builds a new nest, or relines the somewhat damaged old one.

Early in the fall, flocks of robins eat wild cherries and the fruits of other trees that bear fruit in late summer. When the leaves drop, many robins start south. Where there is food they concentrate—in South Carolina it might be among gum trees; in Georgia where there are chinaberries; in Florida among palmettos; in California where there are pepperberries and mistletoe.

**Habits of the American Robin**

Most of us know the American robin only in its breeding season—that quarter or third of the year when it compromises with its natural wildness and, like city squirrels and pigeons, accepts a measure of domesticity, nesting against our houses and getting its living from our lawns and gardens. It shows its adaptiveness in this, because as soon as it is released from family responsibilities it returns to the kind of woodland life it must have led before man came to America. In late summer, fall, and winter the robins live in loose flocks within the borders of the woods and fly from a person in alarm before he has got close enough to discover their presence. It is hard to understand such wild mistrust of man among birds that have recently sought the shelter of his habitation for their nesting.

*Mouths agape, hungry young robins are tended by their mother*

*Robins live in sparsely wooded areas and in forest margins. They also have adjusted well to suburban areas*

The wildness, however, is native, the seasonal domesticity exceptional. The fact that the English settlers associated it with the beloved redbreast of England (quite a different bird), even to calling it by the same affectionate nickname, robin, must have had something to do with its seasonal domestication. In the early American settlements it was undoubtedly shot less freely on that account, although freely enough. As late as the 1870's Elliott Coues was making a plea for legislation to abolish the open season on robins. "There would rarely if ever be difficulty in gaining permission upon proper representation," he wrote "to destroy the very few that might be required for scientific purposes, or to please the capricious palate of an invalid."

This custom of returning to its native wildways at the end of the breeding season accounts for a curiously misconceived human custom in the northern half of this country—that of celebrating the return of the first robin as a sign of spring. While the robin is, in fact, the first, or one of the first, migrants to return, it remains in small numbers throughout the winter, except along the northern border. On the Connecticut boundary of New York one may occasionally see the first robin of the year on January 1st.

One of the American robin's distinctions is its erect military carriage. When feeding on the ground it alternates rapid movement with statuesque immobility. It has no in-between, no slow or leisurely movements. Motionless, it is the picture of alertness, erect and tense, as if listening with its whole body for some signal to be off or some prey to be seized. The head is high, the tail touches ground, the points of the wings are suspended. Then it runs rapidly, like a sandpiper, and freezes again. Or it pounces furiously with its bill on a worm in the grass. Or it takes off as suddenly as it does everything else, flying low at first, then rising to the limb of a tree, uttering a rapidly repeated cluck as it flies. On the limb it stands as erect and alert as on the ground, repeating its cluck a few times and jerking its tail at each repetition.

When alarmed by danger or aroused by a rival robin its call notes rise to loud shrieks, half a dozen in rapid succession when in flight, or repeated at regular intervals when perched. Between the extremes of a cluck and a shriek, it has a complete gradation of single notes, and its repertoire includes as well a high, thin trill, and other thrush sounds. It has the habit of many ground birds, like the killdeer, of uttering a quick series of repeated notes as it takes to the wing. At other times, when perched in a tree, it will give vent to a rapid series of call notes (*tup tup tup . . .*) that starts and ends uncertainly, an expression of sheer excitement or excess vitality, not necessarily addressed to any particular object.

*Robins are among the first to push north with spring. A few even winter in New England*

Sometimes a series of *tups* ends in a shriek, or a shriek is followed by a series of *tups*. The robin seems never quite master of its vitality, unless when singing.

The song is an almost continuous outpouring with little variation, delivered easily and giving the impression of confident serenity. At dawn and dusk, in season, it dominates the atmosphere, it masters the landscape, it commands; and in this the robin betrays its membership in the family of great singers. The song is not tossed out to the world on a momentary impulse, like that of the song sparrow; it is an extended preoccupation, like a religious observance. The robin is at his matins or his vespers and must not be disturbed.

The continuous caroling of robins at dawn and in the evening is, for most of us, the supreme expression of spring, if only by long association. It heightens the seasonal melancholy that occasionally overpowers one, especially in the first spring days, when one should feel glad and relieved at winter's passing. There have been times when its sadness could have made one wish the world at an end while one listens to the spring chorus of robins in the dusk of a day that, by its passing perfection, seems to leave nothing for hope. Yet the sadness is, probably in the season and the time of day, rather than in the robin's music. Perhaps the association explains the comment of W.H. Hudson, an English naturalist and writer, who in writing of the peculiar charm of the song of the dusky thrush, said "that it seems to combine two opposite qualities of bird-music, plaintiveness and joyousness, in some indefinable manner." Both emotions are in the human listener, who feels the characteristic effect of the season.

The American robin is in the second or third rank of singers, not among the great. Its music has none of the qualities of imagination and improvisation that distinguish the mockingbird's song for example; but then these are not the qualities in which our American thrushes (at least) excel. The robin's song also lacks range, in tone and phrasing alike, so that the effect is monotonous. Close up, the tone is not unmusical, but not as full and musical as that of the wood thrush, or of the rose-breasted grosbeak. Most bird songs are best heard, in any case, at some distance; for distance filters out any harshness or stridency of tone and leaves only the best. One would not want even the wood thrush at one's ear. The robin's song at a distance produces, in its tone, an effect of musical sweetness. Even the monotony of phrasing has a pleasing quality, contributing to the impression of sadness or of sad joyfulness so much associated with the song (*See also under Bird*). —L.J.H., Jr.

*How It Got Its Name*

In Europe, country folk of early Normandy referred to any gay blade as *Robert*. Eventually the name was abbreviated to robin and used in many ways. Among others, it was the jocular title of a youth in love. Conquerors took the name with them when they invaded Britain in the eleventh century.

Many persons of the British Isles noticed that a common bird was almost human in its love-making—even choosing a special bit of territory and defending it against rival males. It was logical to give such a feathered swain the name of a giddy adolescent and call him "the red-breasted Robin." In popular speech, the name became *Robin Redbreast*, and finally, *robin*.

Wherever English colonists have gone, they have taken this bird name with them. Failing to find the common European robin redbreast in America, they gave its name to the larger, red-breasted thrush, or American robin. In other parts of the world, the name has been given to birds that have nothing in common with the English robin, except small size and reddish feathers on the breast. —W.B.G.

## ROCK FORMATION

### Rock Stories and How to Read Them

Behind it all there lies a rock. If one stops to think about it, everything in the world is concerned with rocks. They are the foundation on which man lives and builds his cities. Rocks constitute the earth itself. They are the raw materials from which soil is made and out of which all vegetation grows. Rocks are composed of minerals. In them are the ores and metals that are so important to mankind.

The most permanent thing in the world is change. One has only to think of the earth and all the life on it to realize the truth of this seeming paradox. In the study of rocks one is particularly aware of this. Although a rock may seem to be something hard and indestructible, actually it is continuously being altered and even huge masses of rock such as mountain ranges, while fairly permanent when compared to a human life span, are mere incidents in the history of the earth. The Rocky Mountains, for example, are new. Before they existed a vast sea occupied the area, and before that there were plains and other mountains and other plains. Those who understand something of how rocks are formed can read these events by examining the rocky walls of river valleys. Fossil remains of plants and animals, now part of some of these rocks, bear evidence of life in the area while these changes were taking place (*See under Fossil*).

Ability to read a little of the story of earth changes in any area is not as difficult as might be imagined. If one can distinguish the more common members of the three great classes of rocks and if one knows something of the forces at work to alter them, even though this knowledge be gleaned only from the brief paragraphs that follow, it seems probable that a person could go forth wherever he is and read for himself at least a few of the events in earth history that have happened there.

*Sedimentary rocks, such as sandstones and shales, typically occur in layers. The thick beds in the cliff face are sandstones and the thin beds at the bottom are shales*

#### *Kinds of Rocks*

All rocks fall into three great classes: *igneous* rocks, *sedimentary* rocks, and *metamorphic* rocks. Some of the common kinds of rock belonging to these three groupings are: granite, basalt, porphyry, pumice; sand, clay, gravel, sandstone, shale, conglomerate, limestone; schist, gneiss, marble, and slate. The thing for a beginner to remember is that, unlike a plant or an animal, which is always definitely one kind of plant or animal, rocks can be partly several kinds. A rabbit is never part rabbit, part mouse, and part squirrel, but a rock might easily be part gneiss and part schist. These rock mixtures are likely to confuse the beginner in rock study. For this reason only rocks that are typical of their kind should be collected at first, even if that means discarding most of the pebbles brought home from a trip along the beach or upstream. Another thing to remember is that a mere chip or small fragment is seldom typical of any kind of rock. When trying to identify a rock, insist on one at least as big as a fist.

Igneous rocks were once hot and fluid, a sort of mineral "soup," termed by geologists a magma. If this molten rock cools slowly within the earth, the minerals contained in it have time to form crystals, just as hot fudge, if cooled slowly, sugars. The slower the cooling, the larger the crystals. Granite, pegmatite, and gabbro are examples of igneous rock cooled slowly within the earth. Felsite and basalt, composed of tiny crystals as fine or finer than granulated sugar, cooled more rapidly, either within the earth or as a lava that flowed from a volcano. The surface of volcanic lavas cools so rapidly it is glassy, just as fudge cooled rapidly is smooth and creamy. Pumice and obsidian are familiar rocks of this type.

*Erosional processes that cause changes in the earth's topography are apparent everywhere. In a sloping field gullies are formed, exhibiting in miniature how running water carrying a load of sand and silt carves a deep V-shaped channel on its way downhill*

Sedimentary rocks are composed of weathered fragments or sediments of igneous rocks, metamorphic rocks, and older sedimentary rocks. They may be loose, as clay, sand, or gravel, or may be firm and compact, as when these sediments are compressed by weight of overlying deposits and impregnated with solutions of cementing materials, such as lime, silica, and iron. Shale, sandstone, and conglomerate (sand and gravel cemented together) are compact, cemented forms of clay and sand. Often the cementing is done beneath the sea. In the Middle West, riverbanks and road cuts show layer upon layer of shales and sandstones, like a slice through a huge birthday cake. These present a very different picture from the massive, unlayered crystalline walls of igneous rocks common in mountainous regions. But even these cemented rocks break easily and usually feel gritty under one's teeth. Crushed shells of sea animals cemented together form the sedimentary rock limestone.

Metamorphic rocks are those that have become altered by subjection to tremendous pressures and heat. They differ from igneous rocks whose crystals of various minerals are heterogeneously distributed, by having the crystals of each mineral (particularly mica) more or less lined up in bands or layers. They differ from sedimentary rocks that may also have a layered appearance, by being much harder and crystalline. They are not gritty to the teeth as sandstones are (weathered specimens excepted). Common types are schist, gneiss, slate, quartzite, and marble.

*Weathering*

All rocks exposed at the surface are gradually crumbled by the action of heat, cold, rain, snow, and ice. This eroding process is called weathering. It greatly alters the appearance of a rock, softens it, and changes its texture. Since all exposed surfaces of rocks (those usually seen) are somewhat weathered, a fresh surface must be obtained in order to observe the true characteristics of the rock. A few sharp blows of a small stone mason's hammer will do this. The effect is often startling. A dull, nondescript looking rock opens to display a colorful, sparkling, beautiful interior hidden beneath its weathered surface.

In weathering, hot sun causes a rock's surface to expand. Cold contracts it. But this surface does not expand and contract as a unit since the various minerals composing the rock differ in their degree of expansion and contraction. The result is that the rock begins to crack. Water seeps into the cracks and when it freezes widens the cracks. Water is a great solvent, too, and may carry off some of the mineral constituents of the rock in solution. In time, fragments of rock are broken off and these fragments later become smaller fragments, eventually small enough for rains and the force of gravity to carry off to streams and rivers.

As the stream carries along this load of sand and clay, it uses it like a tool to carve ever deeper its V-shaped valleys, as it flows to the quiet waters of the sea, where it deposits its load in huge beds of sand and clay.

In mountainous areas in the North, great rivers of ice, the glaciers, sometimes carry huge fragments of rock along with a load of smaller boulders, pebbles, and finely ground rock slowly down the valleys to be dropped in big hills when the ice melts. The glacier shapes its valley like the letter U.

Wind too is a great weathering force.

*Rock weathering by heat, cold, water, and ice is a major factor in erosion. Rock fragments broken by frost action and a granite boulder split by frost are shown in the top two pictures. Exfoliation, typical of metamorphic rocks is shown at bottom*

It can pick up the finer particles of rock and carry them long distances. It can also hurl them against rock surfaces with such force as to etch them. Some of the curiously shaped rock formations in the Southwest are examples of wind sculpture (*See Canyonlands National Park*). By the combined efforts of these weathering processes, entire mountain systems can be reduced to plains.

Meanwhile, great pressures within the earth may be lifting these plains to form new mountains. In Colorado near the town of Boulder, one can see great beds of sandstone formed there in an ancient sea, now tipped on end by pressures from below to form the foothills of the Great Divide. Higher, where the sandstone cover has worn off, is the massive granite of the lower mountains. This is the rock that pushed the sandstone up. Still higher where both the sandstone and granite cover have worn off, are rocks from nearer the bottom of the pile, rocks altered by tremendous heat and pressure, the metamorphic rocks, schists, and gneisses that form the jagged peaks of the Divide.

Evidences of rock weathering and changes in the earth's topography are everywhere apparent. Out in the sloping field, tiny gulleys are forming, exhibiting in miniature after a rain, how rushing water carrying a load of sand and clay carves for itself an ever deeper V-shaped channel as it winds its way downhill. This is the familiar phenomenon of erosion whereby thousands of tons of good topsoil are removed from fields man has carelessly allowed to remain unprotected by a cover of vegetation—a great loss to agriculture.

A gravel pit reveals the true nature of the area out of which it has been gouged. In the northern part of the country it is a dumping ground of a glacier—a very heterogeneous mixture of sand, clay, and angular pebbles.

A fresh road cut shows the nature of the rock beneath. It may be granite, an igneous rock once molten and slowly cooled within the earth; or metamorphic schists and gneisses, suggesting an old mountaintop; or, in the Great Plains area, layers of shales and sandstones formed long ago within some sea, and often hiding in them fossil remains of ancient life. Near the top of the road cut are fine fragments weathered from the rock below—the elements of soil.

There are rivers dark with mud flowing to the sea where this mud will be dropped, gradually building up great beds of sand and clay, some day to perhaps become great beds of sandstone and shale.

In the mountain canyons are walls of igneous rock that, when molten, intruded and pushed up overlying rock. Through it are streaks of other igneous rocks that intruded later, filling cracks in the older igneous rock.

These are examples of only a few of the rock stories one can learn to read. If one is interested in pursuing this topic further, the books listed at the end of this section will be helpful. The following gives details of some of the common rocks and minerals.

*Common Igneous Rocks*

Granite always contains the minerals *quartz* (usually colorless to smoky) and *feldspar* (pink or white). It usually also contains either *mica* (black or white) or *hornblende* (dark green to black). The mineral grains vary in size from those about an eighth of an inch across to those as large as the end of one's finger. Granite with still larger minerals is called pegmatite.

Pegmatite is a coarse granite containing grains as large as one's thumb to those the size of a grand piano or even larger.

Felsite is a fine grained, light colored igneous rock with mineral crystals almost too small to be recognizable without a hand lens. Dark varieties of this rock are called basalt.

Basalt is a fine grained, very dark colored igneous rock. Basalt is often referred to as *trap rock.*

Porphyry is a rock containing large crystals (phenocrysts) of one or more minerals imbedded in a matrix of fine grained rock. The general appearance may be that of a polka dot or printed fabric.

*Common Sedimentary Rocks*

Some loose fragment varieties familiar

*The Colorado River has carved a channel through a mile of sedimentary rocks at Grand Canyon National Park, Arizona*

to everyone are *pebbles* (gravel), *sand, clay,* and mixtures of these.

Shale is a thin flaky rock formed by the cementing of particles of clay. It looks like slate but is much softer, will usually break easily in one's fingers, and weathers rapidly to clay. It occurs in layers of thin plates sometimes almost paper thin.

Sandstone has a rough, gritty texture, like sandpaper, and is formed by the cementing of particles of sand. It occurs in layers and breaks into flat slabs. The flat stones in stream beds of Ohio are often sandstone. These are often used by the uninitiated camper as pot rests for his stew. Sandstone, being rather porous, contains considerable moisture. When heated by the camper's fire, the moisture changes to steam and explodes the rock, sending sharp rock fragments and hot stew in all directions.

Conglomerate is a mixture of sand and pebbles cemented together and sometimes called "pudding stone," the pebbles suggesting nuts and raisins.

Limestone is made of precipitated calcium carbonate or of fine to coarsely ground sea shells and corals cemented together. It is a soft rock and a scratch by a nail or penknife leaves a broad white streak. If a drop of lemon juice falls on a clean, freshly scraped surface, foamy bubbles of escaping carbon dioxide gas will form. This makes a convenient way to distinguish it from a fine grained sandstone. Sometimes, small fossil shell animals are seen in it.

*Common Metamorphic Rocks*

Gneiss resembles granite but has a banded appearance caused by the lining up of its mineral crystals. It is formed by the alteration of granite, or other rocks with sufficiently varied compositions.

Schist is like a gneiss but usually contains more mica. Its bands appear as

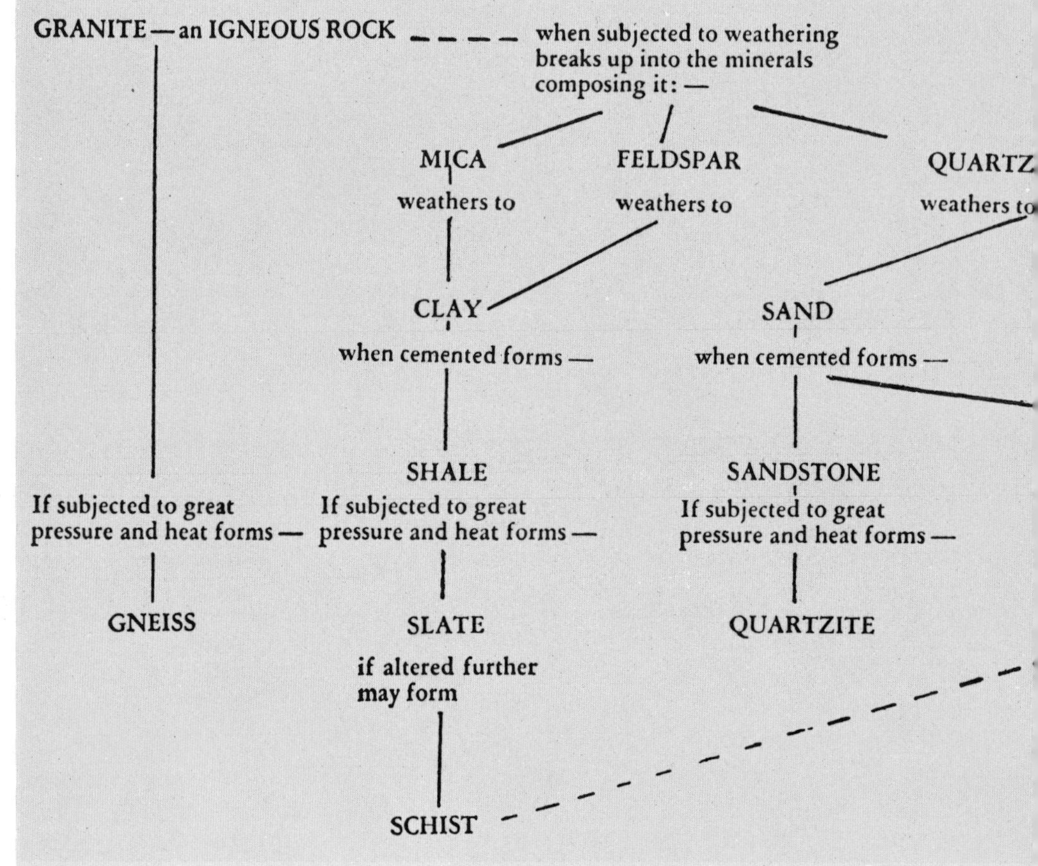


*The diagram above shows how rocks are changed from one type to another*

much more complete layers than those of gneiss and may be almost paper thin.

Quartzite has a granular, sugary appearance not unlike sandstone but has a firm, smooth texture (not gritty), because in breaking, the fracture has gone *through* the sand grains. It is very hard and difficult to break. It is a metamorphic sandstone.

Slate resembles shale but is hard and does not crumble or break easily in the fingers. Unlike shale, which splits in a direction parallel to its natural bedding, the cleavage of slate bears no relation to the natural bedding and may even be at right angles to it.

Minerals compose rocks. They are described technically as natural, inorganic compounds with definite chemical composition and physical properties. It might be said that a mineral, like a cake has a definite recipe. Minerals are made of elements, as hydrogen, oxygen, iron, copper, etc., and the same elements combined in the same arrangement always make the same mineral.

*Common Minerals Found in Granite*

Quartz is a common and widely distributed mineral and is an oxide of the element silicon, $SiO_2$. It may be any color and in large crystals. In granite it is usually colorless, smoky, or pink. It has a glassy appearance and breaks like glass. It is a hard mineral and scratches glass easily. Indians used chips of quartz for arrow points. Flint, agate, chert, jasper, and chalcedony are also

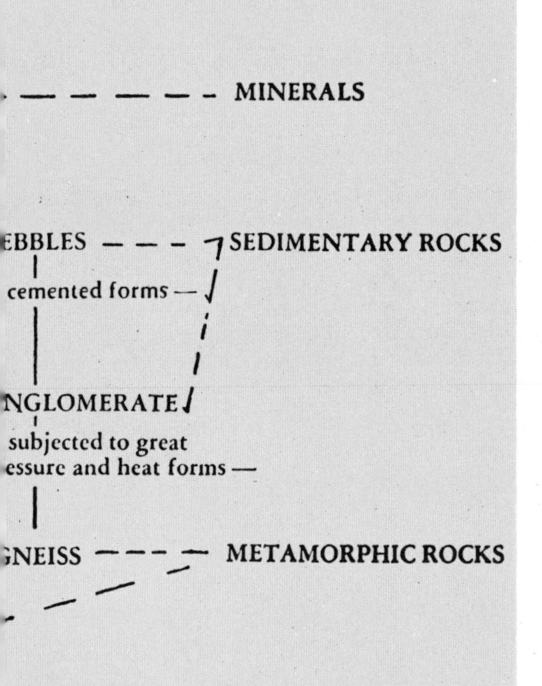


forms of quartz, but the individual crystals are microscopic. Their relationship to the crystallized varieties is the same as that of granite to felsite.

Feldspar is usually pink or whitish and breaks with shiny, flat surfaces. A piece of feldspar by itself usually shows faces shaped like parallelograms. Feldspar is hard enough to scratch glass but does not scratch it as deeply or as easily as quartz. Quartz will scratch feldspar but feldspar will not scratch quartz.

Note: When testing the hardness of a rock by scratching, a sharp edge of the "scratcher" should be held firmly against a smooth surface of the rock to be scratched and drawn across it. One's thumb should be rubbed against the scratched place to remove all powdered rock. If a scratch remains, the scratcher was harder. If no scratch shows, the scratched surface was harder and wore off the edge of the "scratcher."

Common Mica may be either black (*Biotite Mica*) or white (*Muscovite Mica*). Both varieties break into paper thin, shiny, transparent, elastic flakes which can easily be scratched with one's thumbnail. This white mica is sometimes used for windows in stoves, is commonly used as a window for the screw-in type of fuses, and is used for artificial snow at Christmas time.

Hornblende sometimes takes the place of the mica in granite. It is dark green to black in appearance and does not flake.

*Common Iron Ores*

Hematite is a dull, reddish rock often soft enough to stain one's fingers and when drawn across a quartz pebble leaves a reddish streak. It occurs commonly in stream beds and roadsides through the state of Ohio. Indians ground soft colorful varieties, *red ochre,* to fine powder and used it as paint. One can mix some powdered hematite with a thin sugar syrup and try painting with it.

Limonite is another good paint rock, *yellow ochre.* It leaves a yellowish streak on a quartz pebble.

Iron pyrite is a brassy iron ore, known as fool's gold, and is of common occurrence in both igneous and sedimentary rocks. If drawn across a quartz pebble it leaves a black streak. Real gold of course would leave a trail of gold. When hammered, iron pyrite breaks up into a powder; gold is flattened by the hammer, is *malleable.* —D.A.T.

*Recommended Reading*

**Field Book of Common Rocks and Minerals**—Frederick B. Loomis. G. P. Putnam's Sons, New York.

**A Field Guide to Rocks and Minerals**—Frederick H. Pough. Houghton Mifflin Company, Boston.

**The First Book of Stones**—Maribelle Cormack. Franklin Watts Company, New York.

*Rugged mountains and mountain streams are characteristic of Rocky Mountain National Park, Colorado*

**Getting Acquainted with Minerals**—George Letchworth English. McGraw-Hill Book Company, Inc., New York.
**Our Amazing Earth**—Carroll Lane Fenton. Doubleday & Company, Garden City, New York.
**Rocks and Their Stories**—Fenton and Fenton. Doubleday and Company , Garden City, New York.
**The Rock Book**—Fenton and Fenton. Doubleday & Company, Garden City, New York.
**The Story of Rocks**—Dorothy Edwards Shuttlesworth. Garden City Books, Garden City, New York.
**1001 Questions Answered About the Mineral Kingdom**—Richard M. Pearl. Dodd Mead & Company, New York.

**ROCKY MOUNTAIN NATIONAL PARK**

**Location**—Northern Colorado

**Size**—405 square miles

**Mammals**—Mountain lions, bobcats, elk, mule deer, bighorn sheep, beavers, martens, minks, muskrats, squirrels, coyotes, pikas

**Birdlife**—Golden eagles, ptarmigans, grouse, ducks, jays, hummingbirds, many songbirds including water ouzels

**Plants**—Alpine firs, Douglas-firs, Engelmann spruces, Colorado blue spruces, ponderosa pines, limber pines, quaking aspens

This portion of the Front Range of the Rocky Mountains has within it 65 peaks that are over 10,000 feet above sea level. The highest is Long's Peak, at 14,255 feet. The Continental Divide passes through the park. Trail Ridge Road takes visitors high above timberline where alpine tundra life can be observed.

The mountains drop off steeply on their eastern sides, where cliffs 3,000 feet high are common. The western slopes are less precipitous.

There are over 150 lakes in the park, many of them accessible only over a rugged hiking trail. Some 200 miles of trails are available to hikers and horsemen, and skiing facilities are open during the winter.

**Accommodations**—Lodges, inns, and campgrounds within the park and nearby

**Headquarters**—At Estes Park, Colorado

**RODENT**

Rodents are a mighty force in the modern world. Their strength is in numbers and ability to multiply rapidly. Despite a host of enemies that prey upon them, the rodents outnumber all other forms of warm-blooded mammals alive today.

Rodents have spread over all of the great landmasses and most of the islands—from the Arctic to the Antarctic—but none ever went to sea. They show the greatest extremes in body covering, grading from the superfine fur of the chinchilla to the barbed quills of the porcupine. They are the most destructive as well as the most constructive of all mammals and actually show considerable engineering ability. They have played an important part in soil development, preservation of water supply, forestation, and are a power in insect control.

The outstanding characteristic that definitely puts the rodents in an order by themselves is the chisel-like front teeth—only one pair placed side by side in the upper jaw and one pair in the lower. These chisels are separated by a wide space, or diastema, from the molars, or grinding teeth, and they continue to grow throughout the life of the animal. (*See also Beaver; Chipmunk; Gopher; Kangaroo Rat; Lemming; Marmot; Mouse; Porcupine; Prairie Dog; Rat; Squirrel; Vole*) —G.G.G.

A Classification of North American Rodents Occurring North of Mexico (after Hall and Kelson)

Order Rodentia (Rodents)
- Suborder Sciuromorpha (squirrel-like rodents)
  - Family Aplodontidae (mountain beaver)
    - Genus Aplodontia
  - Family Sciuridae (marmots, squirrels, and chipmunks)
    - Genus *Tamias* (eastern chipmunks)
    - Genus *Eutamias* (western chipmunks)
    - Genus *Marmota* (marmots)
    - Genus *Ammospermophilus* (antelope squirrels)
    - Genus *Spermophilus* (spermophiles and ground squirrels)
    - Genus *Cynomys* (prairie dogs)
    - Genus *Sciurus* (tree squirrels)
    - Genus *Tamiasciurus* (red squirrels)
    - Genus *Glaucomys* (American flying squirrels)
  - Family Geomyidae (pocket gophers)
    - Genus *Thomomys* (smooth-toothed pocket gophers)
    - Genus *Geomys* (eastern pocket gophers)
    - Genus *Cratogeomys* (yellow pocket gophers)
  - Family Heteremyidae (pocket mice, kangaroo rats, and allies)
    - Genus *Perognathus* (pocket mice)
    - Genus *Microdipodops* (kangaroo mice)
    - Genus *Dipodomys* (kangaroo rats)
    - Genus *Liomys* (spiny pocket mice)
  - Family Castoridae (beavers)
    - Genus *Castor*
- Suborder Myomorpha
  - Family Cricetidae (mice, rats, voles, and lemmings)
    - Genus *Oryzomys* (rice rats)
    - Genus *Reithrodontomys* (harvest mice)
    - Genus *Peromyscus* (white-footed mice)
    - Genus *Baiomys* (pygmy mice)
    - Genus *Onychomys* (grasshopper mice)
    - Genus *Sigmodon* (cotton rats)
    - Genus *Neotoma* (wood rats)
    - Genus *Clethrionomys* (red-backed mice)
    - Genus *Phenacomys* (heather voles and tree mice)
    - Genus *Microtus* (meadow voles)
    - Genus *Lagurus* (sagebrush voles)
    - Genus *Neofiber* (round-tailed muskrats)
    - Genus *Ondatra* (muskrats)
    - Genus *Lemmus* (lemmings)

Genus *Synaptomys* (bog lemmings)
genus *Dicrostonyx* (collared lemmings)
Family Muridae (Old World rats and mice)
Genus *Rattus* (Old World rats)
Genus *Mus* (house mice)
Family Zapodidae (jumping mice)
Genus *Zapus* (jumping mice)
Genus *Napaeozapus* (woodland jumping mice)
Suborder Hystricomorpha
Family Erethizontidae (New World porcupines)
Genus *Erethizon* (porcupines)

## ROOSTING OF BIRDS

Birdlife in the summertime seems to be idyllic and even the summer nights may seem not to hold especial terrors for them. But much as we know about birds, there is relatively little known about where birds spend the night. A safe place to roost, and a sheltered roost for birds in winter may mean life or death to them.

It is believed that in roosting many species seek, insofar as it is possible, a place similar to that in which they were nestled (*See under Bird: Nesting of Birds*). There are many exceptions to this but it is in general true. Most hole-nesting birds, seek a hollow in a tree, post, or building in which to spend the night. This is true of woodpeckers, chickadees, nuthatches, house sparrows, and perhaps, sparrow hawks. House sparrows have been seen to crawl into nooks and crannies that one would think could interest only a mouse.

Occasionally bluebirds winter well to the north. One case has been recorded of a dozen or more bluebirds wintering in Minnesota, crowding each night into a bluebird box. This has its counterpart in an account of 11 brown creepers that habitually spent the night in the cavity of a beam in a barn. The opening was quite small, and it took quite a while for the creepers to enter. The observer wrote that there was much moving in and out, flying back and forth, and climbing around the beam, the nearby wall, and nearby trees before all of them were settled for the night. Not all brown creepers are so fortunate and most undoubtedly take shelter from the storm and night under a loose strip of bark where they nest habitually. Woodpeckers, as is commonly known, excavate a cavity for a winter roost if no other is handy.

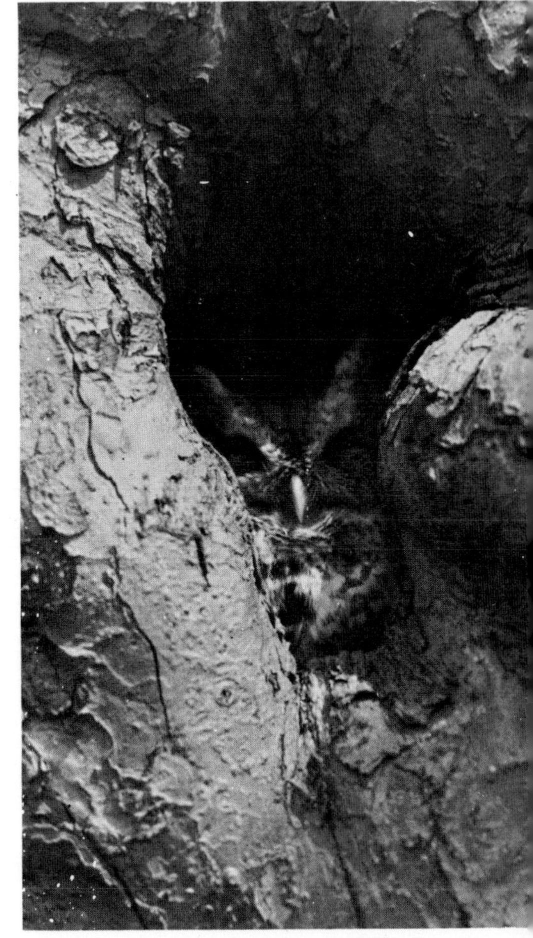

*The screech owl usually roosts in a tree hollow*

The story for ground-dwelling birds is different. In T. Morris Longstreth's book, *Knowing the Weather,* he writes, "A man standing in a foot of snow may be breathing zero air, while at his knees the temperature may be 6° below, at his shins at the snow's surface 14° below, and at his toes where the air has been kept warm by the snow, 14° above." Such conditions might hold true during a calm, but if a strong wind were blowing it might feel 20° colder although the wind is not as strong closer to the ground, because of the friction close to the earth's surface. So, the closer to the ground and the more sheltered a bird can get (if that is its nature), the better for it.

Ptarmigans and grouse of the north country bury themselves in the snow, and perhaps wintering horned larks, longspurs, meadowlarks, and Hungarian partridges also dig down into the snow and get into the lee of the wind, behind some tuft of growth or hummock of ground. Pheasants may also seek shelter in this way, although they have been seen roosting in evergreens and willows like so many chickens.

Juncos, tree sparrows, and cardinals—birds that like a brushy habitat—probably seek shelter from the wind in brushy tangles. One of the favorite roosting places of small birds is a cattail marsh. Pheasants, too, like these places. One fall, during the late migration season, bluebirds and song sparrows were observed settling down for the night in a cattail marsh while one song sparrow sang its summer song in whispered tones as though in memory of warmer, greener days.

Deep in the woods of a forest preserve where there is a rather large cattail marsh, a small flock of juncos were once observed to approach the woods every afternoon during winter. They entered the woods and filtered through the trees toward the marsh, there to spend the night deep down among the dried rushes, out of the wind.

Crows and large owls roost in treetops, preferably in pines. One of the most interesting and picturesque sights of winter is a flock of crows coming to roost—black crows and black trees silhouetted against the vivid sunset of a winter's evening. They arrive in a long stream from some location, where they have previously gathered—some performing aerial acrobatics—and finally, with much shifting about, settle down into treetops. Just about the time one thinks they are settled for the night, the whole flock boils up in a black mass and commences the process of settling down all over again.

One winter at twilight an observer happened upon the roost of a flock of rough-legged hawks (*See under Buteo*). The roost was situated in a group of five old apple trees standing in an otherwise cultivated field. Two rough-legged hawks were perched in the trees. As the observer watched, three more hawks alighted, and a sixth drifted by, still hunting. After a short while, three of the hawks left the roost and flew east to hunt over the darkening fields. Finally they came back, one by one, and settled in the trees for the night.

Evening after evening the observer watched and counted the rough-legged hawks as they came in to roost. One evening he counted a total of eight birds on the roost. Some evenings upon arriving early, he found the hawks perched on fence posts at quite some distance from the trees, while awaiting the approach of dusk. On one such evening crows were flocking in the field, before flying into their own roost, and the hawks waited quietly, unmolested, on the fence posts. On this particular evening, after the crows had left, the hawks deserted their regular roost, after several of them had first gone to it, and settled in another grove of trees near a farmhouse.

Such hardy birds as crows and hawks seem to be able to stand the bitter cold and wind of winter in the open, but occasionally the weather becomes too much even for them. Such was the experience of the rough-legged hawks. On February 14 of that year the worst glaze storm in 15 years occurred. As

*This flock of redwinged blackbirds was photographed at its winter roosting place on a telephone pole*

ice accumulated on the trees, the night was made horrible by the cracking and crashing to earth of overburdened branches. The next evening only one bird was to be found at the usual hawk roost. Underneath the trees was a pile of branches that had fallen during the night. What a hard time the hawks must have had with branches breaking off around and perhaps from under them, and how difficult it must have been for them to find new perches on the ice-laden branches. After that experience the roost was deserted.

*Recommended Reading*

**Recent Studies in Avian Biology**—Edited by Albert Wolfson. University of Illinois Press, Urbana, Illinois.

## ROSE

The fragrant rose has given its name to the large family (Rosaceae) of which it is a member. There are more than a hundred genera in the family, and perhaps as many as 3,000 species. Some are herbs, some shrubs, some vines, and a few are trees.

The west coast of North America has desert sweet and creambush, the deserts have another creambush and Arizona rosewood. Mountain mahogany, chamisebrush, blackbrush, and antelope brush are also western, and are closely related to blackberries and strawberries. Wild cherries, wild plums, and chokecherries are trees or shrubs of the Rosaceae, and are widely distributed. Crabapples, shadberries, serviceberries, and hawthorns belong to still another group within this large family. —G.B.S.

**California Rose**
**Other Common Names**—Wild Rose
**Scientific Name**—*Rosa californica*
**Family**—Rosaceae (rose family)
**Range**—Southern Oregon to northern Baja California
**Habitat**—Low ground or moist slopes, often forming thickets, Upper Sonoran and Transition Zones
**Time of Blooming**—May to September

The wild rose grows from southern California to Alaska. Its best months are May, June, and July. The one in the picture is very common along creek and riverbanks and on bluffs near the sea. The flowers are deep rose color and very fragrant. The branches are close together and have many thorns. A green "ball," or calyx, holds the petals until they die. The ball (or fruit) then turns bright red and is called a hip. Some of our fruit trees belong to the rose family —the cherry, the plum, and the peach being some of them.

*California rose*

**RUMINANT** (*See under Deer*)

**RUSH** (*See under Sedges and Rushes; and under Club Mosses and Horsetails*)

**RUST** (*See under Fungus*)

*Rudbeckia*

**RUDBECKIA**
**Other Common Names**—Coneflower
**Scientific Name**—*Rudbeckia californica*
**Family**—Compositae (composite family)
**Range**—Cascade Range, Chelan and Kittitas counties Washington
**Habitat**—Mountain slopes
**Time of Blooming**—July to August

We look for this flower in wet places in high mountains. The flower is at the top of a single tall stem that is from three to five feet high. The center of the flower is a high brown cone—like a thimble. The wide petals are deep yellow. They make a gay frill at the bottom of the brown cone, standing straight out. The leaves are a foot long and are near the ground. They are very rough to the touch. Along with this coneflower we find black-eyed susan, that has yellow petals and a low brown center (*See Black-eyed Susan*).

# S

**SAGEBRUSH**
**Big Sagebrush**
**Other Common Names**—sage, black sage, blue sage
**Scientific Name**—*Artemisia tridentata*
**Family**—Compositae (composite family)
**Size**—Rarely to 20 feet; usually shrubby, 5 to 8 feet
**Range**—Southwestern North Dakota and Montana west to southern British Columbia, south to Baja California, east to northern Arizona.

Probably the most abundant shrub in western United States, big sagebrush grows in arid regions. Its dusky green leaves set the dominant color for thousands of square miles of open lands, and are the food of many of the small mammals and birds that live where it grows.

The leaves are small, numerous, and each one has three points at the tip. The flowers, which appear in the fall, are yellow and fragrant. The bark is light in color, and shredded in texture.

Other members of the family, smaller in size and more restricted in range, are the silvery sage, white sage, and prairie sage. —G.B.S.

**SAGE**
**Thistle Sage**
**Other Common Names**—Chia
**Scientific Name**—*Salvia carduacea*
**Family**—Labiatae (mint family)

*Sage deserts are common in many parts of the western plains*

*Thistle sage*

**Range**—Contra Costa County, California, south to northern Baja California and eastward to the western parts of the Mojave and Colorado deserts
**Habitat**—Sandy and gravelly soils. Upper and Lower Sonoran Zones
**Time of Blooming**—March to June

This plant is a foot or more high. The long leaves are in a rosette on the ground and have many sharp spines on them. On the stems are woolly white balls, held up by sharp pointed bracts. The lavender flowers sit in these balls. The lower lip of the flower has a ruffle of white and the anthers are tiny balls of orange color. Thistle sage grows in the valleys and in the deserts. There are many other sages—black sage, white sage, purple sage. They all furnish much honey and are valuable to beemen.

**SAGUARO**
**Other Common Names**—Giant cactus
**Scientific Name**—*Cereus giganteus*
**Family**—Cactaceae (cactus family)
**Range**—Arizona, southern California, and Sonora, Mexico
**Habitat**—Desert, forming cactus forests in the Lower Sonoran Zone
**Flower**—Nocturnal white or yellowish flowers borne singly on upper areoles
**Fruit**—A berry with pulpy interior containing many shiny black seeds. Edible

The saguaro is related to a quite varied and widely distributed group of cacti, which include tall "climbing" forms of slender proportions and others the shape and size of pumpkins or small barrels. Of the several genera all have a pronounced ridged or fluted appearance but only the saguaros exhibit the combination of stoutness and height that gives them tree proportions. Insomuch as they grow in areas that are usually unsuitable for any true trees, the saguaros occupy the same niche in the low altitude of the Sonoran Zone in the desert Southwest that the pitch pines and scrub oaks occupy in the sandy coastal plains of the East—namely to form rather open, extensive cover forests. Together with many smaller undergrowth plants and animals the saguaro forests form a quite distinctive biotic area in parts of the arid desert. They offer housing or refuge for a considerable variety of birds and mammals. Woodpeckers peck nesting holes in their upper branches, and hawks and owls frequently nest in these after they have been abandoned (*See under Cactus*).

Like most cacti the saguaros are able to retain water and reduce evaporation because of a thick, leathery skin and a compact form. When cut open this cactus can provide emergency water for lost desert travelers. —M.H.B.

*Towering saguaros are an attraction in the desert*

*Saguaro National Monument*

**SAGUARO NATIONAL MONUMENT**
**Location**—Southern Arizona
**Size**—98 square miles
**Mammals**—Mule deer, black bears, coyotes, gray foxes, peccaries, ringtails, ground squirrels, kangaroo rats, jackrabbits
**Birdlife**—Gilded flickers, Gila woodpeckers, roadrunners, screech owls, elf owls, Inca doves, crissal thrashers, Bendire's thrashers, phainopeplas, pyrrhuloxias, many others
**Plants**— Saguaros, prickly pears, hedgehog cacti, barrel cacti, chollas, palo verdes, ocotillos, other desert flora

The stately saguaros, some of them 50 feet tall, occur in scattered groves in this portion of the Sonoran Desert. They tower over the more lowly cactus and thorn scrub. Woodpeckers nest in them, and abandoned nestholes are taken over by elf owls and cactus wrens.

The Tanque Verde Mountains and Rincon Range lie within the monument, and pine forests grow in their higher elevations.

A loop road, with signs naming the plants, runs through one of the best sections of the monument.
**Accommodations**—In nearby Tucson, Arizona
**Headquarters**—Within the monument; address at Tucson, Arizona

**SAILFISH**
**Atlantic Sailfish**
**Other Common Names**—Florida sailfish
**Scientific Name**—*Istiophorus albicans*
**Family**—Istiophoridae (billfishes)
**Order**—Perciformes
**Size**—Length, 6 to 8 feet
**Range**—In the warm waters of the Atlantic and in the Mediterranean. Occasionally strays as far north as Cape Cod

The sailfish has a powerful, elongated body. Its snout is extended into a strong, round sword. There are two dorsal fins. The front dorsal fin is long and high with a notch, or indentation, in its upper margin. The fish often swims near the surface with this fin out of the water looking very much like a sailboat. There is a groove on the fish's back into which it can fold the front dorsal fin at will. The tail fin is deeply forked.

The sailfish's back is silver blue, its sides and belly are lighter, its magnificent dorsal fin, deep blue with black spots. The sailfish is much sought after as a trophy by fishermen and is one of the best fighters known. It has been estimated that it can swim in excess of 60 miles per hour and when hooked it may make leaps covering 40 feet. Sailfish have attacked boats, driving their swords so far in that they had to break them off to free themselves. —M.R.

**SAITAS**
**Common Saitas**
**Other Common Names**—Blue dick
**Scientific Name**—*Dichelostemma capitatum*
**Family**—Liliaceae (lily family)

*Common saitas*

**Range**—Southern Oregon to northern Baja California
**Habitat**—Dry open ridges and grassy fields, Sonoran and Transition Zones
**Time of Blooming**—March to April

Various common names are attached to this member of the lily family—such as blue dick, cluster lily, Spanish lily, and wild hyacinth. Frequently the long slim leaves have disappeared by the time the flower has reached perfection. In March or April, after a season of heavy rain, a most magnificent wildflower display is officially presented by

Kern County in an out-of-door spectacle. Countless species unite to produce this show, chief among them being blue dicks, various of the lupines, and the gorgeous California poppy of that section. They make a carpet of royal purple over miles of territory south and east of Bakersfield, California, although found abundantly in many other sections of the state.

Blue dicks are also wrongly called wild onion, which belongs to the genus *Allium* (Latin name for garlic), whose lilylike leaves have the distinctly characteristic taste and odor of onions and with flowers of the loosely formed head usually in shades of rose and lavender.

**SALAMANDER** (*For general account see Amphibian; for Homing of, see Animal: Navigation of Animals*)

of these characteristics include long bodies; a well developed adipose fin (a small, fatty fin behind the dorsal fin); a single dorsal fin with 10 to 12 soft rays; strong teeth lining the jaw, palatines, and tongue.

**Atlantic Salmon**
**Other Common Names**—Silver salmon, black salmon, sea salmon
**Scientific Name**—*Salmo salar*
**Family**—Salmonidae (trouts, whitefishes, and graylings)
**Order**—Clupeiformes
**Size**—Length, about three feet
**Range**—Both the European and North American sides of the Atlantic. North American shores from northeastern Labrador to Cape Cod. Stragglers found as far south as New York

Adult Atlantic salmon live most of their lives at sea but swim up into freshwater rivers to spawn. The young remain in fresh water for two or three years and then swim back to the sea. Atlantic salmon that have become landlocked in lakes do not grow very large. They are commonly called ovananiche, or Sebago salmon. The life history of the Atlantic salmon is very complex. Its

*Salmon is one of man's most important food fishes*

**SALMON**

There are a number of fish commonly called salmon; some are the most important of man's food fishes. Six species of salmon inhabit North American waters five of which live in Pacific Coast waters. Of the six, two will be discussed here. Both have the common characteristics of their family, Salmonidae. Some

color, size, and habits vary considerably with its age and whether it is in marine or fresh water.

The Atlantic salmon is one of the many fishes that has been seriously threatened by man's careless treatment. Their numbers are decreasing rapidly due to water pollution, impassable dams, intense fishing, destruction of spawning grounds through deforestration of slopes above freshwater rivers and even the killing of young in power-plant turbines.

**Chinook Salmon**
**Other Common Names**—King salmon
**Scientific Name**—*Oncorhynchus tschawytscha*
**Family**—Salmonidae (trouts, whitefishes, and graylings)
**Order**—Clupeiformes
**Size**—Length, up to 5 feet
**Range**—Waters of southern California to Alaska

The chinook salmon spends most of its life in the ocean but swims up rivers into fresh waters to spawn. It is the largest of five Pacific Coast species of salmon.

The fish's back is dusky gray and its sides and belly are silver. Its back and its dorsal and caudal fins are covered with round black spots.

Three other species of salmon are the pink salmon, *Oncorhynchus gorbuscha;* chum salmon, *Oncorhynchus keta;* and sockeye salmon *Oncorhynchus nerka.*

—M.R.

## SANCTUARY

*What is a Wildlife Sanctuary?*

A sanctuary is a place of refuge. In olden days a fugitive could find sanctuary by going into a temple or church where he would be safe from secular law as long as he remained. Though most of us today think of sanctuaries in terms of birds or wildlife, many sanctuaries are areas where people may find peace and a renewed contact with the realities of nature; as our population continues to grow, and our lives are increasingly regimented, this latter use of natural areas will become increasingly important (*See Nature Center*).

It may be well, at the outset, to distinguish two very different kinds of sanctuaries. First there are strategic wildlife sanctuary areas protecting the breeding, roosting, or feeding grounds of rare birds or colonial species dependent on such protection if they are to survive. Good examples are the Gulf Coast refuges of the National Audubon Society, where colonies of graceful herons, spoonbills, and ibises occur in large numbers; or some of the federal refuges that protect the whooping crane's breeding and wintering grounds, or the year-round homes of the trumpeter swan and the California condor. The maintenance of such sanctuaries is a grave responsibility.

The second type involves sanctuaries for kinds of wildlife not so vulnerable to persecution, where the provision of habitat will suffice, and where such other activities as public education through the enjoyment of this wildlife can be conducted without seriously interfering with the primary conservation objective. These sanctuaries, which may be of almost any size (though their value will vary as they do or do not provide adequate living room for species with a large "cruising radius"), lend themselves to creation and administration by local groups or individuals. Indeed, the need for them is so widespread, and their local importance so great, that they must be a local responsibility.

The term *wildlife refuge* is widely used in this country and has a slightly different meaning from wildlife sanctuary. A *refuge* has come to mean an area designed specifically for the perpetuation of gamebirds or other game animals. Sanctuaries are inviolate areas, but refuges may not be, since hunting is often allowed on at least part of our national wildlife refuges, for example. However, since hunting is restricted to game species, the refuge does in fact serve as a sanctuary for nongame species, and our national wildlife refuges thus make important contributions to the preservation of a great many species.

*Why Create Wildlife Sanctuaries?*

Charles Elton, the famous English ecologist, has pointed out that. . . "sanctuaries are set up for a great many reasons. The Hudson Memorial Sanctuary in Hyde Park, London, was started chiefly for sentimental reasons and to give visitors the pleasure of a few birdsongs uncommon to London. But little harm would be done to the birds themselves if they were unable to breed in Hyde Park. The rest of England is there for them to choose from."

What then are the chief reasons for establishing a wildlife sanctuary? The following appear to be most important:

1. To maintain a natural area
2. For personal enjoyment
3. For educational purposes
4. To increase and maintain diversity of wildlife species
5. To balance local land use and increase the pleasure of living in the community

Although these aims have been listed separately they are all closely allied and interrelated and are almost all applicable to any land being set aside for sanctuary purposes.

*When is a Sanctuary Worth the Name?*

A gift of a few acres of land, a neat sign, and a resolution on the books of the local bird club are not enough to create a useful wildlife sanctuary. If it is to increase the local wildlife population, even the addition of a warden and a fence will not achieve the purpose. The object of wildlife conservation is not only the preservation of a few species but also the providing of proper living conditions to insure a varied population of many species.

If the sanctuary is one with stable vegetation which will perpetuate appro-

*Lake Okeechobee Sanctuary*

priate habitat conditions without man's interference, the area may need nothing but protection.

But very often, land acquired for sanctuary purposes has vegetation which is undergoing change (plant succession) from one type to another. Here man can intercede helpfully, providing he understands the trends that affect vegetation. The land must be managed so that more mammals, birds, and plants can find their living on it—so as to increase the "carrying capacity" of the land. Management of animal populations is very largely management of the plant environment on which they depend. Without food, cover, and water, or any one of the three, wildlife cannot exist (*See Plants and Water for Birds*).

The development of a sanctuary to serve as park or "living museum" is a rewarding community project. Groups such as the Scouts, Campfire Girls, Garden Clubs, YMCA and YWCA, Service Clubs, League of Women Voters, Izaak Walton League, Church groups, and local Audubon Clubs are interested in conservation projects and could be called upon to organize such a project. A committee can be organized with representatives from each interested group, and with proper publicity and enthusiasm can usually enroll the support of town officials. The more people participate in the project, the more it will truly represent a community endeavor and be cherished by the townspeople as their very own. There can be no surer protection of a municipal sanctuary than the support and interest of the town's residents.

When a committee has once established the need for open areas, and wishes to increase diversity of wildlife within a town, the actual work may begin on the area selected. The following are ideas to be kept in mind or to be developed as the situation warrants:

Plant ground cover to stop erosion and provide shelter for wildlife.

Plant trees and berry-bearing shrubs in clumps.

Allow clumps of shrubby plants to run wild in areas where no tangles exist.

Strive for balance between evergreen and deciduous trees and shrubs.

Allow tangles of shrubbery and vines to develop in rocky areas.

Open up patches of cleared land in uniformly wooded areas, unless these be prize groves.

Develop small dams along streams to hold water in pools, again increasing diversity.

Avoid giving the area a manicured look. It won't be natural.

Communities may plant flowering trees along the streets and roads. —D.M.

*Make Your Community a Bird Sanctuary*

The following ordinance has been adopted by the City Council of Goldston, North Carolina, and many other city and town boards. The National Audubon Society recommends the ordinance to communities that have not yet declared themselves to be official bird sanctuaries.

BE IT ORDAINED by the Mayor and Council of the City of Goldston (North Carolina) in Council assembled: That the entire area embraced within the corporate limits of the City of Goldston be, and the same is hereby designated as, a *Bird Sanctuary*.

That it shall be unlawful to trap, shoot, hunt, or attempt to shoot or molest in any manner any bird or wild fowl or to rob bird nests or wild fowl nests. Provided, however, if starlings or similar birds are found to be congregating in such numbers in a particular locality that they constitute a nuisance or menace to health or property in the opinion of the health authorities of the City of Goldston, then in such event such health authorities shall meet with the representatives of the Audubon Society, Bird Club, Garden Club, or Humane Society, or as many of said clubs as are found to exist in the City of Goldston, after having given at least three days actual notice of the time and place of said meeting to the representatives of said clubs.

If as a result of said meeting no satisfactory alternative is found to abate such nuisance, then said birds may be destroyed in such numbers and in such manner as is deemed advisable by said health authorities under the supervision of the Chief of Police of the City of Goldston.

Anyone violating the provisions of this Ordinance shall be punishable by a fine of not more than $100 or imprisonment not exceeding 30 days.

This ordinance shall take effect immediately upon its adoption.

*Recommended Reading*

**A Helping Hand to the Bluebird**—John K. Terres. *Flower Grower,* June 1964.

**The Audubon Guide to Attracting Birds**—John H. Baker. Doubleday, Doran & Company, Garden City, New York.

**The New Handbook of Attracting Birds**—Thomas P. McElroy, Jr. Alfred E. Knopf, New York.

**Our Wildlife Legacy**—Durward L. Allen. Funk & Wagnalls, New York.

**Songbirds in Your Garden**—John K. Terres. Thomas Y. Crowell Company, New York.

**This Land of Ours**—Alice Harvey Hubbard. The Macmillan Company, New York.

## Establishing a Wildlife Sanctuary

Before undertaking a wildlife sanctuary program in the community, those in charge should ask the five W's that a reporter unconsciously answers when covering an assignment: "Who, What, When, Where, Why," and in this case, "How?" In other words, what is the purpose or objective and how will it be accomplished? How will it be maintained and perpetuated? What will it accomplish and what will be the benefits?

### *Location*

Is the site, tract, or area already determined? If so, future developments automatically depend upon a plan and a course of action. If the site is merely prospective, is it actually available? Is the organization able to obtain it by purchase, lease, or gift?

On the other hand, if a group must "start from scratch," there will be an opportunity to investigate, survey, and finally acquire an area that is perhaps more accessible and easier to control and maintain. Also an area may, by chance, be found that is endowed with a relatively natural wealth of birds, other animals, and plantlife, or a good potential without requiring extreme measures to develop, create, or restore suitable habitat.

### *Size*

It is true that one's concept of a sanctuary can be anything from one's yard and feeding station for birds to hundreds—or even thousands—of acres. The size of a sanctuary, it seems, depends upon the resources, personnel, and time that the sponsoring group has available. The size then becomes narrowed to: 1) What the group can adequately handle; 2) animal biology and wildlife conservation.

The first point has been briefly touched upon. The second involves the birds and other animals themselves. If the group merely wants to undertake a project to attract birds artificially, one can stop there; however, if the intent is to go into a wide-scale program, then a knowledge of the birds and other animals of the region can be a guide.

Most pairs of small birds have relatively small territorial requirements (each pair needs from less than one, to several acres) for their nesting and feeding activities. These vary with the habits of the species and may change with the seasons.

The proposed sanctuary should, ideally, be large enough to be managed so as to increase or attract animal species that are characteristic of the general region. The size will be determined by a combination of factors, but in its

*Remote wilderness areas in national forests are set aside as wildlife sanctuaries*

truest sense, the sanctuary should be planned and conducted to provide the most good for the greatest variety and number of birds and other animals. Again, knowing the habitat requirements of animals or acquiring a knowledge of ecology will help one to set up a management plan that is sound and practical (*See Ecology*).

*Type of Sanctuary*

The type of sanctuary is necessarily tied in with the locality, size, and the present use of the site under consideration. Perhaps the sponsoring group can enlist the cooperation of municipal or state agencies to develop a city or a state park, a forest, or a recreation area. If such a plan is undertaken, many of the long-range problems of maintenance and protection may be eased, but they may also introduce other ones that involve the relationship or personalities of the supervisors or administrators.

Occasionally, a sponsoring group will fail to get the aid or cooperation of public officials because the officials are not sympathetic toward birds and other wildlife; the officials may be hamstrung by policy or precedent; they don't want to be bothered with working with an "outside" group. If the sanctuary-sponsoring group contemplates the use of a public area, it should carefully lay its course, make sure that public opinion and influential persons are in sympathy with the idea, and that a legally accepted sanctuary agreement is drawn and agreed to by the parties concerned. If the group feels that it should be granted the privilege of developing a sanctuary on public property, and the public officials resist or are apathetic, one will discover that these officials are usually sensitive to strong public opinion, especially the opinions of citizens with influence and prestige.

Another type of bird sanctuary may be an undeveloped block or a section in or near a downtown or urban area where it is available and can be called to the attention and utilized by many people. A sanctuary may also be established on an abandoned farm or an old estate that can be developed for the strict private use of the sponsoring group; or it can be opened to special persons or groups by invitation or upon request; or to full use of the public.

Finally, a sanctuary may be a remote, isolated, wilderness type where the purpose is that of a refuge or an inviolate area set aside for the welfare of a certain kind of wildlife. This may involve the protection or special management of its habitat by providing it with the proper requirements during the critical portion of the species' life cycle.

*Development and Management of the Sanctuary*

A group that decides to take over an area must necessarily make long range plans. Unless an area is closely supervised or protected, one can expect it to be subjected to vandalism and become a dumping grounds for trash. The disrespect and an almost traditional lack of appreciation and consideration for public property by some people must be reckoned with. One of the first problems is to create the sympathy and interest of unsympathetic and apathetic people. Working with nature and with birds, by contrast, is relatively easy.

One must consider buildings or other structures on the property, if present, and their upkeep. One also must think of trails or paths and their maintenance (*See Nature Trail*). On a big area this can be a sizable chore. A long list of questions and problems must be deliberated. A few follow.

1. Can or will the area be fenced?
2. Does the existing plantlife need immediate control or management?
3. Should plantings be made of various trees and shrubs and of grain and seed plants?
4. Should or can a pond or a series of them be constructed?
5. Are there streams or springs present that must be managed?
6. How extensively will wildlife be furnished with their requirements artificially? Will it need a number of feeders, birdbaths, nesting and roosting boxes, or even nesting materials?
7. Is the area large enough to manage different sections for different types of birds? Can part of it be left in permanent woods? Brushy areas and thickets of trees and shrubs are highly important. Can they be encouraged? Can some of the open field areas be mowed occasionally or left partially clear for field and field border species of wildlife?
8. What can be done to the land to provide swampy or marshy spots?
9. Certain cultivated plants belong. What about those for hummingbirds?

*Educational and Interpretive Programs*

If the sanctuary is large enough to support a building, shelter, or other structure, quarters can be provided for a whole or a part-time custodian, a meeting place, possibly a museum, and a library. This can be a center or a meeting place for lectures, bird study classes, programs, field trips, and conducted tours (*See Nature Center*). These can be limited to members only or to school groups, adults, and the general public. An active program can add to the esthetic, cultural, and recreational activities of the community.

Individual members and committees of the sponsoring group can conduct informal programs and lectures in the schools and before biology classes, youth groups, and civic club meetings. Small nature trails can be established and labeled. Checklists of birds and other informational material about the sanctuary can be compiled to distribute to members, to visitors, and to be mailed to interested people. Perhaps some members can conduct a series of articles or regular columns on wildlife in the local newspapers. Specialists on bird study and conservation can be invited to give lectures and to lead field trips, programs, and discussions.

A combination of these sanctuary activities can have profound effect on a community and the lives of various individuals in it.

*Conclusion*

The person or committee in charge of the sanctuary program should endeavor to anticipate every problem, need, and opportunity. Various wildlife and conservation specialists of state and federal agencies, colleges, and museums should be consulted before and during the establishment of the sanctuary. Such personnel can give practical suggestions and help one to avoid unexpected pitfalls. A wildlife sanctuary will require continuous planning and supervision. Without continuity it will disintegrate. The sponsoring group should never become discouraged. All problems should be taken as a matter of course and dealt with accordingly.

Every community should and can have a wildlife sanctuary. The persons or groups with the willingness to undertake the responsibility should accept it as a challenge.

—J.H.B.

*Sanderlings are common on almost all ocean beaches where they feed on a variety of small aquatic creatures*

**SANDERLING**
**Other Common Names**—Ruddy plover, beach bird, surf snipe
**Scientific Name**—*Crocethia alba*
**Family**—Scolopacidae (woodcock, snipe, and sandpipers)
**Order**—Charadriiformes
**Size**—Length, 8 inches
**Range**—Breeds on the Arctic Islands, Southampton, and northern Greenland; also in Iceland, Spitzbergen, and northern Siberia. It winters along ocean and gulf beaches from central California, Texas, Virginia, and Bermuda to Patagonia in South America. It occurs casually or occasionally in winter in Massachusetts and British Columbia (Vancouver Island); in the Eastern Hemisphere from the Mediterranean, Burma, and Japan, to South Africa and various Pacific Islands. In summer, sanderlings that may not breed sometimes linger along the coasts of Florida and on certain Pacific islands

The flight of shorebirds on a rising tide shows a wild ecstacy capable of carrying them considerable distances before the impulse fades and hunger makes them pause. Coastal distances of the western hemisphere mean little to their long pinions. A hundred-mile flight from the mouth of the Kennebec River in Maine to Highland Light in Massachusetts—what do such short travels mean to migrants that annually flit from Baffin Bay to the Argentine and return?

Taking off from some northern coastal beach, many of them have barely struck their stride when they sight the tip of old Cape Cod, flung like a sickle in the sea. Whether they will stop or not depends largely on the tides. They seem to follow the air trails as long as the water is rising, particularly when driven by storms. The very instant the ebbing water bares flats and bars, the migrants arrive like magic, as if they had timed

their voyage accordingly. Before the sea has receded a foot, one frequently hears their voices high overhead, and presently a few yellowlegs or plover drop down out of nowhere. They whirl alongshore for a few minutes, as if looking for a place to land, and throng the flats as the lowering tide uncovers them.

It is the same story all the way from the St. Lawrence River in Canada to Plymouth, Massachusetts, and thence round the Cape to Chatham and Monomoy, also in Massachusetts. Everywhere the emerging land crooks a beckoning finger to the shorebirds, the green of the meadows tolls them in, and a sandy universe is a playground for their twinkling feet.

Just as the outside beaches give the best glimpses of migrating shorebirds, so the inshore flats and lagoons are the most convenient places to observe their feeding habits. The sands of Barnstable, Wellfleet, Monomoy, Martha's Vineyard, Montauk, and dozens of other harbors and promontories on the Atlantic coast, are visited by innumerable sandpipers, snipe, and plover from the arrival of the first ring-necked plover early in July to the disappearance of the last sanderling in mid-October or later.

Almost any day between these dates one could watch many different species without stirring from a Provincetown, Massachusetts, wharf. When the tide ebbs, flurries of shorebirds arrive everywhere and alight, elevating their wings and peeping complacently. They start feeding immediately and keep it up almost without interruption until the next high tide chases them into the air. They seem the winged embodiment of the tide—their flight a ripple, or a series of ripples, and their bodies are aerial minnows, dark above and glistening white underneath.

Myriads of these little beach waifs run about devouring minute crabs, algae, hoppers, sand worms, and various marine insects. All feed eagerly but none can compete for an instant with those hungriest of sandpipers, the beautiful san-

*The sanderling is a big-headed sandpiper that has a stout, black bill*

derling. Sanderlings dash about as if they were famished, often holding their mandibles submerged to the nostrils but working them like scissors. One might think from the way they stuff themselves that they would burst.

In May and in early June, sanderlings pass northward along the New England coast bound for their nesting grounds in northern Alaska, the shores of the Arctic Ocean, and northern Greenland. They are cosmopolitan in their distribution, breeding also in Iceland, Spitzbergen, and northern Siberia. Their southern migration, during which we see them along our coasts in greatest numbers, extends to southern Patagonia in South America, to South Africa, Ceylon, Java, Borneo, the Philippines, Australia, New Zealand, and Hawaii.

Despite this wide dispersal, considerable numbers of sanderlings winter along the Atlantic Coast in the middle latitudes of the United States, where they add a touch of life and beauty to the cold and deserted sands.

Although common on the inshore flats at low tide, sanderlings are preeminently the sandpipers of the sounding ocean beaches, and are appropriately termed surf snipe. They prefer those vast, tide-scoured, rolling strands where breakers crash and roar. When the tremendous backwash seethes down the slope, bearing minute crustaceans and hoppers, these bold little birds dash after the water, snapping up the tiny marine animals that kick themselves clear of the spume (*See under Crustacean*).

Often, too, sanderlings probe the hard, wet sand for sand fleas, mussels, and other sea spoil, leaving lines of holes two or three feet long and deep enough to survive the scouring of several waves. Following a flock of these birds along the barren, outside strand, it is pleasant to hear their contented peeping and whistling, and to watch them at a distance swarming over some rise in the sands.

At other times the observer may be

surprised to see a flock spring from the margin of the sea, where their pale protective coloration renders them indistinguishable until they move.

Their heads and upper parts are somewhat rusty in the breeding season, with blackish back and scapulars and some gray. Their underparts are white, their bills short and black, and their legs are brown or black. Males and females look alike, and are from 7 to 8¾ inches long. They are the only species of American

*Shown in light winter and dark summer plumage are least sandpipers (upper left); semipalmated sandpipers (upper right); western sandpipers (center); dunlins, or red-backed sandpipers (lower left); sanderlings (lower right)*

sandpiper lacking a fourth toe. In their winter plumage, after the summer molt, sanderlings lose most of their rusty tints and look as gray and white as the sand on which they scamper.

Sanderlings lay their top-shaped, spotted eggs in hollows lined with dried grass on pans of clay or stone slightly raised above the surrounding tundra in the Far North. The young are said to be as precocial as most of the order are, and they run about and feed themselves soon after hatching. They are mighty travelers. As soon as they are fledged they start south and by midsummer become the commonest birdlife on the Atlantic coast.

–H.M.H.

**SANDPIPER**

The sandpipers are that attractive group of graceful shorebirds which are combined in the family *Scolopacidae*. There are actually twelve families of shorebirds, a diverse group of over 300 species which are related to the gulls and alcids. The sandpipers are themselves subdivided into some 80 species, 34 of which occur in North America.

The British call these birds waders, a term used much less in America because of the competitive term, "wading birds", which includes the herons and their long-legged relatives. This emphasis on relationship and terminology is introduced only to show how difficult it is to pigeon-hole any large group of living things.

In general, however, the sandpipers are slender birds with longish legs and bills; they inhabit grasslands, tundra, and shores. Because they engage in long, spectacular migrations, they sometimes concentrate in large numbers at certain favorable sites, most often along the margins of the continents, and this is where most of us come to know and study them. The tidal flats of Massachusetts, Long Island, New York, New Jersey, and elsewhere along the eastern seaboard; as also those of San Francisco Bay and a lesser number of Pacific coast sites, swarm with these birds spring and fall.

These large gatherings contain other shorebirds, not just sandpipers as a rule. Often numerous are the plovers, a closely related group that beginners easily confuse. Plovers, however, are stockier birds, somewhat shorter-legged, and have larger heads and stouter bills, the tip of the bill being swollen.

All the sandpipers—indeed, all the shorebirds—and more particularly the larger ones, were once hunted avidly and mercilessly. It was not until 1927 that federal protection was extended fully to these birds, and even today, some forty years later, some species have not recovered from the persecution they suffered in the late nineteenth and early twentieth century, due both to market hunting and sport (*See under Curlew; and under Extinct and Threatened Animals*). Although these birds are technically game birds, since they are so listed in the migratory bird treaties with Canada and Mexico, only two, the woodcock and the snipe, may be legally hunted today.

Some of the small sandpipers that flock together on mud flats and sand bars are commonly called "peeps," a useful vernacular group name when they are not or cannot be identified to species.

Most of the sandpipers are very inconspicuously colored, with drab browns grays, and buff tones predominating. These are protective colors that cause the bird to "melt" into the landscape when immobile.

A majority of the sandpipers nest on the arctic tundra, some of them right around the top of the world. They are all ground nesters except for the solitary sandpiper which lays its 4 eggs in an old songbird nest, most often that of a robin or blackbird.

On the tundra, sandpipers eat prodigious quantities of insects. During their long migrations, however, and during the weeks and months they spend along the edges of lakes, bays and oceans, they feed mostly on small aquatic organisms, including crustaceans, mollusks, and marine worms. Some species feed on the low-growing blueberries and crowberries of the arctic and subarctic before launching themselves down the long over-water routes.

The habitat preferences of sandpipers, along with details of form and marking, and their varied voices, are all helpful in distinguishing the many species. They are similar enough, however, especially in the nondescript winter dress, to be a real challenge to the field student.

Perhaps the most exciting trait of these fascinating birds is the ability to navigate from one extreme of the planet to another. Birds which nest on the arctic tundra, only a few hundred miles from the north pole, may fly all the way to the pampas of Argentina to spend the winter, or to the tiny southern hemisphere islands of Oceania. Some go all the way to Australia (*See under Migration*).

*Least sandpipers feed on beach fleas, flies, mosquitoes, and other insects.*

In so large and varied a tribe it is of course possible to provide a mere selection of species for individual treatment, as is done beyond. Although much remains to be learned about these long-winged travellers, the books listed below will provide much additional information and prove a useful introduction to the intriguing sandpipers.

*Recommended Reading*

**A Gathering of Shorebirds**—Henry Marion Hall. The Devin-Adair Company, New York.
**A History of the Gamebirds, Wildfowl, and Shorebirds**—Edward Howe Forbush. Massachusetts State Board of Agriculture.
**Life Histories of North American Shorebirds**—A.C. Bent. Dover Publications, New York.

**Least Sandpiper**
**Other Common Names**—American stint, Wilson's stint, mud peep, sand peep
**Scientific Name**—*Erolia minutilla*
**Family**—Scolopacidae (woodcock, snipe, and sandpipers)
**Order**—Charadriiformes
**Size**—Length, 6 inches
**Range**—Breeds from central western Alaska and northern Mackenzie southeastward to central eastern Mackenzie, central eastern coast of Hudson Bay, northern Labrador, eastern Quebec, and Newfoundland. Winters on the coast of California and Oregon, also southern Nevada, central New Mexico and Texas,

and western and central Arizona to southern Louisiana, Alabama, Mississippi, North Carolina, south through Mexico, Central America, West Indies, Peru, and central Brazil

For all beach waifs the ocean strand southward is the road to palm-green islands and the southern seas. The endless crescents of the beach are transient and unsubstantial. Drowned, fathoms deep, every few hours they are always being created again, never two days alike, but molded by every whim of the waves.

To have closeup views of the shorebirds that throng the North American coastal beaches in autumn, it is necessary to reach the shore very early and while the tide is rising. Scoop a hiding place some four feet deep among the flotsam at the beach crest. Then set out on the sandy beach a dozen snipe or plover decoys, matching them in groups facing the breeze and so far down the incline that the skirts of the breakers trail about them every little while. That is the best place for them, although one must shift some every so often, as the tide creeps up.

Meanwhile only the tide disturbs the birds at their breakfast, driving them up the beaches or forcing them to flit elsewhere for better fare. The decoys are scarcely in place when there comes a ripple of light as a flock of least sandpipers, tiniest of the order, flash in from nowhere. Steady and close as a school of minnows slipping over a shoal, they settle among the decoys, but if one raises a hand they vanish in a flurry, just as fishes underwater will do. Once in a while one will see them coming from a distance, seeds of light that grow visibly, flower briefly in the air, and then are gone. They remind one of flying fishes that flitter away when something noses them out of the weeds in the Gulf Stream, then plump into the first big wave they meet. *(See Flying Fish)*

The least sandpiper, this smallest of shorebirds, is extremely tame and unsuspicious. A flock will trip past one's beach hiding place so close that he can see them wink or scratch their heads. Bands of these peep trip along the strand, pausing every second to seize some minute crustacean from the weeds uprooted by the rollers. Sometimes several stand around a fish stranded on the beach and swallow the flies buzzing above its carcass.

Everytime a wave slides back, myriads of beach fleas—small crustaceans—kick themselves from the foam only to be gobbled by the sandpipers that dash down and snatch them before another breaker can chase the food-seeking birds back to dry spaces once more. Not that they risk danger, for, like all shorebirds, they can swim when the need arises. Running on the sand they are sometimes difficult to see. Their necks and breasts show a brownish wash, their backs are mottled gray-brown, with darker fight feathers, and below they are white. One might think that they had taken these hues from the sand over which they scamper. They have silver bosoms but their brightness blends with that of the breaker which puts them to flight. When they fly back to shore a few rods farther on, they seem to vanish. They appear and disappear like the watery ripples that spill their lustrous lining on the beach and then subside.

Least sandpipers are even more abundant on the harbor flats and on the muddy margins of brackish ponds or creeks. Everywhere their small size—5 to 6½ inches long—and their pleasing cries of *Peetweet! Weet! Weet!* disinguish them from larger shorebirds with which they throng the flats and bars. Their range includes both North and South America, but like so many others of their kind they nest far to the north.

Least sandpipers lay their buffy eggs, three or four to a set, in a grass-lined

*The least sandpiper is the smallest of the sandpiper group*

hollow on some arctic island, or along the shores of the Arctic Ocean, or farther south in Labrador and regions west of that rocky peninsula. The female is a trifle larger than the male, and the male, like a phalarope, is said to do most of the brooding. Their young hatched are scarcely bigger than bumblebees. Yet they run about and pick up their own food as soon as their natal down has dried. One never sees sandpipers feed their chicks, although they shelter them at night or during storms, holding them snugly under their warm breast feathers. The young grow rapidly and by midsummer are as big as their parents.

Least sandpipers feed on beach fleas, flies, mosquitoes, mosquito larvae, crickets, and other insects. Alongshore they devour bloodworms, minute crustacea, and marine animalcules. On all such flotsam they grow fat and trim. They are cheerful, social little creatures, consorting with semipalmated sandpipers, sanderlings, and other larger shorebirds. The range of the least sandpiper includes North and South America, and they winter south to Central America, Bermuda, Chile, and Brazil. They are commonest on our coasts late in the summer, but move farther south in September and October. The smallest of all shorebirds they sometimes span the broad Atlantic Ocean, and have been seen in the British Isles, Finland, and France. Blown about the world like spindrift they seem at home everywhere. Their color patterns are not markedly different from those of other closely related "peep," but they may always be known by their tameness, their greenish or yellowish legs, and by their tiny size. Their voices are as sweet and gentle as their natures. —H.M.H.

**Spotted Sandpiper**
**Other Common Names**—Peep; peetweet, teeter-peep, teeter-tail, sand lark, river snipe
**Scientific Name**—*Actitis macularia*
**Family**—Scolopacidae (woodcock, snipe, and sandpipers)
**Order**—Charadriiformes
**Size**—Length, 7 to 8 inches
**Range**—Breeds from tree limit in Alaska, northern Mackenzie, northern Manitoba, Ontario, Quebec, and Newfoundland south to California, Arizona, New Mexico, central Texas, northern Alabama, and North Carolina. Winters from southern British Columbia south to the southern United States, and from Mexico to Argentina

The spotted sandpiper does not gather in great flocks as do the other sandpipers, but it searches the beach alone, teetering as it goes, as if it were too delicately balanced on its slim legs. Also know as teeter-tail, it utters a sharp *peet-weet* as it flies. The wingstroke is very short, the wings keeping a stiff-bowed position. This almost makes it look as if the bird were flying along on its wing tips—a very good field mark. Many other shorebirds are streaked, but the spotted sandpiper is the only one that is definitely spotted with round spots like a thrush.

The spotted sandpiper does not seem to require remote ocean beaches and vast mud flats, but lives even along tiny brooks and around stagnant pools in abandoned quarries. Sandy shores, rocky coasts, mud flats, plowed fields, or golf courses are all just as attractive to these adaptable waders.

Not long after their arrival in May, the males fight with each other over their territories, then nesting begins. The nest is a simple scraped-out spot on the ground, sometimes out in the open, but more often in a little hollow among the weeds or at the base of a bush. It might be just a scoop in the sand, with no lining, or it might be well lined with grasses or weeds. The birds that live in more northerly regions build bulkier nests. In Labrador, nests made of moss are sometimes six to nine inches thick. Four pear-shaped eggs are laid, the small ends placed together in a four-leaf-clover design. Because of their protective color, creamy white with dark splotches, they are easily overlooked among the surrounding stones and pebbles. In 15 or 16 days they hatch into the most appealing of all bird fledglings. In less than half an hour they dry out, all soft and fluffy, and are able to run around after their parents. At the least sign of danger they hide, their mottled brown colors blending with the surroundings.

In the late summer the youngsters look very much like their parents, olive-brown above and white below. They have no spots, however, but by this time, neither have their parents; the breeding plumage has been molted for a less distinctive garb. Independent by this time, they wander up and down the shores, capturing all sorts of insects, crustaceans, and other tiny creatures that live in the line of debris thrown up by the waves. A sandpiper after a fly somehow reminds one of a cat stalking a mouse.

The spotted sandpiper is an early migrant—just as its relatives that nest in the Arctic are also. Some of them reach Mexico and South America by the end of July. Others do not leave the northern beaches until early October but most of them have gone long before that. Winter finds them scattered from the warm beaches of the south Atlantic, the Gulf States, and the Pacific Coast south to Argentina. In late April and

*Spotted sandpipers, young (left); adult (right)*

May their shrill *peet-weet* can be occasionally heard overhead in the black night sky—the first sign that the spotted sandpipers are back. —A.B., Jr.

**Upland Sandpiper**
**Other Common Names**— Upland plover, Bartramian sandpiper, uplander, prairie plover, prairie snipe, quaily
**Scientific Name**—*Bartramia longicauda*
**Family**—Scolopacidae (woodcock, snipe, and sandpipers)
**Order**—Charadriiformes
**Size**—Length, 12 inches
**Range**—Breeds from southern Alaska, Mackenzie, Manitoba, central Saskatchewan, Minnesota, Wisconsin, Michigan, southern Ontario, Quebec, central Maine, to eastern Washington, northeastern Oregon, Idaho, southern Montana, southeastern Wyoming, central Colorado, northwestern Oklahoma, southern Ohio, Indiana, and Illinois, north-central Texas and central Missouri, northern and eastern West Virginia, central Virginia, Maryland. Winters in southern South America on the pampas of Argentina to Brazil.

If some day while driving through the open country one chances to see a long-legged, long-tailed, slim-necked, and small-headed brown bird alight on a fence post—hold its pointed wings aloft for a moment and then gently fold them—one may be quite sure that he has seen that spirit bird of the grasslands, the upland sandpiper, formerly called the upland plover. One's first impression is apt to be that here is a shorebird, strangely out of place in pasture fields and daisy-flecked meadows. But a shorebird it is, although merely in relationship, for this bird shuns the shores in favor of the rolling seas of grass. It is not a plover, but a sandpiper that has many ploverlike and even dovelike traits.

The upland sandpiper is truly a bird of the open spaces. Its original home was the western prairie, and it probably extended its range eastward to the Atlantic Coast only after the white man converted a large part of the prevailing forest into farms of spacious pastures and meadows. A few generations ago it was a common inhabitant of rural areas throughout the Northeast; and on the vast prairies of the Midwest it existed in almost unbelievable abundance. In those days it was considered to be a very fine gamebird.

When America's vast flocks of passenger pigeons were all but gone, the market hunters turned to other birds, among them the upland sandpiper. Its flesh delighted epicures, and carloads of the birds were shipped to the markets. There were no closed seasons or bag limits on the birds in those days, and year after year the slaughter continued until they were so thinned that they hung on the very brink of extinction. In 1919, Dr. Thomas S. Roberts, writing in a biennial report of the Minnesota State Game and Fish Commission stated:

"Fifty years ago it (the upland sandpiper) was present all through the summer, everywhere in the open country, in countless thousands. Now it is nearing extinction. Here and there an occasional breeding pair may yet be found, but they are lonely occupants of the places where their ancestors dwelt in vast numbers."

Fortunately the upland sandpiper was spared the ill fate of the passenger pigeon, the Eskimo curlew, and the heath hen (*See under Extinct and Threatened Animals of North America*). It is now on the road back, slowly increasing as a result of long years of protection.

The birds usually reach their breeding grounds sometime during the latter part of March or during the month of April after a winter's sojourn on the pampas of southern South America, some 7,000 to 8,000 miles away from their summer

*The upland sandpiper characteristically holds its wings in an elevated position upon alighting*

home. Some night, if one is in upland sandpiper country, he may hear a rolling trill, infinitely sweet and mellow; a voice drifting out of the sky, that might be mistaken for the whistling of the wind were the night not so calm. Thus the upland sandpiper eloquently announces its arrival. It has done so since time immemorial. What a loss it would have been had that sound become but a vague memory.

Courtship begins almost as soon as the birds arrive in their nesting grounds. Then their eerie, long-drawn whistled calls come more frequently. Shrill and penetrating, under favorable conditions, they may be heard at a distance of a half mile or more. This call, once heard, is never to be forgotten, for it is unlike any other bird call. It is a prolonged and windlike whistle which starts with a tree toadlike rattle, ascending in the first part and descending in the second, like *whip-whip-whee-ee-ee-loo-oo-oo!* At times the bird will ascend in great circles into the sky, then plummet earthward. On the ground the male will sometimes approach his prospective mate with a peculiar hopping motion, at the same time uttering musical twittering notes; then he may fly away a short distance, returning again and again to repeat the performance. Although the upland sandpiper's normal flight is swift and buoyant, on the breeding ground it often indulges in a wavering flight much like that of the smaller spotted sandpiper.

A nest of the upland sandpiper, hidden among the tall grasses of a June meadow, is not at all easy to locate. It is modestly built, for it consists merely of a hollowed out space in the earth, sometimes lined with a few blades of grass. At times the nests are placed in tufts of grasses or sedges in comparatively open situations; but, generally, they are artfully concealed. True to shorebird tradition, the upland sandpiper lays the usual complement of four eggs which may vary from pinkish or olive-buff to greenish-white, quite evenly spotted with brown. The eggs are usually laid sometime between mid-May and mid-June.

The young are running about by the latter part of June. Although they are able to leave the nest almost as soon as they are hatched, they are at first quite weak and too timid to investigate much of the world about them. When about half-grown the downy youngsters are clumsy-appearing, for their long legs seem to be all out of proportion to their bodies. Both of the parent birds show great concern for their progeny, and will defend them courageously even against superior odds. The mother will often resort to feigning injury in order to lure an invader from the vicnity of her youngsters, and both birds often vigorously protest the presence of an intruder with their cry of alarm—a rapid and emphatic *quip-ip-ip-ip.*

In its food habits the upland sandpiper is one of the farmer's staunchest friends. The greater part of its food consists of grasshoppers, crickets, weevils, cutworms, army worms, white grubs, and many others. Experts who have made a study of the bird's food habits, claim that almost 97 percent of its food consists of such animal matter. The rest is made up of weed seeds and a small amount of waste grain which they glean from the fields after the harvest.

Those who live with the upland sandpiper often affectionately call it the quaily the name, of course, being suggested by certain of its melodious notes that resemble those of quail. Not many years ago, the bird books considered the name of *plover* as utterly inappropriate —the bird was not a plover but a sandpiper—and that it should properly be referred to as a sandpiper. In the bird's scientific name, *Bartramia longicauda,* the *Bartramia* honors the Quaker naturalist from Philadelphia, John Bartram; its specific name of *longicauda* simply means long-tailed.

*An upland sandpiper nesting in a meadow (above) is flushed from its nest containing four eggs (below)*

To know the upland sandpiper is to love it, for no bird adds so much charm to the expanses of meadow or prairie. It is not so uncommon in our farming sections today and may be seen in the expanses of field and meadow surrounding Pymatuning Lake, in Crawford County Pennsylvania, for example. It has also been observed elsewhere in various parts of Pennsylvania. One can only regret that when the upland sandpipers leave the sanctuary of the United States in late August or September, and return to their ancestral winter home in the grasslands of far-off South America, they are even today slaughtered by the market gunners. Given more adequate protection on their wintering grounds, there is little doubt that their numbers would soon be greatly augmented.

–W.C.G.

**SAND VERBENA**
**Beach Sand Verbena**
**Other Common Names**—Abronia
**Scientific Name**—*Abronia umbellata*
**Family**—Nyctaginaceae (four-o'clock family)
**Range**—British Columbia to Baja California
**Habitat**—Sea beaches, Upper Sonoran, Humid Transition, and Canadian Zones
**Time of Blooming**—January to December

From the beginning of the year almost to the end the common sand verbena spreads delightful color over sand dunes along the entire coast from San Diego to Vancouver Island. The flower heads, set on long, trailing, crimson-flushed stems, later develop into a compact head of fruit. With it along the coast appears the deep dark red of *Abronia maritima* and the white of *Abronia alba,* the latter present on California's Channel Islands. From Santa Barbara north is the stout-stemmed yellow species, *Abronia latifolia,* from the sandy meadows at 9,000 feet elevation near Mt. Whitney comes *Albronia alpina,* pink or white flowered, growing in small dense mats. Very similar in appearance to the common sand verbena is *Abronia villosa,* which trails for miles over the Colorado and Mojave deserts where it makes stirring pictures with the patches of snowy desert evening-primrose.

*Sand verbena*

**SAPROPHYTE**

A comparatively small number of plants, mostly fungi and bacteria, do not have chlorophyll and are unable to manufacture food by photosynthesis. Those that live by robbing living

*Mushrooms are saprophytic plants and are unable to manufacture their own food*

organisms of the food they must have are called parasites; those that subsist upon dead matter are called saprophytes. Some species change their roles, depending upon circumstances, and complete categorization is impossible.

Saprophytes play an important role in nature, for it is these organisms that break down the complex chemicals in dead organic matter into simple constituents that can be utilized by other plants.

Some of the more familiar saprophytes are mushrooms, puffballs, and molds. Among the higher plants, Indian pipe, an unusual member of the heath family, became a saprophyte, probably in association with certain bacteria of decay. —G.B.S.

**SAPSUCKER**

**Yellow-bellied Sapsucker**

**Other Common Names**—Yellow-bellied woodpecker, red-throated sapsucker

**Scientific Name**—*Sphyrapicus varius*

**Family**—Picidae (woodpeckers and wrynecks)

**Order**—Piciformes

**Size**—Length, 8 to 8½ inches

**Range**—Breeds from Cape Breton Island, Quebec, Alberta, and Alaska, south to California, Arizona, Texas, Missouri, Tennessee, and Georgia

The yellow-bellied sapsucker makes little rows of holes in the bark of trees. Sometimes these holes are in rings around the trunk, sometimes in rows up and down. The downy woodpecker and some other woodpeckers make perforations in the bark, but symmetrical rows are made by the yellow-bellied sapsucker. Each little hole has slightly squared corners, and goes through the bark to the cambium layer through which the lifeblood of the tree flows. Each one tilts slightly downward, so as to collect the sap that oozes into it.

A single tree might have a thousand or more of these small pits. Poplars and maples are the trees most utilized by the yellow-bellied sapsuckers, but spruces, pines, and others may also be used. When a group of trees has been worked on by a yellow-bellied sapsucker, it is called a "sapsucker orchard." These trees are patronized by many of the other small creatures of the woodlands —bees buzz about the flowing pits, butterflies sip with their long, coiled tongues, and hummingbirds are nearly always around. Even red squirrels and chipmunks share the food, enlarging the holes so they can lap up the sap more easily. Usually, the sapsucker itself will come back to gather the sticky harvest, along with whatever insects have been attracted.

Most woodpeckers have a very long tongue, equipped at the end with sharp barbs with which to spear struggling grubs that have been uncovered. The sapsucker's tongue is shorter, tipped with a fringe of stiff hairs, like a brush, with which it laps up the sap. The yellow-bellied sapsucker is a small woodpecker and has a long white patch on its black wing. This is perhaps its best field mark. Whereas the male downy woodpecker has a red patch on the back of its head, the yellow-bellied sapsucker has one on its forehead. In addition, the males have red throat patches, a mark shared by no other woodpecker. The female's throat is white.

In many parts of the eastern United States, the sapsucker is a migrant during late March and April, seeming to arrive mysteriously overnight. The red-throated males are the first to arrive; the females follow a few days later. They seldom make a sound, and would escape notice were it not for their occasional short, bounding flights from tree to tree. When they reach their nesting grounds in Canada, or in the cool mountain woodlands along the northern edge of the United States, they are more noisy; in fact, their squealing or mewing calls become a familiar sound.

The nests range between 15 to 40 feet from the ground. Most of these nests are made in dead trees or stubs, but live trees are sometimes used. The small opening, about one-and-a-half inches in diameter, drops into a gourd-like chamber a foot or more deep. There, on a rough bed of chips, lie five, six, or seven glossy white eggs. Both parents take turns incubating the eggs. In about two weeks, they hatch. The hissing calls of the young birds announce the return of their parents to the nest with a supply of sap. As they grow larger, they are weaned to insects. When they are feathered out well enough to leave the nest, they resemble the female parent, but their colors are duller. Abandoning the stuffy, dark nesting cavity, they follow their parents to a nearby sap orchard to feed on the dripping fluid. Soon they learn to dart out after insects, and snap them up in the air like flycatchers. They will also eat wild cherries, dogwood berries, and other small, wild fruits with which the trees and shrubs are heavily laden in late summer.

By late September of October, when sap ceases to flow and many small wild fruits have already been gleaned from the trees, the yellow-bellied sapsuckers start south. Some go to the West Indies and Mexico, but the majority winter in the southern United States.

A subspecies of the yellow-bellied sapsucker that inhabits the Pacific States is very different, having the entire head and upper breast red. It is called the red-breasted sapsucker. Although its pattern is different, it belongs to the same species as the eastern bird. It lives in the high mountains, and drops down to the warmer lowlands during the winter months. This accomplishes the same purpose as the 1,000 or 2,000-mile journey that the eastern sapsucker has to make each fall. —A.B., Jr.

*Fifty-one percent of the yellow-bellied sapsuckers' diet is plant matter*

*The leaves of the sassafras tree may have entire margins, or have one or two lobes*

## SASSAFRAS

**Other Common Names**—Aguetree
**Scientific Name**— *Sassafras albidum*
**Family**—Lauraceae (laurel family)
**Range**—Southern Maine to southern Iowa and eastern Kansas, south to eastern Texas and central Florida
**Habitat**—Woods and thickets. A prolific sprouter. Invades abandoned fields in the Middle Atlantic States
**Leaves**—3 to 7, occasionally 10 inches long, lustrous green and of three types: plain oval, a mitten-shape with a thumb (right of left), and a three-fingered leaf of varying shape and proportion. Spring buds large, yellow
**Bark**—Gray on smaller trunks and branches; turning cinnamon-brown with age, and deeply furrowed and aromatic. Terminal twigs are shining and green throughout winter
**Flowers**—Bright yellow-green clusters about two inches across appearing with the unfolding new leaves
**Fruit**—Single or small groups of dark blue berries, one-half inch or so long, on scarlet stems, ripening in September or October

Various parts of the sassafras tree were used for medicinal purposes in the days when people relied more upon wild herbs and plants in treating ailments—sassafras tea being one of the better-known infusions, made usually from the roots and considered to be a stimulant and spring tonic.

Children, of course, are always delighted by the mitten-shaped leaves of this species and may start learning tree identification through such an interest.

Sassafras fruits are also rather unique as is the tendency of the twigs to remain green even on larger trees. A height of 90 feet, with trunks up to 6 feet in diameter is approaching maximum size. This figure represents an extremely large specimen, for even quite old sassafras trees are seldom more than a yard thick, and the vast majority are much smaller. In some areas of the sandy coastal plain where fires take a frequent toll of vegetation and humus, sassafras may grow to only twenty or thirty feet in height with trunks well under a foot thick at the base. Along heavily cindered railroad tracks it may appear as hardly more than a shrub, but wherever it grows to anywhere near tree size sassafras can be recognized at a fair distance by its dense crown and secondary foliage masses that are hollow underneath and supported by many-twigged branching. In autumn the leaves turn an attractive variety of colors, predominately yellow, and it is altogether a pleasant species to have around private property. It is somewhat neglected as a park and public-buildings tree. —M.H.B.

## SAWFISH

**Smalltooth Sawfish**
**Other Common Names**—Common sawfish; sawray
**Scientific Name**—*Pristis pectinatus*
**Family**—Pristidae (sawfishes)
**Order**—Rajiformes
**Size**—Rarely over 16 feet long and 700 pounds in weight. Sometimes over 18 feet and 1,000 pounds
**Range**—Tropical and subtropical waters of the Atlantic and in the eastern Mediterranean. In the western Atlantic it ranges from northern Florida to Brazil and sometimes strays as far north as the waters off Long Island, New York

The outstanding physical characteristic of this fish is its elongated, flat snout. Commonly called the saw because it is lined on both sides with large, sharp, toothlike structures, it often reaches two or three feet—sometimes as much as six feet—in length. Its underside is flat; the mouth is located on the flattened under-surface of the head and contains small, blunt teeth. There are no gills, but breathing apertures are behind the fish's eyes. The upper part of the sawfish's body is dark gray to dark brown. The bottom part is gray, light yellow, or white.

Although most common in salt water, sawfishes may be found in brackish or even fresh waters. They catch the fishes they eat by swimming into large schools and hacking from side to side with their formidable saws. Those fishes that the sawfish stuns or injures are then consumed by it. —M.R.

**SAWFLY**

Sawflies, along with the closely related related horntails, are members of the order Hymenoptera (wasps, ants, bees, and allies). Adult sawflies and horntails (*see Pigeon Horntail*) can be distinguished from other Hymenoptera in that their bodies are thick-waisted, not "wasp-waisted," or with the second abdominal segment narrowly constricted into a stem, or pedicel, as in the ants, bees, and wasps.

Adult sawflies are generally small, with rather broad wings. The body is usually black, sometimes with yellow or brown markings. The ovipositor (egg-layer) at the tip of the abdomen, instead of having a "sting" as in the bees, wasps, and some ants, has two saw-toothed blades (thus the name *sawfly*). These are sheathed within two short outer plates that serve as guides when the female is moving the two blades in opposite directions to slit a leaf or plant stem in which to insert an egg.

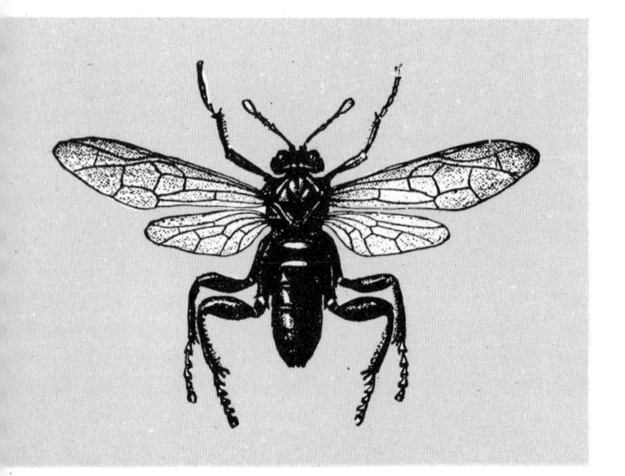

*Sawfly*

Most of the sawfly larvae, which resemble small caterpillars, feed on plants.

The larvae of the larch sawfly, *Pristiphora erichsoni,* occasionally defoliate larch trees in Canada and the northern United States. The European spruce sawfly, *Pristiphora polytomus,* when accidentally introduced into Canada proved so devastating in its destruction of trees by the larvae that large sums of money have been spent to control it by introducing millions of parasites of this sawfly from Europe (*See Biological Control*).

The imported currantworm, *Nematus ribesii,* one of the best known of the sawflies, is also widely distributed in the United States and the larvae thrive on currant and gooseberry plants. The best know and one of the most destructive sawflies to man's economy is the cherry, or pear, slug, *Caliroa limacina*. It was accidentally introduced into New England from Europe during the early settlement of the United States. It thrives wherever its host trees of cherry, pear, or plum are extensively cultivated.

Sawflies (the larvae) of certain species attack a wide number of evergreen and broad-leaved trees and shrubs, and even grasses and sedges. All the larvae eat foliage, and those of a species that lives on rose bushes, at maturity, enter the pithy stems to hollow out a pupal chamber before transforming into adults.

More than 30 species of birds feed upon sawfly larvae and from 50 to 100 sawfly larvae have been found in a single stomach of a mockingbird. Ten to twenty-five sawfly larvae have been found in the stomachs of some individual bird species that feed on the sawflies. —J.K.T.

*Recommended Reading*

**College Entomology**—E.O. Essig. Stechert-Hafner, New York.

**Destructive and Useful Insects: Their Habits and Control**—C.L. Metcalfe and W.P. Flint. McGraw-Hill Book Company, New York.

*Common scallop*

**SCALLOP**
**Common Scallop**
**Other Common Names**—Bay scallop
**Scientific Name**—*Pectens irradians*
**Family**—Pectinidae (scallops)
**Order**—Prionodesmacea
**Size**—Diameter, 2 to 3 inches
**Range**—Cape Cod to Cape Hatteras

An economically important mollusk, (*see Mollusk*), the harvesting of the common scallop supports an extensive fishery. The edible portion of the animal is the large muscle that closes the two shells.

The scallop has the unusual ability of moving rapidly through the water by opening then closing the shells with considerable force. It progresses in a zigzag line that quite possibly confuses an animal pursuer bent on catching and eating it.

The two shells are hinged at the umbo, and a wing stands out on either side. The radiating ribs of each valve interlock with corresponding depressions in the other shell. The valves are not quite equal, the right one generally is the smaller, lighter in color. and is underneath the scallop when it is at rest. (*See illustrations under Bivalve*).

The mantle of the scallop has a number of eyes. These light-sensitive organs are blue, and each has a lens, a retina, and an optic nerve.

The bay scallop of the Pacific Coast, *Pecten aequisulcatus*, closely resembles the common scallop of the East Coast. The calico scallop, smaller and more colorful, occurs in the Gulf of Mexico north to North Carolina.

The sea scallop, found in deep water from Newfoundland to New Jersey, is often six inches across. It is also edible and has one flat shell and one concave one.

Other scallops, of lesser importance, include the rough, thorny, ornate, Iceland, and striate scallops, among others.
—G.B.S.

**SCAUP**
**Greater Scaup**
**Other Common Names**—Big bluebill
**Scientific Name**—*Aythya marila*
**Family**—Anatidae (swans, geese, and ducks)
**Order**—Anseriformes
**Size**—Length, 17¾ inches
**Range**—Iceland, Scandinavia, Russia, and Siberia; winters in British Isles, Denmark, France, Asia Minor, western India, China, Japan, and Korea. From Arctic coast of Canada east to Michigan, southern California, Atlantic coast from Maine to Florida

This bird has a twin—the lesser scaup duck, *Aythya affinis*. Bluebills as these two species are both called, are difficult to distinguish when seen in the wild.

The greater scaup is the more northern nester and winters on both coasts, mostly north of the principal concentrations of the lesser scaup. This latter is a prairie province nester, and has therefore suffered more from man's drainage of swamps and marshes. It is the common

*Greater scaups, male (foreground); female (rear)*

winter duck of Florida. The scaups are typical diving ducks and need ample take-off space.

The greater scaup spends the winter on salt water, usually in large flocks. These so-called rafts are often concentrated over beds of mussels, one of their favorite foods. Scaups swallow shellfish whole and their strong gizzards, which are always well filled with gravel, quickly break the hard shells and grind them up. Most ducks seem able to break up hard-shelled food items. Mallards are very fond of acorns and the wood duck eats quantities of the very hard-shelled bitter pecan. (*See Mallard*)

Of all our ducks the greater scaup is the most completely omnivorous. It thrives on either plant or animal food. When on salt water its diet is largely animal matter; while on fresh water it is predominately vegetable varied to some extent with small fish, tadpoles, snails and various freshwater insects.

**SCIONWOOD** (*See under Chestnut*)

**SCORPION**
**Other Common Name**—None
**Scientific Name**—*Centruriodes sculpturatus*
**Family**—Centruridae (scorpions)
**Order**—Scorpiones
**Size**—Length, 2½ inches
**Range**—Arizona and Mexico

Of the scorpions in the genus *Centrurus*, there are about fifteen American species. Besides those that live in Arizona, some live in the southern United States. Scorpions are nocturnal and most of those one finds are practically harmless. The sting is usually no more severe than that of a bee or wasp—hot and painful in the beginning but disappearing within an hour or two. There is one other species living in the southwestern deserts besides *Centruriodes sculpturatus* that can inject a poison so virulent that it may kill a child.

The poison injected into its victims by these two species is classed as a neurotoxin. The symptoms of a bitten person are labored breathing, extreme restlessness, and a large flow of saliva. Ice packs on the wound and an antivenin are used in treating the patient.

The scorpions are the most primitive member of the land arachnids, and also the oldest. Fossil scorpions are known from the Silurian Period some 400 million years ago.

A scorpion's most obvious characteristic is the spinelike sting at the end of what appears to be its tail, but which is really a narrowed elongation of the abdomen. A live scorpion holds the elongated part of its abdomen curved forward over its back, with the poisonous sting directed forward. In this position it is ready to strike its prey

*Land scorpions are known to have inhabited the earth 400 million years ago*

of spiders and insects. A scorpion slowly approaching a large spider, when within a few inches of it, reaches out and catches it in its lobsterlike pincers. While holding the helpless spider aloft, the scorpion whips forward its sting-tipped tail and injects its poison into the spider's body. In seconds the spider is dead.

The scorpion cannot eat solid foods. After killing its victim the scorpion brings it up to its mouth to make the wounds necessary to inject into it digestive juices. These soon reduce the inner parts of its victim to a pulp, which the scorpion slowly sucks up with the aid of its elastic-walled muscular pharynx. The scorpion feeds very slowly and it may require half an hour to finish its meal after which it casts aside the empty skin of its victim.

The "tail" of the scorpion, the narrow extension of its abdomen, has a digestive tube, or gut, running almost to its end. To the last body segment is joined the telson, a bulblike reservoir that contains the poison glands. At the end of the last segment is the gracefully curved sting through which the poison is injected into its prey.

The scorpion's eggs mature within its body and the young scorpions are born alive. They attach themselves to the mother's back and live for a few days there on the embryonic yolk that fills the mid-gut of the new born scorpion. The young scorpions are carried about by the parent until after their first molt. Then the young ones drop to the ground and begin getting a living for themselves.

Some of the species that live in desert woodlands of juniper and pinyon pines hide by day under fallen trees, pieces of wood, and stones. They spend the hot desert day in shallow tunnels scarcely more than an inch wide that they dig into the earth at a slight angle downward. A long pile of earth or sand that the scorpions push out smoothly in front of the tunnel betrays their presence. Each scorpion may occupy its tunnel for many days, going out to hunt its prey at night and returning to its burrow to spend the day.

Of the more than 300 species of scorpions, about 25 live in the southern and western United States, north to North Dakota. —J.K.T.

*Recommended Reading*

**A Manual of the Common Invertebrate Animals (Exclusive of Insects)**—Henry Sherring Pratt. The Blakiston Company, Philadelphia.
**American Spiders**—Willis J. Gertsch. D. Van Nostrand Company, Princeton, New Jersey.
**Our Desert Neighbors**—Edmund C. Jaeger. Stanford University Press, Standford, California.

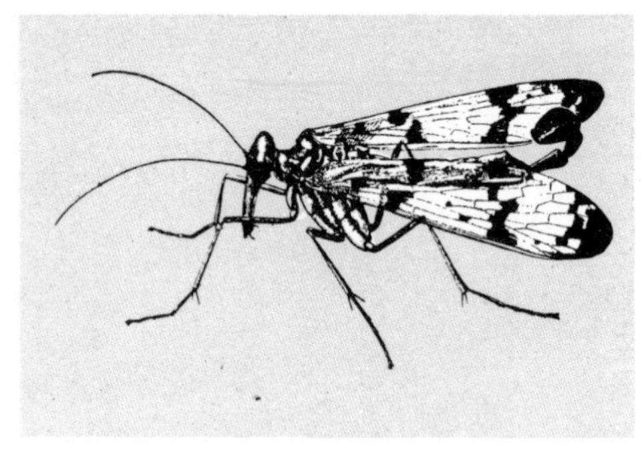

*Scorpionfly*

**SCORPIONFLY**
**Common Scorpionfly**
**Other Common Names**—None
**Scientific Name**—*Panorpa venosa*
**Family**—Panorpidae (scorpionflies)
**Order**—Mecoptera
**Size**—Length, up to one inch
**Range**—Eastern North America

Scorpionflies can be identified by the somewhat elephantine appearance of the head. The long, trunklike beak has the mouth at the tip, however, and instead of ears the insects have long antennae that grow from low between the eyes. The name of scorpionfly is given to these creatures because of the long, recurved male genitalia, which resemble the narrow elongated, and recurved abdomen of the scorpion (*See under Scorpion*).

The common scorpionfly has two nearly equal pairs of spotted wings, which are usually yellow and black. Snow scorpionflies (often called "snow fleas") which resemble nymphal grasshoppers, are active during the winter, often on the surface of the snow. They are wingless, but have the typical scorpion fly head.

Scoprionflies generally feed upon dead insects, both as adults and in the caterpillarlike larval form. The eggs are laid on the ground, usually in the wooded regions that the adults frequent. —G.B.S.

**SCOURING RUSH** (*See under Club Mosses and Horsetails*)

**SCULPIN** (*See Miller's Thumb under Fish: Common Freshwater Fishes of North America*)

**SEA ANEMONE**

Sea anemones are polyps, soft-bodied marine animals of the phylum Coelertera (*See under Coelenterate*). Like the other chief members of this group, the jellyfishes and the corals (*see Coral*), sea anemones are basically a digestive tube whose mouth is surrounded by tentacles containing stinging cells, and whose outer wall surrounds the entire animal when it contracts its tentacles and empties its digestive tube of water.

Unlike corals, sea anemones do not make calcium carbonate skeletons for themselves, and unlike jellyfishes, they do not swim, but creep slowly over rocks and shells on their pedal disks.

Most sea anemones attach themselves to a solid support, while they catch and kill small marine animals with the stinging cells. Others burrow in sand, exposing only the tentacles and the mouth when feeding.

Individual sea anemones are both male and female, but discharge only one kind of sex cells at a time. The fertilized egg develops into a free-swimming larva that soon settles to the bottom to be-

*A colony of sea anemones*

come an adult. Most are about an inch in length, but a West Indian species is about a foot high and somewhat more in diameter. Sea anemones are found in all oceans. —G.B.S.

**SEA CUCUMBER** (*See under Echinoderm*)

**SEA-DAHLIA**
**Other Common Names**—Coreopsis
**Scientific Name**—*Coreopsis maritima*
**Family**—Compositae (composite)
**Range**—San Diego County California to northern lower California and adjacent islands
**Habitat**—Beaches, coastal bluffs, hillsides
**Time of Blooming**—March to June

As early as March fine specimens of the sea-dahlia will be found on the coast of southern California. The stem, from 1 to 3 feet high, is stout and hollow, the bright green leaves divided into many spreading lobes; the flower stems, from 7 to 14 inches high, support the gay yellow heads whose prominently notched petals make a spread of four inches. Farther north along the coast is the shrublike species, *Coreopsis gigantea*, with distinct trunk four inches through, the lighter yellow flowers slightly smaller but forming drifts of color on the six-foot-high branches. This latter species also frequents the Islands of Santa Cruz, Santa Rosa, and Santa Catalina. In the Colorado and Mojave deserts there are several species, the plants being much smaller, the petals sometimes white on the upper third.

**SEA HORSE**
**Atlantic Sea Horse**
**Other Common Names**—None
**Scientific Name** —*Hippocampus hudsonius*
**Family**—Syngnathidae (sea horses and pipefishes)
**Order**—Solenichthys
**Size**—Length, to 4 inches
**Range**—Nova Scotia to Argentina

*Sea horse*

Patches of seaweed, marine grasses, and coral heads are the home of this remarkable little fish. It is the only one that holds the head at a 90° angle from the backbone and that bears a striking resemblance, in miniature, to the horse.

There are two species of sea horses on the Pacific Coast and six along the Atlantic shore. About sixteen other species occur throughout the world, most of them in southeast Asia and Australia. All of them are marine, and all are found only in shallow water.

Sea horses belong to an order of small fishes that are distinguished by the possession of a tubelike mouth. Feeding is by suction; tiny shrimps and other marine animals are drawn into the mouth in a sudden sucking motion. Pipefishes and trumpet fishes are among the better known members of the group.

Not all members of the order have the bony external plates developed to the degree that they are in the sea horse and the pipefish. In the sea horse they show as large and sturdy, with flexible joints on all sides. Despite their rigidity, the sea horse can twist and turn with remarkable freedom.

The tail of the sea horse is without fins. It is long, tapering, and prehensile, and the creature uses it to grasp seaweed, anchoring itself to the plant. Its position is upright, maintained thus by the pectoral fins, which are situated just behind the gills. The dorsal fin is well developed, and is the principal organ of locomotion.

The eyes are set on the sides of the head, and move independently of each other. They are quite sensitive to light changes, and probably have a lot to do with the color of the fish, which frequently matches its background. They are dark gray or black most commonly, but red, dull white, green, and silver also occur.

One of the most interesting traits of the sea horse concerns the birth of the young. The female deposits the eggs in a pouch on the abdomen on the male.

The male's pouch is just above the juncture of its tail with its body. About 200 eggs are transferred into this brood pouch, and the female swims away, her duties done. The pouch swells, and a tiny pocket forms about each egg. The embryo sea horses take three weeks, sometimes slightly less, to develop. At the end of that time, the male must expel them from the pouch, and birth is not easy. He writhes, struggles, and often rubs the swollen pouch against rocks or other hard objects. The young do not appear all at once, but a few at a time over several days.

Young sea horses are transparent at birth, but develop color pigment in a few days. The eyes are very large, proportionately, and the beak short and wide. They swim horizontally for a few days, then begin to bend the head forward and to bring the body into the normal vertical sea horse position.

—G.B.S.

*Recommended Reading*

**The Illustrated Library of the Natural Sciences**—American Museum of Natural History. Simon & Schuster, New York.

**Living Fishes of the World**—Earl S. Herald. Doubleday, New York.

**SEA LILY** (*See under Echinoderm*)

**SEA LIONS and SEALS**

Though reaching their greatest develoment in the cool waters of the northern and southern seas, the pinnipeds have a world oceanic distribution. Along with the schools of cetaceans (whales, dolphins, and porpoises) that cruise the high seas, the herds of sea lions, walruses, and true seals occupy the ocean surface and correspond in this realm with the multitudes of ungulates that once covered the great land masses.

Marine vegetation as a source of sustenance for seafaring animals is almost negative and animals of the ocean must of necessity, rather than choice, subsist for the most part as predators on other animals (*See Predator*). All pinnipeds are carnivorous and feed on fishes, crustaceans, squids, and sometimes on warm-blooded animals. Superceded in actual speed by the streamlined cetaceans and the big game fishes, the pinnipeds are past masters in aquatic sports. They can maneuver with perfect safety in boiling surf bursting with all the might of an angry sea on jagged rocks.

*Sea Lions*

In their evolution, the sea lions pushed out to sea at a later date than the true seals and are not as highly specialized for an aquatic life. They still retain a small but distinct external ear. Their hind limbs are capable of rotating forward to support the body and permit comparatively free progress on land. Young sea lions are born on land and must learn to swim.

In North American waters the sea lions are restricted to the Pacific Coast. They are represented there by the fur seal which is not a true seal but a typical sea lion, the California sea lion, *Zalophus californianus*, popular in zoos and circuses, and the northern, or Steller's sea lion, largest of all the sea lions. Our sea lions are all gregarious and love company. During the breeding season they congregate in colonies or rookeries at suitable localities along the Pacific Coast. The mature bulls come ashore first and take up their stands in positions best suited for each to get the greatest number of cows which arrive a little later. Furious battles are fought for possession of the females and the stronger the bull the greater will be its harem.

The northern fur seal, *Callorhinus ursinus*, is the most prized and the finest of all the sea lions but it is rarely seen in captivity. In May, herds of fur seals arrive on the Pribilof Islands to breed. The bulls remain on shore without food during the entire mating period. Should they relax their vigilance

*A male northern sea lion does not have the head crest of the California sea lion*

even for an instant the neighboring bulls would quickly invade the harem and soon the whole colony would be in utter chaos.

The pup, or calf (twins are rare), is born in June or July. As the mother mates soon after the pup is born the period of gestation is only a few days short of a year. The female pup is ready to mate when two years old but males are not sufficiently mature to compete for females until two or three years later. Immature males or bachelors consort together. The breeding season which starts in May extends until November when the entire colony puts out to sea. The cows and pups winter together at sea somewhere near the latitude of southern California. The bulls now living harmoniously together, spend the winter farther north. The life-span of the fur seal is about fifteen years. Its greatest natural foe is the killer whale.

The presence of a soft dense fur underlying the long coarse cover hairs put a price on the pelt of the fur seal that very nearly exterminated the race. However, government enforcements of strict conservation measures came just in time and the herds are now approaching their former magnitude.

The northern, or Steller's sea lion, *Eumetopias jubata*, has the distinction of being the largest and most ferocious of the eared seals, or sea lions. A large bull may weigh up to 1,800 pounds. It approaches the walrus and elephant seal in actual size. It frequents the stoniest and most dangerous shorelines of our land—the rocky coasts and islands of the northern Pacific. Discipline in its harem is not very strict and there is continuous strife between the males during breeding seasons. In fact, a constant roar of abuse by the irate bulls rises in a savage chorus above the booming of the surf pounding on the very threshold of their refuge.

Despite their might and remarkable power of endurance, colonies or rookeries of northern sea lions are never very large. The rate of mortality among the young is very great. Many are crushed by the fighting bulls that pay no heed to their pitiful cries. High seas frequently break over their refuge and many of the pups, unable to swim, are drawn into the sea and drown. When old enough, the pup is protestingly dumped into the sea by its mother. She may accompany her young but offers no assistance or sympathy; it must swim or drown.

*True Seals or Hair Seals*

Boasting an ancestral lineage antedating that of the sea lions, the true seal may also have been derived from a different stock and followed a somewhat different line of development. In the true seals there is no external ear; the hind limbs extend straight out behind and are incapable of rotating forward; they are the primary means of propulsion in the water, operating as twin screws; the forelimbs are short and are brought into action merely for the purpose of balance. The entire body, including the feet, is covered with hair and is without any underfur. Body heat is retained by a layer of blubber, or fat, under the skin. The true seals have invaded not only all the oceans of the world but have ascended far up many large rivers and even entered inland lakes. They have evolved into many diversified forms; at least eight different seals inhabit North American waters.

Sealing as a commercial industry has been practiced for many years and is of considerable economic importance.

Credited with being the most handsome and spectacular of the true seals, the ribbon seal, *Phoca fasciata*, has a unique color pattern. Contrasting with its dark brown coat, it has a sharply defined yellowish-white ribbon around its neck, another around each shoulder, and a third across the rump. These strange markings stand out boldly in the male but are less conspicuous in the female.

They represent an extreme in some form of protective coloration, possibly representing cracks in the ice. Recorded only sparingly about the Aleutian Islands and the coast of Alaska, the ribbon seal is one of the rarest of all seals and is seen only occasionally, either singly or in pairs. It is scarcely larger than the harbor seal and is much prized by the Eskimos for its attractive markings.

A native of the Arctic, the ringed seal, or jar seal, *Phoca hispida*, ranges far north into the ice helds of the polar regions and it is not found south of Labrador in the northern Atlantic or south of the Bering Sea in the Pacific. Its dark brown is curiously marked with irregular rings of blotches of yellowish-white. Newborn young have a snow-white, warm, wooly coat of hair that is retained for about four weeks. Except for a more northern habitat, characteristics of the ringed seal are much the same as those of the harbor seal that it resembles in size. Much of its life is spent near a breathing hole in the ice through which it is ready to slip at the first sign of danger and for its regular fishing trips.

The small seal frequently seen along the reefs, islands, and in sheltered harbors of the temperate zone is the harbor, or leopard seal, *Phoca vitulina*. This seal never strays far from land but on occasion will ascend far up large rivers and even beyond the influence of the tide. Its coarse hair is yellowish-gray dappled with black, but individuals may vary from this color to almost black spotted with white. The first coat of the baby harbor seal is a white wool but this is shed immediately after or even before its birth in the early spring.

Though normally shy and evasive, the harbor seal readily responds to protection and may even become friendly when a sympathetic understanding with it has been established. Family groups of a male and two or three females, each with one pup, are not uncommon but large numbers do not associate together. A harbor seal, when taken young, is easily trained and makes a devoted and loyal pet. In northern waters the harbor seal does not migrate with the seasons, but when the wintery blasts enclose the Arctic Coasts in ice, which gradually creeps out to sea, the seal, by constant use, keeps a breathing hole open. Periodically it visits this connection with the outside world to breathe or come out on the ice to rest. It is there that the Eskimos lie in wait to harpoon the unsuspecting seal, for they largely depend on it as a supply of winter food.

Occurring sparingly on both the Atlantic and Pacific coasts in the northern hemisphere, limited numbers of harbor seals still survive in favored localities. It is graceful and swift in pursuit of its finny prey but it is not a menace to our commercial fisheries.

The harp seal, *Phoca groenlandica*, sometimes known as the saddleback, is a large North Atlantic and arctic species that may weigh six to eight hundred pounds. Primitive numbers of harp seals are estimated in hundreds of thousands and probably millions. Its yellow coat with the characteristic broad lunate band of brown extending from the shoulders along the side to the tail are in the general form of a harp. The young are born on the floating ice in March, and, as might be expected, all are white at first. It takes four years for the young to reach maturity and not until this time do they show the harplike marking.

The harp seal is a sea rover and frequents the offshore ice fields, migrating north and south with the seasons. It follows the whitefishes and cod which are its principal food supply. Although lacking its former abundance, it still congregates in large numbers on the breeding grounds of Newfoundland. About 100,000 harp seals are still taken annually by commercial sealers.

A peculiar festoon of coarse, flattened bristles on each side of the muzzle suggested the popular name of bearded seal, *Erignathus barbatus*, for the largest of the northern seals. This uniformly colored, grayish-brown species may weigh up to 1,500 pounds when fully mature. Sealers, however, named it *squareflipper* because its flippers are squared at the tip. Credited with being rather a solitary creature, the bearded seal avoids the company of other species and is nowhere very abundant throughout its range in the arctic regions. The bulls fight fierce battles for possession of the females, using their fore flippers rather than their teeth in combat.

In diving, the bearded seal makes a somersault and descends to a considerable depth in search of its food which consists of crustaceans and mollusks found on the ocean floor. Unlike most other northern seals born on the floating ice, the newborn bearded seal has a coat of dark gray wool instead of white. A few days after birth, however, the gray wool is shed for one of attractive steel-blue hairs that are clouded with dull white patches.

Eskimos consider the *ogjook*, or bearded seal, a great prize, not only because of the amount of flesh and blubber found on one of these great seals but because of the thickness of the hide which is especially suited for hunting lines and harnesses and the construction of skin boats.

Often spending the cold winter months at sea, the gray seal, or horsehead, *Halichoerus grypus*, summers along the rockbound coasts and outlying islands of the northern Atlantic where the sea is deep and the rough and troubled waters are seldom still. Its range is a relatively narrow belt that does not penetrate north into the ice fields nor does it extend very far south of Nova Scotia. However, endowed with a strong homing instinct the gray seal cruises at sea somewhere near the breeding grounds and a few individuals regularly visit these rocky shores the year round.

Gray may be its dominant color but individuals vary from almost gray-black to a pale light gray often blotched with dark irregular spots. The gray seal is more or less sociable though it is not gregarious in any sense of the word. Family groups of a male, two or three females and pups in various stages of development may associate together. It is shy, suspicious, and is rarely seen on the rocks except in the late spring or early fall when the snow-white pups are born.

The gray seal is about equal in size to the harp seal; large males average about 8 feet in length and weigh approximately 600 pounds.

The hooded seal or bladdernose, *Cystophora cristata*, is of particular interest because of an inflatable bag of muscular tissue on top of the head in males. When enraged or excited this animal can distend the sac nine inches in height giving it a formidable and grotesque appearance. Full-grown males measure 7 to 8 feet in length and weigh up to 900 pounds. The females are smaller and do not have the inflatable bag. In color the hooded seal is dark gray or bluish-black, irregularly marked with yellowish spots and blotches. The pups, snow-white at birth, are born on the floating ice about a week later than those of the harp seal.

Having a life history and habits much like those of the harp seal, the hooded seal frequents the offshore ice packs in the northern Atlantic and migrates with the seasons.

Few animals in the world today have such a strange and mysterious background as the elephant seal, or sea elehant, *Mirounga angustirostris.* This unexplainable creature is a true seal that obviously derived its name from the peculiar elongated snout of cavernous tissue which when relaxed hangs eight inches below the mouth. That this remarkable appendage serves any useful purpose other than in courtship is questionable. The females do not have a proboscis. When the bull utters its deep ventriloquial bellow the end of the

*Its whiskers green with algae, a monk seal sounds off at Hawaii National Wildlife Refuge*

trunk is unfolded like a balloon and is curled into the mouth. Its huge ponderous body is not only grotesque but almost formless. The coarse skin is wrinkled, furrowed, and cracked.

Formerly the herds of this huge seal, which when fully grown may weigh 2,000 or 3,000 pounds and measure up to 22 feet in length, numbered many thousands. However, they have been so persistently and indiscriminately hunted for blubber that today there are not more than a few hundred left and these are restricted to the Island of Guadalupe, Mexico, southwest of San Diego, California. Quantities of pebbles found in the stomachs of these animals suggest a diet of shellfish and other forms of marine life found on the ocean floor. —G.G.G.

**California Sea Lion**
**Other Common Names**—Black sea lion
**Scientific Name**- *Zalophus californianus*
**Family**—Otariidae (eared seals)
**Order**—Pinnipedia
**Size**—Male: body length, 8 feet; weight, 500 to 620 pounds. Females somewhat smaller
**Range**—Pacific Coast; British Columbia south to Nayarit state Mexico and Tres Marias Islands

The California sea lion, *Zalophus californianus,* is the best known and the most popular of all the pinnipeds. The graceful motion of its slender, sleek body and long, supple neck as it glides through the water, is the principal attraction at most zoos. Seemingly, it gets as much pleasure out of exhibiting its ability in aquatic sports as those who look on. Its usual cry, *how-woo,* is a bid for attention—the larger the crowd of onlookers the greater its efforts to show off. While lacking the power of reason attributed to the dogs, the sea lion is intelligent. Its wonderful sense of balance and ability to learn tricks has often been exhibited on the stage and in circuses.

The life of the California sea lion follows much the same pattern as the northern fur seal except that its breeding grounds are the rocky coast and islands of the Californias. The black mark placed against its name, as a destroyer of salmon and other marketable fishes has proved erroneous. The staple diet of the California sea lion consists of squids and octopuses. No doubt for some unknown digestive purpose, the sea lion swallows countless small round pebbles, an inch or two in diameter. Sixteen pounds of pebbles were actually taken from the stomach of one individual. —G.G.G.

*Recommended Reading*

**Field Book of North American Mammals**—H.E. Anthony. G.P. Putnam's Sons, New York.
**The Mammal Guide**—Ralph S. Palmer. Doubleday & Company, Inc. New York.
**Return of the Sea Elephant**—Lewis W. Walker. *Natural History,* November 1947.

**Harbor Seal**
**Other Common Names**—Common Seal
**Scientific Name**—*Phoca vitulina*
**Family**—Phocidae (earless seals)
**Order**—Pinnipedia
**Size**—Length, 5 feet
**Range**—Northern coasts throughout the world. Atlantic: Europe, North America south to southern New England. Pacific: Arctic to Baja California on the North American coast, south to Japan on the Asiatic coast

Harbor seal bask at low tide on exposed sandbars or seaweed covered rocks in protected coves and bays. If disturbed by an approaching man or boat they inch caterpillar like toward the water, for unlike a sea lion, a seal cannot use its stubby flippers as legs. Usually reluctant to leave their sunbaths, they may move until the rising tide washes them away. Once in water, a seal is streamlined and graceful, although it lacks the sea lion's speed. Harbor seals live entirely on seafood, including tomcod, flounders, alewives, squids, octopuses, and some cructaceans. In waters of the Pacific Northwest, seals have been accused of destroying salmon, but actually they rarely molest these fish.

Although polygamus, the male harbor seal has no harem. The female has a single pup in the spring, which may be snowy white at birth but soon becomes spotted like its parents. Against an algae and barnacle covered rock this mottled coloration makes the seals difficult to see. Their natural enemies are sharks and killer whales, and in the North the Eskimos hunt harbor seals for meat and hides.

*Harbor seal*

## SEASHORE

### Life of the Seashore

The science of the sea, called oceanography, has made great strides as a result of the application of many modern inventions. Such equipment as the aqualung, sonar and other electronic devices have made observation and measurement much easier and more accurate than before. As a result, more and more is being discovered about this fascinating area that covers nearly three-fourths of the surface of the globe.

Just what is the sea like? First of all it is a habitat in which salt water is the principal element. This does not mean just so many teaspoons of salt in each gallon of water, for if we analyze sea water in a laboratory we find it contains more than fifty of the natural chemical elements. In recent years we have learned how to use this resource by extracting chemicals such as bromine and magnesium from the sea in large quantities.

More important to the larger forms of life in the ocean is the presence of countless hordes of microscopic plants and animals, collectively called *plankton* (*See also under Plankton*). This drifting life forms the base of the food pyramid in the salt water. As we know, animals cannot live on land unless plants first convert the energy of sunlight into food materials, using that remarkable substance *chlorophyll* to do it. The same is true for the sea, but almost all the plants are microscopic algae such as diatoms and other forms which drift in the plankton near the surface and absorb the sunlight that shines into the water. Small animals feed on these plants and larger animals feed on them, thus building up the chain (*See Food Chain*).

For most people the easiest place to study the sea is to go down along the seashore and look for the life that can be found there. In many places on the ocean front the force of water breaking on the shore makes life difficult for

*The rocky coast of Maine*

both plants and animals. Also the rising and falling of the tide leaves many organisms exposed to the air part of each 24 hours and submerged the rest of the time.

In some parts of North America there is less than one foot of tidal change to be expected, while the maximum which occurs in the upper end of the Bay of Fundy may be more than fifty feet. Influences of importance here are whether or not the shore slopes rapidly or gradually and how close to the low tide an animal may live. Free swimming animals like fishes are not usually affected by these changes because they can shift with the tide unless they happen to become trapped in a tidal pool as they sometimes do. But animals that are sessile or attached to some permanent base must make some other provision for this problem. This usually means the development of some protective coat of shell or heavy membrane which keeps them from drying out during the intervals when the tide is out.

*Rocky Shores*

The rocky shores that occur along the northeast coast of the Atlantic and on many parts of the Pacific Coast afford a rich habitat for a great variety of marine animals. They provide for most animals the best type of shelter from the effects of the ocean and from their natural enemies. The action of waves along such a shore assures an abundance of dissolved oxygen in the water, but it also presents severe problems of protection from the tremendous hydraulic force that can be generated by tons of water breaking against the rocky surfaces during storms. A variety of seaweeds, especially those belonging to the brown algae, and commonly called rockweed or kelp (*see under Kelp*), attach themselves rigidly to these rocks and form great masses of dense plant life. These are often supported by air bladders in their fronds when the tide is in, and when the tide is out their heavy mats retain moisture and thus prevent many of the animals that seek shelter under them, or those attached to their fronds, from the drying effect of exposure to the sun and air.

Crevices in the rocks afford shelter or points of attachment for animals that fasten themselves down to avoid damage by wave action. Examples of these would include barnacles, which secrete a calcareous shell that is attached solidly to rock surfaces; mussels, whose attachment is a strong, silklike thread secreted by the byssal gland; chitons, limpets, and other mollusks whose shells are flattened to lessen their resistance to the water. These hang on to the rock surface by the powerful sucking force of the large broad foot. A number of animals, including a variety of hydroids, some sponges, and many bryozoans or moss animals attach themselves either to the rock surface or directly to the fronds, stipes or holdfasts of the seaweed, thus becoming almost an integral part of the plant itself. From such a point of vantage they are able to thrust out tentacles and capture from the water the tiny microscopic plankton organisms that float past, carried by the motion of the waves.

One of the most impressive things about the tidal zone is the great concentrations of animals that often occur there. Rock surfaces may be entirely covered with barnacles, thousands of hydroid individuals may grow on a single plant of rockweed, and in some of the tidal pools snails are often piled two or three deep. The chances of survival for the offspring of these animals are relatively low because of these crowded conditions and as a result the rate of reproduction is often fantastically high. Most of the eggs hatch into microscopic, free-swimming larvae that are able to move to new locations and establish new colonies in areas that may not be so heavily populated. Barnacles, crabs, and other crustaceans produce such free-swimming larvae. In

*Algae-covered rocks edge the ocean at Cape May, New Jersey*

barnacles, after a period of larval existence the individual attaches itself to a rock or piling and secretes a protective shell of calcium. Thereafter it literally stands on its head and waves the featherlike feet, or cirri, through the water, drawing in the tiny plankton organisms on which it feeds.

Wherever the contour of the shoreline is such that pockets are formed there will occur tidal pools, and these are apt to become living rock gardens of beautiful algae (*See Alga*). Among these gardens will be found a variety of animals: tiny amphipod crustaceans, usually called scud, snails of several species, crabs, starfishes, and sometimes shrimps or small fishes. Where muddy or sandy pockets occur between the rocks one may find marine worms or bivalve mollusks similar to those to be described as characteristic of muddy or sandy shores (*See Tidal Pool*).

What are the food requirements of all these animals? Some, like the common periwinkle, are herbivorous, feeding on the many kinds of algae to be found in great abundance growing on the rocks. A great majority are plankton-feeders. The feeding habits of hydroids and barnacles have already been described. Many of the sponges, worms, mollusks and even fishes have adaptations that enable them to strain these microscopic forms from the water as they pass it through their digestive tracts. Another group of animals are carnivorous, preying upon smaller forms. Such predators would include many of the crabs, starfishes and sea urchins. Others are the birds that prey upon these seashore animals: gulls, shorebirds, and even some of the ducks, like the eider. Still another group of animals are scavengers, patrolling the shore and removing the remains of animals that have died or been destroyed. Such a group might include crabs, lobsters, some snails, and fishes. So it is that we find animals of the rocky shore preying and preyed upon, often crowded together so tightly that it seems impossible for all to find room.

*The Sand Beach*

Great stretches of the ocean front on both the Atlantic and Pacific coasts are composed of sand beach, varying actually from coarse gravel to the finest of sand. In general it might be said that such beaches are among the poorest places to study marine life. There is little protection there for animals and the severe action of waves, turning over and shifting the sand, leaves little opportunity for animals to get established. It is true that many shells of mollusks and some of the other more rigid skeletons may be washed up on the sand and found by the collector, but there are not many living forms that can adapt themselves to these surroundings. During certain seasons where great number of jellyfishes swarm in the sea offshore, many of them will be washed ashore by wind and tide and great windrows of them will be seen along the beach front.

*Mud Flats*

Behind the barrier beaches of the sandy shores, and wherever estuaries of rivers occur, there are extensive tidal flats of varying character and composition. Some of them are composed of fine sand, others of mud; extensive shallow areas of these bays may be exposed by the low tide and covered at high tide. In these shallow water areas the algae are often replaced by that fascinating aquatic flowering plant, the eelgrass (*See under Eelgrass*). This plant is exceptionally interesting because it is the base of a great pyramidal food chain second in importance only to the plankton in providing the sustenance for many invertebrate animals, and fishes and birds in the coastal

*The Atlantic Ocean breaks on flat, sandy beaches at East Hampton, Long Island*

areas. During the 1930's a serious epidemic disease threatened to wipe out the eelgrass and as a result populations of fishes and birds were seriously unbalanced. This was especially true of the American brant whose population was reduced to a dangerously low level for a period of time. Fortunately the worst of this cycle has passed and the eelgrass is making good progress toward recovery. It is a fine example of the way in which dislocation of one living form may seriously affect the living conditions of others that are closely dependent on it. The great masses of eelgrass (*Zostera*) provide shelter and food for myriads of tiny shrimps and baby fishes such as flounder, herring, and others, which in turn are the basic food of many of the larger fishes such as mackerel and cod.

The animals that live on the surface of shallow sandy bottoms or in the eelgrass are usually protectively colored to resemble the sand or the plant on which they live. The flounder becomes almost invisible. The pipefish appears to move sideways and looks almost exactly like a blade of the eelgrass. There also we may find sand dollars, those curious relatives of the sea urchin, that crawl slowly along the bottom.

The greatest number of animals in these mud flat zones protect themselves by burrowing down into sand or mud and thus hiding from their enemies. The two most important groups of animals that have made this kind of adaptation are bivalve mollusks and worms. Some of the bivalves (*see Bivalve*), including the oyster, which fastens itself rigidly to a base support, and the mussels, which tie themselves down by their byssal threads, occur on the surface of the sand or mud, often in great shoals or beds that may cover the surface almost entirely. Another group of bivalves make use of their muscular foot to dig their way through the mud and only expose the opening of the siphon at the surface. Through

*A shell collector examines a razor clam and a hard clam on a barrier island. Other items in his collection include whelks, oysters, clams, horseshoe crab*

the siphon they take in seawater, extract from it the plankton food and oxygen and then return it through an excurrent tube of the siphon. Examples of these would be the hard-and soft-shell clam, the razor clam and similar forms, many of which are of great economic importance as a source of food (*See under Clam; and under Mollusk*). Marine worms fall into two general types those that are free-swimming and predatory like the clam worm, having complicated and effective rows of parapodia or swimming organs, and those that secrete protective tubes about themselves and remain within them for protection. Many of this latter group have feathery and beautifully colored mouthparts and gill structures that project up out of the parchment or sand tubes.

Just offshore beyond the tidal zone the bottom may be inhabited by a great variety of marine forms. Unfortunately the average student of the sea cannot easily observe these animals because of the difficulties involved in collecting them, but the use of a dredge will re-

*A whelk deposits a long string of egg cases*

*Fucus, or rockweed, is a widely distributed brown algae that grows along the cool, rocky New England and eastern Canadian shores*

ward the collector with a great variety of hydroids, anemones, sponges, bryozoans, worms, echinoderms, tunicates, and other fascinating forms of which it is impossible to treat in this brief survey. Off rocky coasts the great forests of kelp become a dwelling place for innumerable populations of fascinating creatures, many of them, like the lobster, of great commercial value.

*Wharves, Docks, and Pilings*

On well-established wooden or stone structures that have been built by man a great variety of marine animals often live. After a period of time these structures get thoroughly covered with a heavy growth of seaweed and form a shelter for many of the same creatures that would ordinarily inhabit the seaweeds along a rocky shore. In addition to this, there are a number of animals that can attach themselves firmly to the surface of the wooden pilings. Some of these become an economic nuisance because they attach themselves to the bottoms of boats, thus impeding their progress and increasing the use of fuel. The best known of such animals is the barnacle, but there are many others that will choose a similar habitat if given the opportunity.

Mussels, boat snails, and limpets will fasten themselves on underwater wooden structures and among the seaweeds that grow there may be found tiny fishes or perhaps a few sea slugs, those peculiar mollusks that have lost their shells and often have developed beautiful branching gill structures on their backs. The wood itself is often attacked and riddled by a peculiarly modified clam, *Teredo*, more commonly known as the shipworm. Sea anemones attach themselves to the wood and occasionally either solitary or colonial tunicates or sea squirts may be found. These are distant relatives of the vertebrates, or backboned animals, because they start with the beginnings of a spinal cord when they are larvae. But somewhere along the line they backtrack and as adults live a simple existence surrounded by a leathery covering or "tunic" which they secrete to protect themselves. They are called sea squirts because, when distrubed, they will often squirt water out of one of the two external openings.

This description of the life of the seashore is very incomplete and only suggests the type of life that may exist in several common habitats that the average student of natural history might visit. For example, the tropical waters of our southern coasts contain a great variety of animals that have not even been mentioned. Coral reefs are interesting, not only in the marvelous way that these tiny animals build up the complex and often vividly beautiful calcareous structures, but also in the great variety of characteristic life that associates with them. In more northern waters there are tremendous offshore banks where a variety of interesting bottom life occurs.

One shoud note how important many of the marine animals are to man as a source of food and other products. Along the shore the gathering of shellfishes such as oysters, clams, scallops, crabs, and lobsters, is an important industry. Off the banks may be found the great fisheries where fleets of trawlers have been collecting fishes for market since the earliest days of our history. Though the methods of fishing have changed, the actual fishing operation is still fascinating and sometimes dangerous. Today we must concern ourselves with scientific research to determine the best way to operate these fisheries without depleting or destroying the resource. This will require careful study and intelligent application of what we learn.

It is important to remember that all of these marine organisms are related by that complex and fascinating association characteristic of all life on the earth. Each species plays a part in the balance

*Barnacles are sedentary marine animals that often attach themselves to pilings*

of the whole, and the destruction of one form, as in the case of the eelgrass, may have profound effects on many other animals that are closely or indirectly related to it. It is only by studying these relationships that we are able gradually to unravel the mysteries of this closely woven life and come to a better understanding of the world in which we live (*See Balance of Nature, Ecology; Food Chain; and Wildlife: The Wildlife Community*). —B.B.C.

*Recommended Reading*

**Animals Without Backbones**—R. Buchsbaum. University of Chicago Press, Chicago.

**The Seashore**—C.M. Yonge. Collins, London.

**Beginner's Guide To Seashore Life**—L.A. Hausman. G.P. Putnam's Sons, New York.

**Field Book Of Seashore Life**—R.W. Miner. G.P. Putnam's Sons, New York.

**Introducing Sea Shells**—R.T. Abbott. Van Nostrand Company, Princeton, New Jersy.

**The Lower Animals; Living Invertebrates Of The World**—Ralph Buchsbaum and Lorus J. Milne. Doubleday, Garden City, New York.

**1001 Questions Answered About The Seashore**—N.J. and Jacquelyn Berrill. Dodd, Mead & Company, New York.

**Seashores**—Zim and Ingle. (Golden Nature Guide) Simon & Schuster, Inc., New York.

**This Great And Wide Sea**—R.E. Coker. University of North Carolina Press, Chapel Hill, North Carolina.

**The Wonderful World Of The Sea**—James Fisher. Garden City Books, Garden City, New York.

## SEASON

### The Circle of the Seasons

When winter comes, the mercury in the thermometer falls toward zero, ponds and streams freeze over, thousands of birds migrate southward, and many species of animals dig in below the frost level or retreat into caves where they hibernate until spring (*See Hibernation*). Plants that have no protective adaptations to endure the cold and drought, have lost their leaves, and gardens and woods are bare and brown except where the hardy evergreens grow. Man has experienced winter as far back as there are any records. Even before he inhabited the earth, the story in the rocks tells us there was winter. Lacking fur or feathers, or wings with which to fly to a warmer climate, man prepares for winter in the temperate zone by heating his home and dressing warmly.

No natural phenomenon is more familiar to us than the changing seasons. It is as well known as the alternation of day and night. But, like the latter, it is something that most of us accept with little thought as to why it happens. The fact that the changing seasons are caused in some mysterious way by a changing relation between the sun and earth is, of course, generally known, although most of us are pretty vague as to exactly what that relation is.

That we may understand why there are seasons, let us consider the relations between the earth and sun that effect these changes. First, we must remember that the earth is really a heavenly body. It is just as much a heavenly body as Mars, Venus, or Saturn. Actually it is a planet—one of nine planets that revolve around the sun.

Now everybody knows that the earth goes all the way around the sun every 365¼ days. This period represents one year. The other planets take different lengths of time to go around the sun. Those whose orbits are nearer to the sun than the earth's go around in a shorter time. Those farther from the sun than the earth, take longer. For example, the planet Venus, which is much nearer to the sun than we are, goes around in about 225 of our days. Thus, a year on Venus would be shorter than a year on the earth. Mars, however, is farther away from the sun than we are, so it takes about 687 of our days to go around the sun. Therefore, a year on Mars is nearly twice as long as it is on the earth.

It is this annual motion of the earth—its revolution around the sun—that is partly responsible for our changing seasons. But this is not the only cause. As a matter of fact, it would be entirely possible to have the earth go around the sun and still experience no change in season. This would be the case if the axis of the earth were always straight up and down (perpendicular) in reference to a line drawn from the sun to the earth. In that case, the sun would always shine directly over the equator and we would have the same season continually. Also, the days and nights would be always the same throughout the world. As we shall see, this condition prevails on two occasions during the year—the first day of spring and the first day of autumn.

But we know that the earth's axis is not perpendicular to a line drawn between the earth and the sun. The axis is tilted away from the perpendicular by an angle of about 23½ degrees. And as a result, we find that during a certain part of the earth's journey the north end of its axis (north pole) is leaning toward the sun, while at the same time, the south end of the axis (south pole) is tilted away from the sun. Just six months afterward the earth has traveled half way around its orbit. This time the south end of its axis is inclined toward the sun and the north end away.

It is this change in the direction of the earth's axis, relative to the sun, that is responsible for our changing seasons. But let us see just why this is so. We will first consider the time of year when the north end of the earth's axis is tilted toward the sun. This is its position on

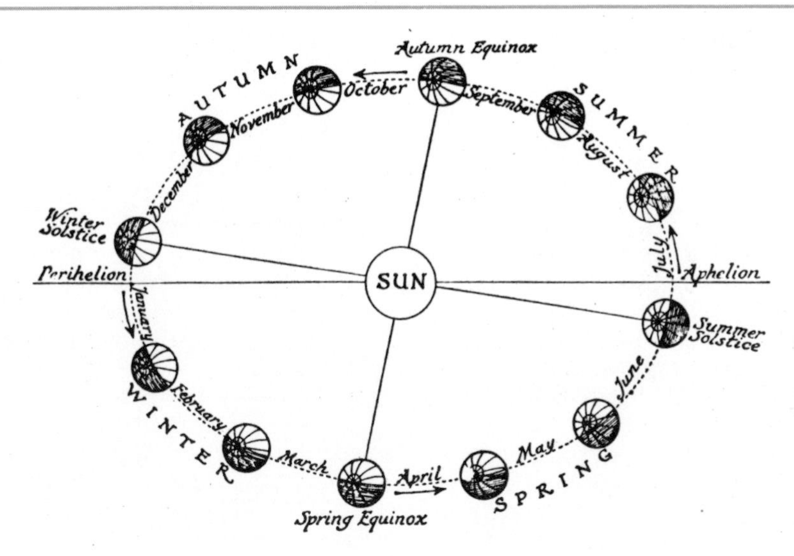


*The positions of the earth relative to the sun, for each of the 12 months of the year, are shown above. The north pole tilts toward the sun in June and away from it in December, causing seasonal changes*

about the 21st of June, which is the first day of summer for all of us who live in the northern hemisphere. The astronomer calls this the summer solstice.

Because the north end of the earth's axis is leaning toward the sun on this date we find that the sun then rises at its farthest point north of east. As the earth turns on its axis, the sun swings across the sky in a great curved path that carries it high in the south. At noontime it hangs directly in the south and at the highest position that it ever attains above the southern horizon. Then, as the hours of the afternoon advance, the sun drops lower and lower toward the western horizon, to set just as far north of west as it had risen north of east. We all know, of course, that on this date the sun rises earlier in the morning than any other time throughout the year, and it sets later in the evening. Actually, in the latitude of New York, there are more than 15 hours of daylight and less than 9 hours of darkness on this longest day of the year. For people who happen to live on the Tropic of Cancer (23½° North Latitude) the sun appears directly overhead at noon on this date. Since we have the sun above the horizon for a longer time at this season and, since its rays fall more directly upon us, large quantities of heat are stored up in the earth north of the equator. The sunshine falls upon gardens and forests, and lakes and oceans store up this radiated warmth from the sun.

But we know that as the weeks advance summer will draw to a close. This is because the earth is advancing on its orbit around the sun and the north end of its axis is slowly moving away from the sun. After the time of summer solstice we find that each morning the sun rises a little farther south and sets a little farther south. The days begin to grow a little shorter and we find that each day at noon the sun is a little lower in the sky than it was on June 21st.

On about September 22nd the sun rises directly in the east and sets directly in the west. On this date, except for the period of twilight and dawn, we have days and nights of equal length. This is the first day of autumn and neither the north nor the south pole is inclined toward the sun. The sun now shines directly over the equator.

After September 22nd the earth journeys toward that part of its orbit which is exactly opposite to the position that it occupied at the time of the summer solstice. Now we find the north pole of the earth gradually moving away from the sun. Each day the sun rises a little farther south of east and sets a little farther south of west than it did on the day before. It is at this time of year that the leaves begin to turn from green to red and gold. Then, as the cold winds blow, they fall from the trees. We say that winter is coming.

On about December 21st the earth arrives at that part of its orbit where the north pole is directed away from the sun. On this date the sun rises far south of east and sets far south of west. We find it hanging low in the south at noon. At noontime it is directly overhead at the Tropic of Capricorn. This is the beginning of winter and at this time the sun is above the horizon for only about 9 hours and below the horizon for 15 hours for the latitude of New York. It is the season of ice and snow, of cold days and long nights.

But with the passage of time our planet continues to move along in its orbit and each day the rising and setting points of the sun creep steadily north. By March 21st (the first day of spring) the sun again rises directly east and sets directly west. We again experience equal day and night. Then the days begin to grow longer than the nights, as the north pole begins to swing away from the sun. By June 21st we find that we in the northern hemisphere are again having long days and short nights. A whole year has gone by, and we have experienced a full cycle of seasons.

Of course, we have been discussing the seasons as they occur in the north. In the southern hemisphere, below the equator, these conditions would be the reverse. Down in the southern part of South America summer comes in December when the south pole of the earth is turned toward the sun. They have winter in June. Spring comes in September and

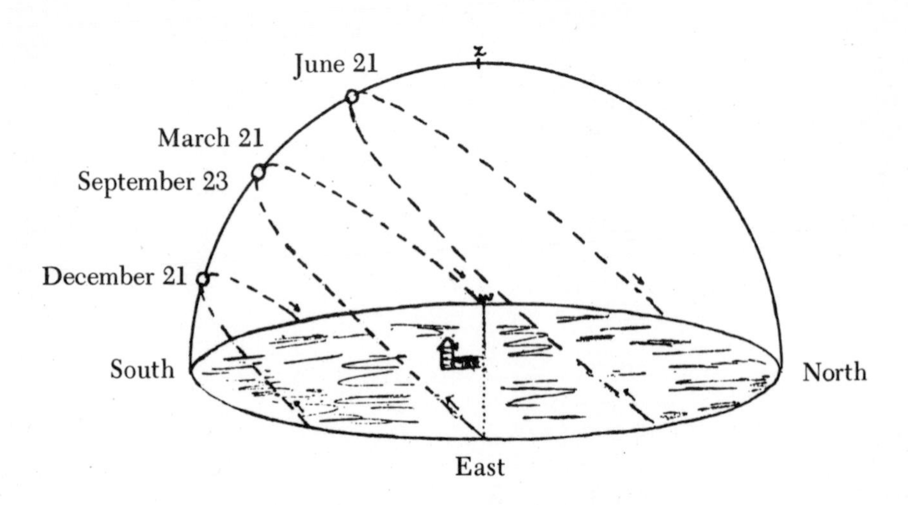


*The rising and setting positions of the sun for an observer at the latitude of New York City on the dates of the summer and winter soltices and at the time of the spring and autumn equinoxes are shown above*

Autumn in March. It all depends upon where you live whether you swim or skate in December. —R.R.C.

*Recommended Reading*

**Astronomy**—Robert H. Baker. Van Nostrand, New York.

**Astronomy**—Clyde Fisher and Marian Lockwood, John Wiley & Sons, Inc., New York.

**Astronomy**—William T. Skilling and Robert S. Richardson. Holt, Rhinehart & Winston, Inc., New York.

**Weather**—Gayle Pickwell. McGraw-Hill, New York.

**Why the Weather?**—Charles F. Brooks. Harcourt, Brace & World, New York.

## SEAWEED

Plants that grow underwater in the oceans are generally termed seaweed. Microscopic, drifting plants of the plankton are not included within the common meaning of the word, which is restricted to those large enough to be easily seen and that are fixed to one location.

Most seaweeds are green, brown, or red algae, primitive plants lacking flowers, roots, trunks, and true leaves. The rootlike structures are called *holdfasts,* the thick, branchlike structures that are attached to them are *stipes,* and the leaflike tissues that grow from the stipes are the *blades.*

Seaweeds contain chlorophyll, as do land plants, and manufacture their food from sunlight and chemicals in the water. They derive no nourishment from the holdfasts. Their reliance on sunlight restricts them to the shallower parts of the oceans (*See under Kelp*). —G.B.S.

## SEDGES AND RUSHES

### Sedges

Sedges are grasslike plants of the family Cyperaceae. Seeing a sedge with its narrow grasslike leaves growing close to others in a dense community, just as grasses do, one might mistake it for a grass. These two plant groups are closely related, and have some characteristics in common. Both have:

1. Flowers which, though having stamens and pistils, lack a perianth (calyx and corolla). Note: some sedges have fine hairs surrounding stamens and pistils which may be considered a primitive perianth.

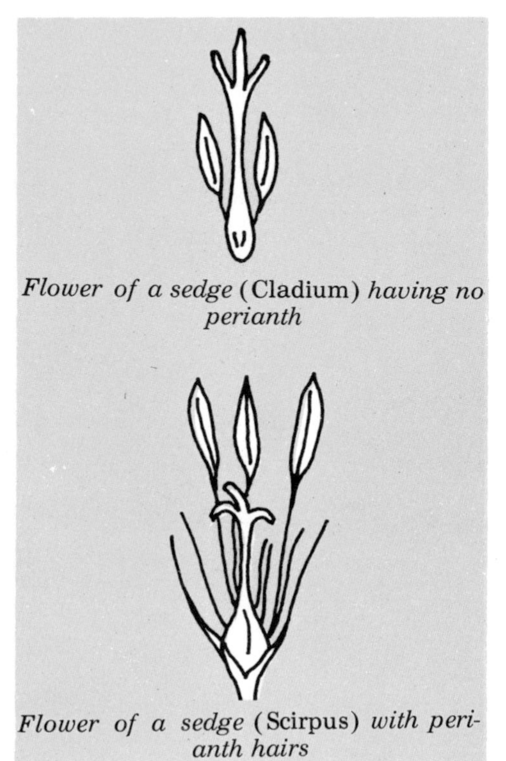

*Flower of a sedge* (Cladium) *having no perianth*

*Flower of a sedge* (Scirpus) *with perianth hairs*

2. Flowers more or less enclosed by husklike scales and grouped in spikes.
3. Part of the leaf, or all of it, wrapped around the stems like a sheath.
4. Only one seed formed in the fruit.

The close and discriminating observer finds differences that set these two families apart.

*Comparison of stems*

Grasses—stems cylindrical or flattened; hollow.

Sedges—stems usually triangular, at least at the top; solid.

*Comparison of leaf sheath*

Grasses—Sheath split, ligule present.

Sedges—Sheath closed, no ligule present.

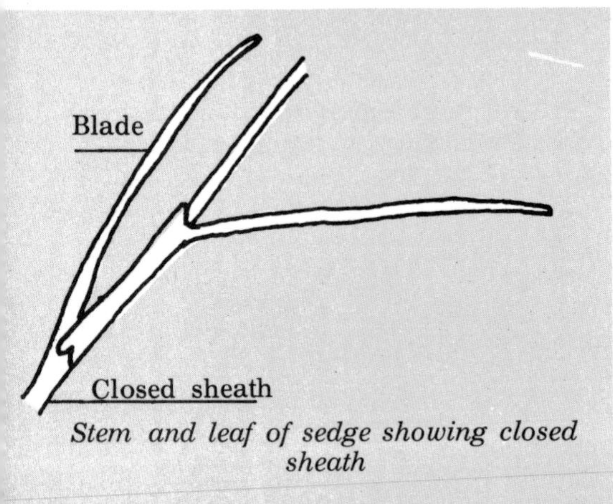


*Stem and leaf of sedge showing closed sheath*

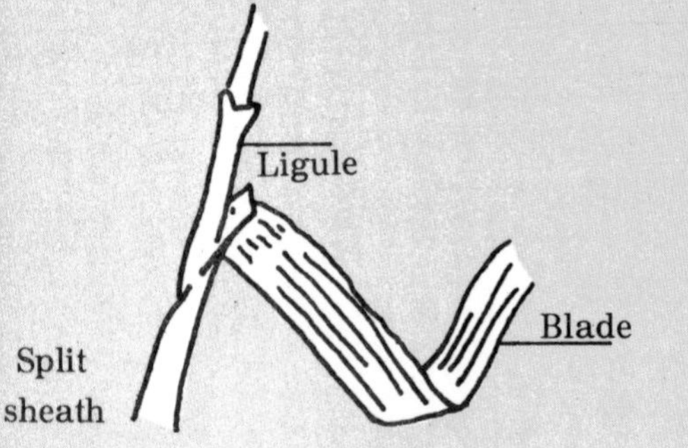


*Stem and leaf of a grass showing split sheath and ligule*

*Comparison of stamens*
Grasses—Anther attached to filament by the middle, easily swinging to the wind.
Sedges—Anther attached to filament by the base.

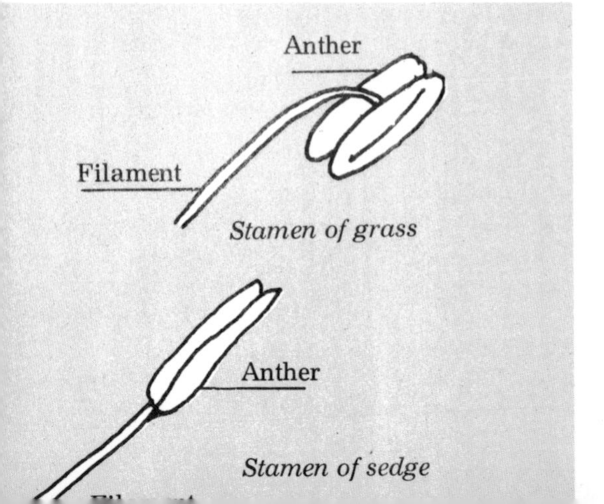


*Stamen of grass*

*Stamen of sedge*

*Comparison of stigma*
Grasses—feathery stigma.
Sedges—stigma not feathery.

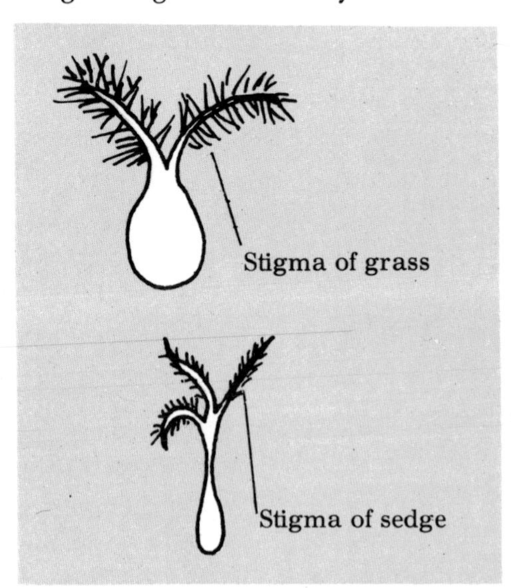


Look for sedges in marshy places, banks of streams and shores of lakes, occasionally in dry or sandy soil. Like grasses, they are widely distributed over the whole world. One genus alone (*Carex*) includes about 1,000 species. Economically, they are apparently less useful than grasses. They are not important as fodder, because they are dry and contain a large amount of silica. The edges of many of the triangular stems or leaves are exceedingly sharp. Some have such beauty that they are used for planting in gardens or for making winter bouquets. One of the most ornamental is cotton "grass" (note the misnomer), (*Eriophorum*), which grows in cold mossy bogs. Around the stamens and pistils are numerous soft white bristles which become greatly elongated in fruit. They make a lovely sight in June or July, looking like waving white plumes. In another species of *Eriophorum* the bristles are a beautiful tawny color.

The most universally known sedge is *Cyperus papyrus*. It is one of the tallest sedges, growing to a height of 10 feet. The "paper" of the ancients was made of the pith of the flowering stems, split into fine sheets, laid side by side with edge overlapping edge and this overlaid crosswise with similar strips under pressure. Papyrus is native in Syria, Palestine, and the Upper Nile region.

Umbrella sedge, or umbrella plant, a common house plant, *Cyperus alternifolius,* has a terminal umbel of many long spreading leaves that give the plant its umbrellalike appearance.

*Rushes*

Rushes are grasslike or rushlike herbs in the family Juncacae. The grasslike appearance of some rushes is more marked in those whose leaves are flat as, for example, the common wood rushes of the genus *Luzula.* Those rushes with cylindrical leaves are not so readily mistaken for grasses. They are indeed more like sedges. There are leaf sheaths in this group, split (in the genus *Juncus*) or closed (in the genus *Luzula*). There are no ligules. The stems are hollow or pithy. So far, then, we have no sure and quick identification features. The small flower of a *Luzula* resembles a tiny lily.

The diameter of a lilylike flower of a

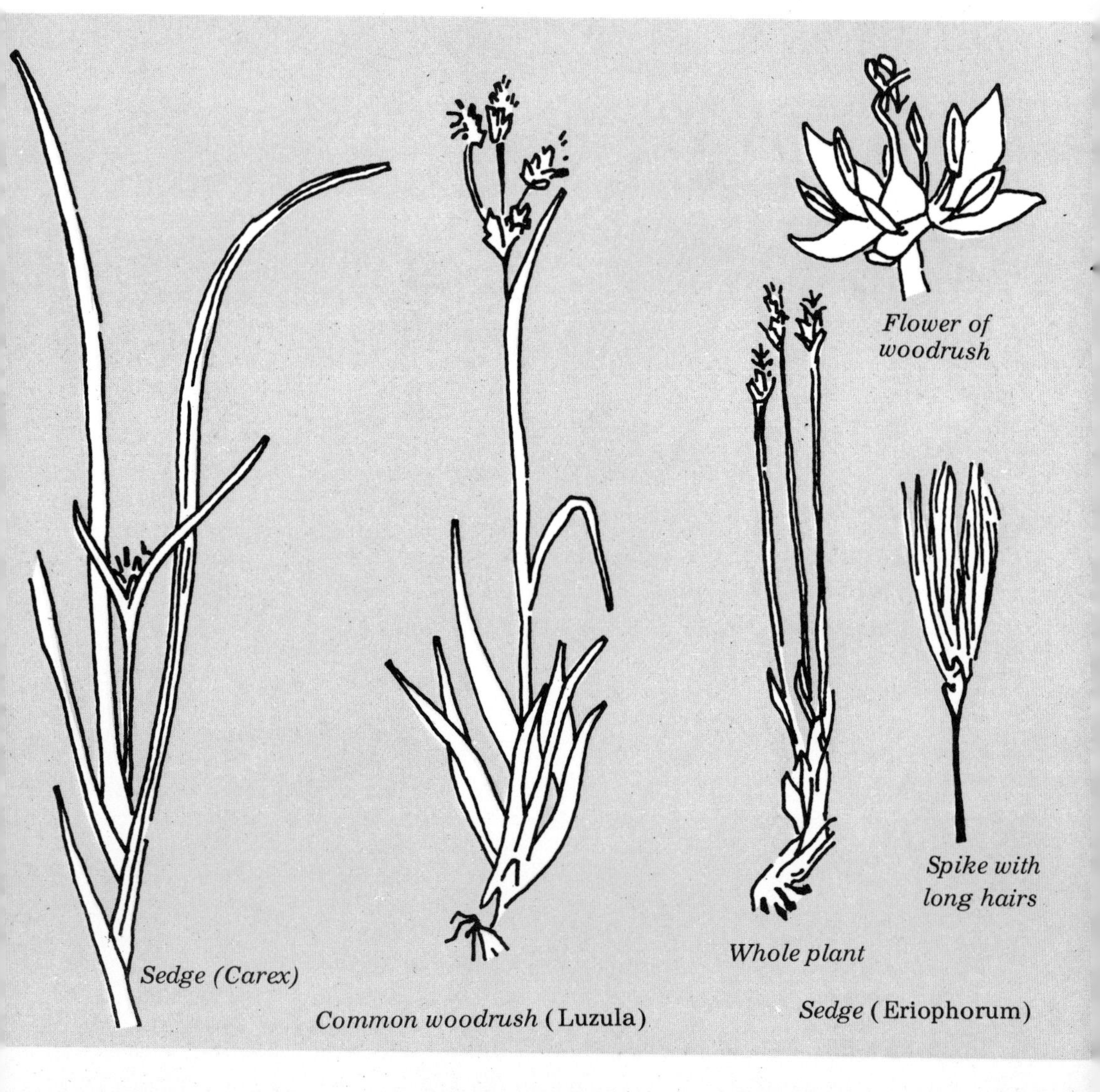

wood rush is about one-quarter of an inch; the color of the perianth, greenish or brownish and of a rather dry and papery texture. The flower is more complete than those of grasses and sedges, allying the rushes more closely with the lily family than with the grasses.

Other rushes have similar flowers, some even smaller (one needs a pocket lens to see them clearly). One need not be at a loss at a rush's identity after the flower has faded, for the fruit too is quite different from the one-seeded grain of achene of grasses and sedges. The fruit of rushes splits open at maturity into three parts, freeing the three to many seeds.

Rushes are as cosmopolitan as grasses and sedges, but are especially abundant in cold and temperate regions. Their uses are limited. One has heard of rush lights. They were made of the pith of bog-rush stems dipped in tallow. Some are used for plaiting mats. One common rush of salt marshes, *Juncus bulbosus,* makes good hay. To add to the confusion of names, certain sedges are commonly spoken of as rushes, e.g., bulrushes (*Scirpus*), one species of which is used for bottoming chairs.

*Recommended Reading*

**All About the Flowering World**—Ferdinand C. Lane. Random House, New York.
**Gray's Manual of Botany**—M.L. Fernald. American Book Company, New York.
**How to Know the Grasses**—Richard W. Pohl. William C. Brown, Dubuque, Iowa.
**Introductory Botany**—Arthur Cronquist. Harper & Row, Publishers, Inc., New York.

## SEED

A seed is a plant embryo, the union of the female egg cell and the male sperm cell, plus some tissues that develop as food by the sprouting plant.

The outer portion of the seed is the coat. It is thin and papery in some species, thick and hard in others. Its function is to prevent loss of moisture from within the seed and to protect the delicate inner tissues.

The endosperm tissues store the food that the new plant will need until it can manufacture its own. In some plants this tissue is within the embryo, as in the beans, and appears as two thick seed leaves. In others, such as buckwheat, the endosperm is separate.

The embryo itself is composed of three parts. The primitive stem and root is known as the *hypocotyl,* the seed leaves as the *cotyledons,* and the developing bud as the *plumule.* —G.B.S.

### Seeds and How They Travel

Late summer is the peak season for seed ripening. It is called harvest time because the world's most valuable food crops (the cereals) of corn, wheat, oats, barley, rye, buckwheat, and rice are seeds.

A seed is a masterpiece of efficient design. Typically it has three features: The *germ* is a living plant, microscopic in size, complete with root, stalk and leaf; the germ is buried inside a nugget of concentrated food; this provides nourishment when the plant starts to grow, before its own roots and leaves can go to work making food; the third feature (not always present) is a mechanical distributor. This accessory may be a pair of wings as on maple seeds, or a propeller as on ailanthus seeds (*see Ailanthus*), or a parachute as on milkweed, or sharp hooks as on the burdock. Seeds not so equipped (e.g. the grasses) are apt to be very light so that they simply blow around. Or they may be very smooth, like apple seeds, and contained inside a fruit eaten by birds or other animals. These pass through the alimentary canal of the animal and are thus scattered. The world's biggest seed, the coconut, is built to float away. Coconut trees typically lean over seas, lakes, or streams.

All types of this remarkable product of nature comprise an embryonic plant that is broken away from its parent, provided with independent food, sealed for protection, and sent traveling.

As evident from the tonnage of grain crops, seeds are produced in enormous

*When ripe, milkweed seed pods eject many parachute seeds that are carried away by the wind*

numbers. A modest red clover plant will grow 500 seeds; a single crabgrass plant can produce 90,000 seeds; pigweed, a million seeds per plant.

The length of time a germ can stay alive inside its food nugget waiting for favorable conditions to grow varies enormously. The normal lapse is from summer to the following spring. Grass and weed seeds may germinate after ten or fifteen years under natural conditions. One scientist kept tab on weed seeds he planted under controlled conditions and some species grew after forty years. Some tell of seeds taken from the hand of an Egyptian mummy germinating after several thousand years! But this story still needs to be proved.

The food nuggets of seeds are not only enjoyed by man but also by birds and other animals. A tiny meadow mouse eats 24 to 36 pounds of food in its lifetime and it loves seeds.

All the massive activity of plants from spring to fall has been leading up to the "still small voice" of the seed. When that is reached, leaves drop, flowers fade, stems shrivel, and life is scaled down to such minute proportion that people who see trees and flowers by the acre think the outdoors has turned dark.

To make seeds, thousands of miles of root hairs were driven by a plant through refractory ground; gallons of solution were gathered, filtered, lifted; countless leaves expanded and produced food; flowers sparkled in every part of the field and woods; petals and sepals, stamens and pistils moved through their routines while myriads of pollen grains were transported by wind or insects. (*See Pollination*)

Botanists call the seeds of any plant its fruit. The casing of the seed was the beginning of many types of fruits: nuts, pods, capsules. Put to another use, the casing, which begins as the ovary of a flower, supplies a living compartment in which amazing kinds of seeds can be cradled while they develop.

The ovary case usually clings to its seeds. If it does not turn into an apple

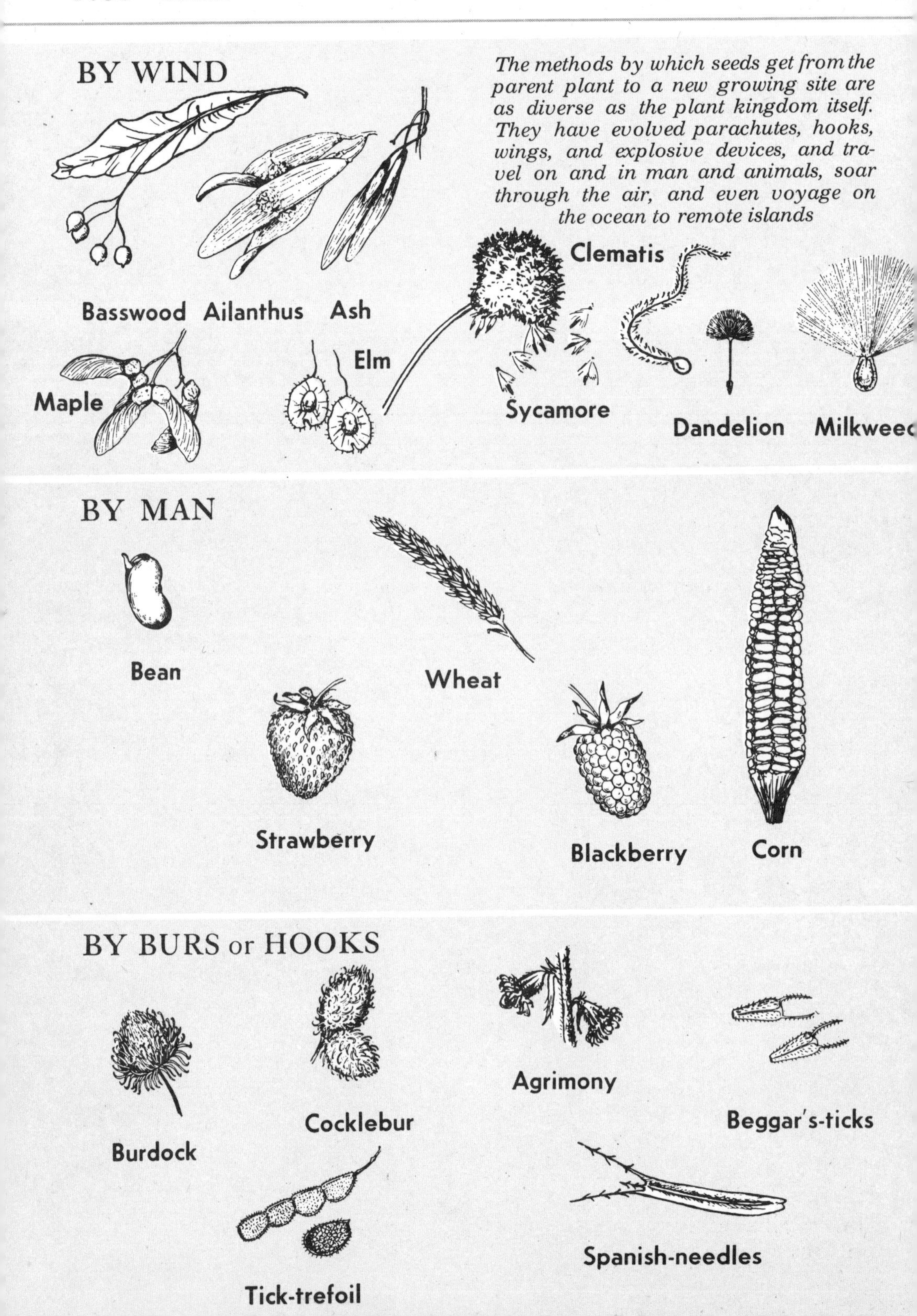
BY WIND
*The methods by which seeds get from the parent plant to a new growing site are as diverse as the plant kingdom itself. They have evolved parachutes, hooks, wings, and explosive devices, and travel on and in man and animals, soar through the air, and even voyage on the ocean to remote islands*
Basswood
Ailanthus
Ash
Clematis
Elm
Maple
Sycamore
Dandelion
Milkweed
BY MAN
Bean
Wheat
Strawberry
Blackberry
Corn
BY BURS or HOOKS
Agrimony
Beggar's-ticks
Cocklebur
Burdock
Spanish-needles
Tick-trefoil

## BY WATER

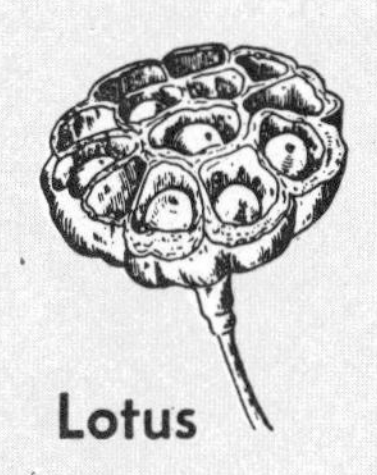

Lotus

Coconut

Arum

Pearlwort

Raindrops splash seeds of tiny pearlwort from their pods.

## BY EXPULSION

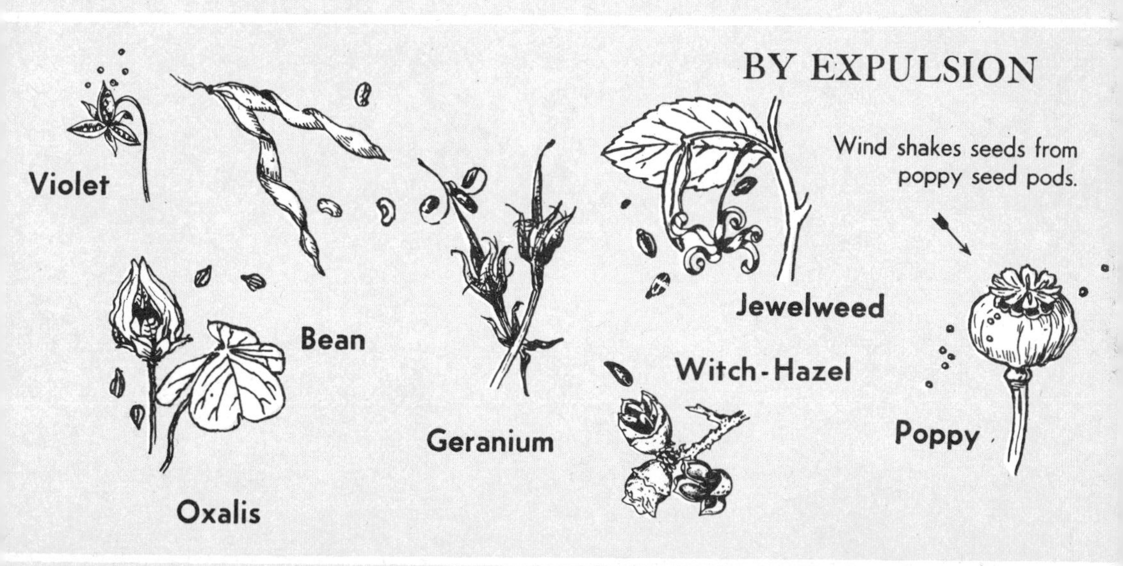


## BY ANIMALS

Acorn

Cherry

Hickory Nut

Beech Nut

or acorn or berry, it may grow wings, as the maple, elm, ash; or form propeller blades, as ailanthus; or develop barbs that stick to passing animals, as burdock or tick trefoil or Spanish needles. This phenomenon would be incredible if it were not spread out before our eyes.

Thus plants, with fanfare of leaf and flower, make miniatures of themselves within their seeds. These are set free with food to keep them alive, equipped to take advantage of every outside agent to keep them moving. Nuts and acorns use squirrels for transportation and planting; berries and grains use birds; hooked and sticky seeds use furry animals. Some seeds use rain, rivers, or sea; many, wind. Anemone and hellebore equip their seeds with oil used by ants which lug them off.

If this seems like uncanny ingenuity, what shall we say about mechanisms that kick off seeds with the same kind of energy used to kick off footballs? Of all contraptions that scatter seeds, these are the most startling.

*The Outdoor Machine Shop*

During the summer, plantlife has been installing mechanisms for seed distribution. This machine shop goes into peak production in October, and will operate all winter. We have an impression that plantlife is dead and that the remains are merely crisp weeds that crackle under foot or rattle in the cold wind. To say that this trash contains a machine shop is no mere metaphor. Seed containers operate with marvelous precision. This fact is all the more remarkable when we consider that seed containers include no living cells. Their materials have no more "life" than springs and hinges. Yet in some mysterious way these are endowed with a capacity to perform when the seed is ripe.

A seed case has symmetry and often jewel-like beauty. It may be round or square. It may be very long and slender or chunky. It may open at the top, side, or bottom by a round hole, a trap door, a hinged lid, a rolling back of the walls, or in other ways. If the walls are very thin and brittle, they will be reinforced with perfect engineering. The capacity, the shape, and the method of operating depend on the size of the seeds and the way they are attached. The whole thing is a unit well poised with efficiency, fitness, economy—a means perfectly adapted to its end.

The opening power of a seed case is wind, moisture, and temperature that act on the stresses and strains within the walls and hinges of the seed case. However, a seed case must mature its seeds before it can operate. Strangely enough, if the seeds are eaten by insect larvae before they are ripe or suffer some accident which prevents them from maturing, the pod will not open, and the ejection mechanism will not operate.

In October one may see the milkweed sending out its cottony parachute seeds along the roadside. Examine one carefully and discover that this is not just a pod breaking open and the seeds tumbling out. A milkweed pod has a line down one side that separates clearly and cleanly by rolling back its lips gradually from top to bottom. As it opens, the seeds, which are arranged in a compact spiral, will loosen one by one, each seed in its turn peeling off from the assembly line. Even with a buoyant parachute, the milkweed seed might drop to the base of the plant on a windless day. Therefore, when it peels off, the loosened seed remains attached by the tip end of its parachute. This looks like a bubble emerging. It holds on that way until a breeze springs up just strong enough to detach it and carry it off.

In the fall the witch hazel bushes have yellow flowers (few native plants bloom in the late fall). At the same time the branches carry heavy pods with two thick lips and rounded at the bottom. These pods have taken a year to build from last fall's flowers. With the right combination of weather, the lips will part the way a duck opens its mouth, opening to a 90° angle, and the seeds that are shaped like tiny slender footballs will be shot out violently some six feet.

The common native shrub called New Jersey tea is another example of violent seed dispersal. Its fall fruit looks superficially like the shoe buttons with three grooves. The three segments between the grooves are folded over and joined together to make the container. When one sees these on the shrub, one would not think twice about them. But presently when one is not looking, after the seeds have ripened, the alternation of warm sun and cool damp nights causes this drab little fruit to explode. The secret lies in the fact that the segments had been under powerful tension when they were folded around to make the fruit. When they suddenly flatten out, separating along the grooves, they fling three large seeds a considerable distance into the woods. The whole contrivance vanishes instantaneously.

The out-of-season activity of seed cases which is, mechanically, the most astonishing behavior in all plantlife, is scarcely known or recognized, only because the mechanisms are so small in proportion to the big outdoors.

Touch the ripe seedpod of touch-me-not, or jewelweed. Jostle it, or try to take it in one's fingers. This innocent looking bean explodes at one's touch. What happens will be so sudden one cannot follow it with the eye. The seeds will pop off into the surrounding jungle and if anything is left in one's hand it will be a tangle of tiny squirming curls.

The touch-me-not pod uses the same principle as a watch spring. It is equipped with five mainsprings. These are strap-shaped, forming the segments of the pod from tip to tip. They are perfectly fitted together and sealed along the edges with light shellac that makes the pod waterproof but offers no resistance to the springs flying apart at the right moment. The pods are "wound up" (a mysterious act, when one stops to think of it) as they grow. When elongated, they are in

*Winged maple seeds*

tense position, the reverse of the watch spring. To relax this pressure, they must curl up. Thus, this static innocent-looking bean packs violence.

Through the center of this device, runs a core, resembling a silver ribbon. To this, five seeds are attached at equally spaced intervals both around the core and along its length. The tip of this core is firmly fixed in the point of the pod formed by the joining of the tips of the springs. At first the base of the core is attached to the stem while it is drawing on sap and nourishment to build the seeds. But when the seeds mature the core becomes loosened from the stem. This happens inside the pod, leaving the bases of the springs still attached to the stem. This curious fruit is held to its plant in this way. However, the attachment to the stem grows weaker and weaker while the pull of the springs grows stronger and stronger. At the precise moment, when the seeds are fully ripe and all is ready, the glue at the base of the springs has weakened to the point when it cannot withstand the tension any longer. Then the whole pod lets go—the contraption held together at its tip travels off through the air like a weird little flying machine. The kinetic energy of the coiling springs carries it off, but not far. It describes a parabola and heads for

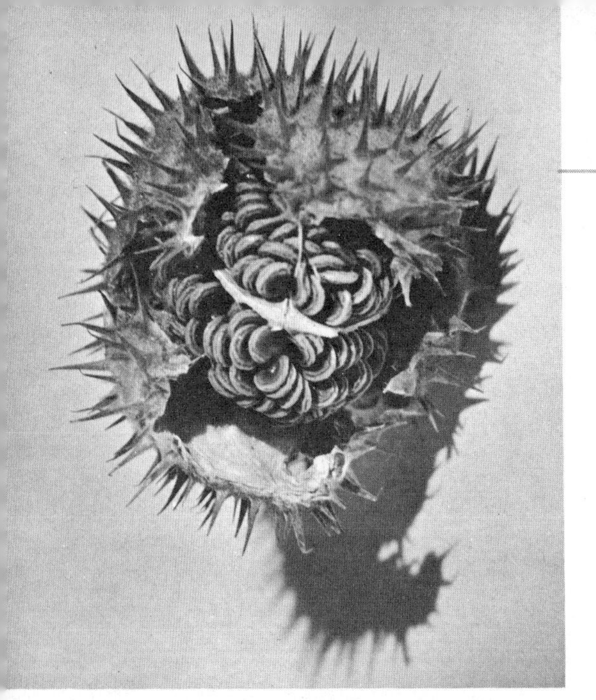

*The burlike seedpods of Jimson weed are transported great distances when they become attached to animals*

*The fuzzy seeds of wild clematis are very light and are blown by the wind to suitable growing sites*

the ground. During the instant while still in the air, this rocket fires off its ammunition. The violence of the uncoiling springs knocks out the seeds. First the flying fruit, then the shooting seed. The seeds disappear in various directions.

*The Baseball Mechanism of Wild Geranium*

When its magenta petals have fallen, the geranium fruit looks like a five-sided awl sticking out about three-fourths of an inch. Its strap-shaped sides are firmly fixed to the peak of the core which makes a supporting column for the whole device. The base of each strap forms a cup for the seed. This resembles a hand around a tiny baseball. At first this is green and partly buried. As the seed ripens, the "hand" is raised and turned exposing the seed-baseball that it is going to fling out.

In a few days, deep purple flushes the green. Quickly the whole device has turned metalic purple and become polished like shining steel. On that day, or one when it is not raining, the first touch of warm dry sunlight pulls the trigger. The steel springs fly up violently, coiling outward, carrying the seed containers upward, turning them in a sharp arc. The opening and the shape of the "hand" that holds the seed are such that the seed is released at the most forceful point, and tossed out with exactly the same sort of force as when a baseball player throws a high ball to the outfield.

*The Violet Squeeze Machine*

Violets prosper because they have a double way of forming seed. The well-known violet flower sets its seeds in the normal manner, but thousands of enthusiasts will pick it before it can take a step. Here is one of those unusual cases where picking this woodland flower, provided the plant is not uprooted, does not threaten its existence. While its flower has bloomed and been picked, the resourceful violet plant has made another flower. This is hidden in the litter on the ground, and, because it has no petals, nobody pays any attention to it. But the hidden flower will manufacture a fine case full of seeds—even more than the flower in full view.

This fruit of the violet ripens all summer, forming an oval capsule, beautifully tinged with purple. If any floral part were born to blush unseen it is this violet fruit. Its position under loose dirt or leaves is hardly strategic for sending forth seeds. Therefore, the maturing of this fruit affects also its stem. This stiffens and lengthens until finally the tension of the stem pulls the fruit out of its hiding place. It may do this gradually or snap it up, depending on how much weight is holding the capsule under. Now it is up in the air, but only a few inches up. The capsule splits into three segments that revolve outward until they lie almost horizontal. Each segment resembles a tiny canoe split open along its upper side. The sides of the canoe contract; they squeeze with an ever-increasing thumbscrew pressure. Finally, the seeds are pinched out violently, one at a time. Those that have the strongest attachment in the pod fly the farthest when they let go. Violet seeds are tossed from their lowly fruits as far as fifteen feet, but the average is around six feet.

*Wood Sorrel's Automatic Seed*

This wild flower grows in the hills—in the heart of the hardwood forest where skunk cabbage, clintonia, bunchberry, sweet gale, and trillium abound. Wood sorrel, *Oxalis montana*, is as lowly as a violet. It carpets a patch of woods with large, wheel-shaped flowers, white or pink, with deep pink veins. It is one of the most delicately beautiful of all woodland flowers.

Wood sorrel is probably best known for the agility of its leaves. They are three-parted like a clover, forming a shamrock design out of three hearts. Sorrel leaves go to sleep at night—they fold up tight and droop until the reappearance of light causes them to expand. This motion is so rapid one can see it. More has been written about the sleep of its leaves than about wood sorrel's unique mechanism for making sure that its seeds travel.

Mechanisms that act as catapults, slingshoots, or popguns, are built out of parts surrounding the seeds. The seed is inert—it takes an outside force to send it whizzing. But in its evolution, wood sorrel hit on a way of making the seed itself do the trick, without any action by surrounding parts.

In relation to the size of its flower, the fruit capsule of wood sorrel is small and remains weak and succulent, never forming anything crisp and dynamic. This seed case cradles one or two seeds in each of its five cavities. The secret of their ejection lies in the thick, three-layer coat of the seed itself. The outer layer is hard, inelastic, but prepared to shrink to about two-thirds of its size. Its middle layer is soft, highly absorbent, and prepared to swell up. Its inner layer is more like the thin coat of any seed.

At a mysterious signal, three days before the seed is fully ripe and ready to

*Horsechestnuts are stored underground by squirrels in the fall. Those that are not eaten during the winter begin to grow the following spring*

*The winged seeds of pines fall from the cone when it opens*

go, water in the wood sorrel plant begins to shift rapidly. The stem of the fruit shows this agitation by swelling up almost to double its size from water that suddenly concentrates in it. This shifting of water results in upsetting the equilibrium of the seed coat. The outside layer loses water and contracts suddenly to one-third of its size. The center layer takes in water and expands or at least resists the terrific contraction. Something is bound to snap! When it does, the seed coat turns practically inside out so violently that its seed takes to the woods. The flacid capsule then hangs like a spent spiral.

Seeds are minute, but they hold the germs of the vast green mantle of our land. Their equipment for travel and agility is marvelous beyond any blueprints of the imagination. —R.P.

*Recommended Reading*

**All About the Flowering World**—Ferdinand C. Lane. Random House, Inc., New York.

**The Basic Science Education Series—Seeds and Seed Travels, Flowers, Fruits, Seeds**—Bertha M. Parker. Row, Peterson & Company, New York.

**The Essentials of Plant Biology**—Frank D. Kern. Harper & Brothers, New York City.

**Flowers and Flowering Plants**—Raymond J. Pool. McGraw Hill Book Company, New York.

**Our Flowering World**—Rutherford Platt. Dodd, Mead & Company, New York.

**1,001 Questions Answered About Trees**—Rutherford Platt. Dodd, Mead & Company, New York.

**Sharp Eyes—A Rambler's Calendar of Fifty-two Weeks Among Insects, Birds and Flowers**—William Hamilton Gibson. Harper & Brothers, New York.

**The Wonders of Seeds**—Alfred Stefferud. Harcourt, Brace & World, Inc., New York.

**SENITA** (*See under Cactus*)